Question & Answers

JAA PPL Revision Papers

Air Law and Operational Procedures;

Meteorology;

Communications;

Human Performance and Limitations;

Aircraft General;

Flight Planning and Performance

and Navigation

<Written and illustrated by

Helena B A Hughes

POOLEY'S

Air Pilot Publishing

Nothing in this manual supersedes any legislation, rules, regulations or procedures contained in any operational document issued by The Stationery Office, the Civil Aviation Authority, the manufacturers of aircraft, engines and systems, or by the operators of aircraft throughout the world. Note that as maps and charts are changed regularly, those extracts reproduced in this book must not be used for flight planning or flight operations.

AUTHOR

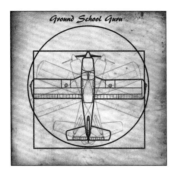

Helena B A Hughes

Helena Hughes was born into an aviation household, having her first informal "flying lesson" at the age of four. Her late father David was a flying instructor and also flew corporate jets. On leaving University Helena went to America to obtain a PPL, converting to a UK licence on return. Shortly afterwards she started work in Air Traffic Control at London Luton Airport earning her Controllers Licence in 1990. Helena continues to be an operational Air Traffic Control Officer and is currently posted to Swanwick working "Thames Radar", "Luton Radar" and "Heathrow Special"; she is involved in controller training as both an Instructor and Assessor. Helena holds a fixed wing CPL/IR and has been a flying instructor since 1996. She also holds a PPL(H) and is a Radio Telephony and Air/Ground Examiner.

Helena would like to thank: Mrs. Brenda "Bedda" Hughes; Mr. Andrew Temple of Solent Flight Ltd; A Vrancken and H Ewing

INTRODUCTION

This book is intended as an aid to revision and examination preparation for those studying for the grant of a JAA PPL. Ideally its use should follow a period of self or directed study to consolidate the knowledge acquired and identify any areas of weakness prior to attempting the PPL examinations themselves.

The questions and answers in this publication are designed to reflect those appearing in the current examination papers and are set out in a representative format. No attempt has been made to replicate any actual examination paper.

Blank answer sheets are provided at the end of the book which may be photocopied to enable multiple attempts at each exam.

INTENTIONALLY BLANK

CONTENTS

INTENTIONALLY BLANK

PART 1: AIR LAW & OPERATIONAL PROCEDURES

The Air Law and Operational Procedures examination consists of 40 questions; the time allowed is one hour.

The pass mark is 75%.

Each question is multiple choice with four possible answers A, B, C and D. You should indicate your chosen answer by placing a cross in the appropriate box on the answer sheet.

Blank answer sheets are to be found at the end of this publication, these may be photocopied.

INTENTIONALLY BLANK

AIR LAW PAPER 1

1. Large white diagonal crosses placed no more than 300 metres apart on a section of runway mean the section between the crosses is:
   a. Unfit for landing, but may be used to taxi
   b. Unfit for landing, but may be used for take-off
   c. Unfit for the movement of aircraft
   d. Unfit for take-off, but may be used for taxi

2. ICAO recommends that the colour used for runway markings should be:
   a. White
   b. Orange
   c. Yellow or white
   d. Yellow

3. At a civil land aerodrome an Aerodrome Identification Beacon is a:
   a. Red beacon flashing a two letter Morse group
   b. Green beacon flashing a two letter Morse group
   c. White beacon flashing a two letter Morse group
   d. Green/white alternating beacon

4. Runway threshold lights are:
   a. Fixed unidirectional lights showing red in the direction of approach to the runway
   b. Fixed omnidirectional lights showing green
   c. Fixed unidirectional lights showing green in the direction of approach to the runway
   d. Flashing unidirectional lights showing red in the direction of the runway

5. The transponder code used to indicate radio failure is:
   a. 7700
   b. 7600
   c. 7500
   d. 7000

6. An aircraft must carry an identification plate inscribed with its registration mark. The plate should be made of:
   a. Iron
   b. Stainless steel
   c. Aluminium
   d. Fireproof metal

7. With QFE set on the altimeter subscale, vertical position is reported as:
   a. Flight level
   b. Altitude
   c. Height
   d. Elevation

8. When two aircraft are converging, the one which has the right of way, must:
   a. Maintain its speed and height
   b. Maintain its heading and height
   c. Maintain its speed and heading
   d. Maintain its speed, heading and height

9.   An Alerting Service is:

     a.   A specialist department of D and D
     b.   A service provided to notify the appropriate organisations of aircraft in need of Search and Rescue aid, and assist such organisations as required
     c.   A network of civil and military stations
     d.   A service provided to notify the appropriate organisations of aircraft in need of navigational assistance

10. A white "T" with a white disc alongside the cross-arm in line with the stem of the "T" displayed in the signal area means:

     a.   Parachute operations on the aerodrome
     b.   The direction of landing and take-off do not necessarily coincide
     c.   Take-offs and landings must be in the same direction
     d.   Tea is made with round bags

11. The following is a definition of what? "The length of the take-off run available plus the length of any available stopway".

     a.   Accelerate Stop Distance Available
     b.   Runway length
     c.   Take-off Distance Available
     d.   Part of the runway declared as suitable for the ground run of an aeroplane taking off

12. The Take-off run available (TORA) may be described as the:

     a.   Length of the clearway and stopway
     b.   Runway length
     c.   Part of the runway declared as suitable for the ground run of an aeroplane taking off plus any associated clearway
     d.   Part of the runway declared as suitable for the ground run of an aeroplane taking off

13. A Control Zone is controlled airspace that extends from:

     a.   A specified altitude to a specified flight level
     b.   The surface to a specified upper limit
     c.   The surface upwards
     d.   Specified lower limit to an upper one

14. An Air Traffic service provided to give advice and information useful for the safe and efficient conduct of flight which may include weather information and general airspace activity, is:

     a.   Basic Service
     b.   Traffic Service
     c.   Deconfliction Service
     d.   Flight Information Service

15. Lower Airspace Radar Service (LARS) is available outside controlled airspace up to and including ....(i)....and within approximately ....(ii).... from a participating ATSU. (UK)

     a.   i) FL 65   ii) 30 nm
     b.   i) FL 95   ii) 25 nm
     c.   i) FL 65   ii) 25 nm
     d.   i) FL 95   ii) 30 nm

16. The criteria for VFR flight in Class D and E when operating above 3000 feet but below FL 100, are:

     a.   Flight visibility 8 km, 1500 m horizontally and 1000 feet vertically from cloud
     b.   Flight visibility 5 km, 1000 m horizontally and 1500 feet vertically from cloud
     c.   Flight visibility 5 km, 1500 m horizontally and 1000 feet vertically from cloud
     d.   Flight visibility 5 km, clear of cloud and in sight of the surface

17. ICAO recognises that, with respect to airspace sovereignty, each contracting state:

   a. Shares sovereignty with any neighbours having a land border
   b. Has complete sovereignty over the airspace above its territory
   c. Must reach regional agreement as to airspace sovereignty
   d. Has no right to sovereignty to the airspace above its territory

18. With regard to the Chicago Convention, when an aircraft enters its territory a contracting state:

   a. May require it to land at a customs airport
   b. Must require it to land at a customs airport
   c. May require it to land at a port of entry
   d. May require it to land at an immigration airport

19. To operate radio transmitting equipment over the territory of a contracting state:

   a. The operator must be licensed by the state of registry of the aircraft
   b. The radio station must be licensed by the state of registry of the aircraft
   c. Both the radio station and the operator must be licensed by the state of registry of the aircraft
   d. Either the radio station and the operator must be licensed by the state of registry of the aircraft

20. ICAO requires that the Certificate of Registration:

   a. Should be kept in a safe place by the operating company
   b. Shall be carried on all flights
   c. Shall be carried on flights not terminating at the aerodrome of departure
   d. Is not necessary on domestic flights, but shall be carried on international flights

21. An aircraft is considered to be overtaking when the faster aircraft is closing within:

   a. 20° of the centreline of the slower aircraft
   b. 90° of the centreline of the slower aircraft
   c. 70° of the centreline of the slower aircraft
   d. 45° of the centreline of the slower aircraft

22. An aircraft operating on a Special VFR clearance is exempt from (UK):

   a. The "1000 feet rule"
   b. The "500 feet rule"
   c. The need to "land clear a the congested area"
   d. Both the "500 feet rule" and the "1000 feet rule"

23. A steady red light directed from an aerodrome to an aircraft in flight means:

   a. Give way to other aircraft and continue circling
   b. Airfield unavailable for landing
   c. Wait for permission to land
   d. Position downwind

24. A Flight Information Service at an aerodrome provides:

   a. Information useful to the safe and efficient conduct of flight within an ATZ
   b. Information useful to the safe and efficient conduct of flight in a CTR
   c. Instructions and advice to aircraft in the ATZ
   d. Clearances to operate within an ATZ

25. At or below the Transition Altitude vertical position is reported in terms of:

   a. Height
   b. Flight Level
   c. Elevation
   d. Altitude

26. A Certificate of Airworthiness would cease to be valid:

    a. After 5 years

    b. If the aircraft, or its equipment, is overhauled, modified or repaired in a non-approved manner

    c. Outside the State of Registry

    d. If the airframe hours exceed the maximum allowed in a twelve month period

27. When a "light" aircraft departs from an intermediate position on the same runway following a "Heavy" aeroplane's departure, the recommended minimum spacing is:

    a. 2 nm

    b. 3 km

    c. 3 minutes

    d. 2 minutes

28. The final authority over the operation of an aircraft in flight belongs to:

    a. The Pilot-in-Command

    b. The aircraft owner

    c. The person manipulating the controls

    d. The aircraft operator

29. To carry passengers the pilot-in-command must have made, as the sole manipulator of the controls, at least:

    a. Three take-offs & landings in the same type or class to be flown within the preceding 90 days

    b. One take-off and landing in the same type or class to be flown within the preceding 28 days

    c. Three take-offs and landings within the preceding 90 days

    d. One take-off and landing in the same type or class to be flown within the preceding 30 days

30. In relation to Search and Rescue operations, the "distress phase" means that:

    a. Air Traffic Control has lost contact with an aircraft

    b. Apprehension exists as to the safety of an aircraft and its occupants

    c. An aircraft has an emergency situation

    d. An aircraft and its occupants are threatened by grave and imminent danger

31. You are a PPL with no instrument qualification flying in the UK and receiving a Traffic Service. The controller instructs you to climb, however this means you would not be able to maintain VMC. What should you do?

    a. Obey the instruction

    b. Ignore the instruction

    c. Advise the controller and request an alternative instruction

    d. Acknowledge the instruction, do not comply and remain VMC

32. At a Government or licensed aerodrome you are absolved from which of the Low Flying Rules, when taking off or landing in accordance with normal aviation practice?

    a. The "1000 feet Rule"

    b. The "500 feet Rule"

    c. The "Land Clear Rule"

    d. All of the low flying rules

33. An air accident occurring in the UK must be reported by the quickest means available to (UK):

    a. The CAA and AAIB

    b. The CAA and the Chief Inspector of Air Accidents

    c. The Chief Inspector of Air Accidents and the local police

    d. The Chief Inspector of Police and the CAA

34. You are flying by day and observe a ground search and rescue signal, to acknowledge you should:

    a.   Fly over the site twice at a low height

    b.   - Rock the aircraft's wings

    c.   Raise and lower undercarriage/flaps

    d.   Rev the engine twice

35. The lowest height to fly under IFR is:

    a.   1000 feet AGL

    b.   1500 feet above the highest obstacle within 10 nm of track

    c.   1000 feet above the highest obstacle within 5 nm of track

    d.   1000 feet above the highest fixed obstacle within 600 m

36. Which of the following would be classed as an aircraft accident?

    a.   A person on the ground is seriously injured after being hit by a component that has become detached from a light aircraft in flight

    b.   A main tyre bursting on landing

    c.   An aerial becomes detached

    d.   A bird strike which slightly dents the leading edge of a wing

37. If making a flight in a single engine aircraft over water it is recommended that:

    a.   Life jackets should be worn by all occupants when flying over water

    b.   Life jackets should be carried for all occupants

    c.   When flying over water beyond gliding distance of land, life jackets should be worn by all occupants

    d.   When flying over water beyond gliding distance of land, life jackets should be on board for all occupants

38. An aircraft's vertical position when measured from mean sea level is:

    a.   Reported at "height" and the subscale is set to QFE

    b.   Reported as "altitude" and the subscale is set to QNH

    c.   Reported as "height" and the subscale is set to QNH

    d.   Reported as "altitude" and the subscale is set to 1013.2 hPa

39. Aviation medicals are issued in accordance with:

    a.   JAR-FCL 3

    b.   JAR-FCL 2

    c.   JAR-FCL 1

    d.   JAR-FCL 4

40. Unless otherwise prescribed by an appropriate authority, "Night" is between:

    a.   The end of morning civil twilight and the beginning of evening civil twilight

    b.   The end of evening civil twilight and the beginning of morning civil twilight

    c.   The end of evening civil twilight and the end of morning civil twilight

    d.   The beginning of morning civil twilight and the end of evening civil twilight

---

END OF LAW PAPER 1

AIR LAW PAPER 1: ANSWERS

No.	A	B	C	D
1			X	
2	X			
3		X		
4			X	
5		X		
6				X
7			X	
8			X	
9		X		
10		X		
11	X			
12				X
13		X		
14	X			
15				X
16			X	
17		X		
18	X			
19			X	
20				X
21			X	
22	X			
23	X			
24	X			
25				X
26		X		
27		X		
28	X			
29	X			
30				X
31			X	
32				X
33			X	
34		X		
35			X	
36	X			
37			X	
38		X		
39	X			
40		X		

CORRECT ANSWERS: PERCENTAGES										
30	31	32	33	34	35	36	37	38	39	40
75%	77%	80%	82%	85%	87%	90%	92%	95%	97%	100%

1. **(Answer: C)** Large white diagonal crosses not more than 300 m apart on a runway mean that the area between the crosses is unfit for the movement of aircraft.

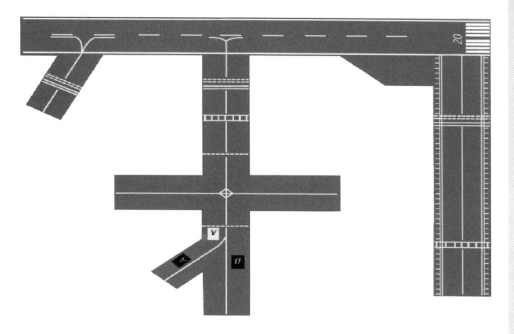

2. **(Answer: A)** ICAO recommends that runway markings are white and taxiway markings are yellow.

3. **(Answer: B)** A civil Aerodrome Identification beacon is green and flashes a two letter Morse group. Those at military aerodromes are red.

Aerodrome beacons are a different system and flash white/white or, less commonly, green/white. These are installed where aircraft usually locate the airfield by visual means, when reduced visibility is frequently an issue or should the aerodrome be difficult to locate because of the surrounding terrain.

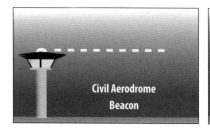

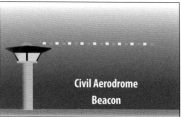

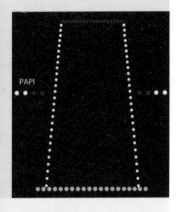

4. Answer C

Runway threshold lights shown in the colour green

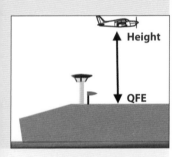

7. Answer C

With QFE set vertical position is reported as a 'Height'

10. Answer B

4.   **(Answer: C)** Runway threshold lights are required to be fixed unidirectional lights showing green in the direction of the approach to the runway.

5.   **(Answer: B)** The special purpose transponder codes are:

7700	**=**	**emergency**
7600	**=**	**radio failure**
7500	**=**	**unlawful interference**

6.   **(Answer: D)** An aircraft identification plate must be made of fireproof metal or other suitable fireproof material. It must be inscribed with the aircraft's nationality/common mark and registration mark and fixed to the aircraft near the main entrance.

7.   **(Answer: C)** With QFE set vertical position is reported as a "height".

    QFE is the pressure setting at aerodrome elevation.
    •   This is normally the highest point on the landing area
    •   When we have QFE set on the altimeter it indicates HEIGHT.
    •   HEIGHT is defined as the vertical distance above a specified datum (usually above aerodrome level AAL).
    •   This setting is useful when the only concern is height above the aerodrome, so QFE is a common setting to use for take-offs, circuits and landings.

8.   **(Answer: C)** An aircraft which has the right of way must maintain its heading (course) and speed.

NOTE: WITH REGARD TO COLLISION AVOIDANCE ICAO USES SLIGHTLY DIFFERENT WORDING, & REFERS TO HEADING RATHER THAN COURSE.

9.   **(Answer: B)** An Alerting Service is provided to notify the appropriate organisations regarding aircraft in need of Search and Rescue aid, and assist such organisations as required. It is provided automatically to all aircraft known by the Air Traffic Services to be operating within the UK FIRs.

10.   **(Answer: B)** In a signal area the symbol on the right indicates that the direction of take-off and landing does not necessarily coincide.

11.   **(Answer: A)** The Accelerate/Stop Distance Available (ASDA) is the length of the take-off run available plus the length of any associated stopway. A stopway is a defined rectangular at the end of the Take-Off Run Available prepared as a suitable area upon which an aircraft can be stopped in the event of an abandoned take-off.

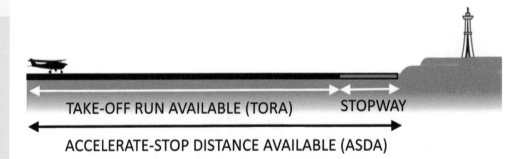

TAKE-OFF RUN AVAILABLE (TORA)

12. **(Answer: D)** The Take-Off Run Available (TORA) is that part of the runway declared as suitable for the ground run of an aircraft taking off.

    Landing Distance Available, or LDA, is the length of the runway declared as available and suitable for the ground run of an aircraft landing.

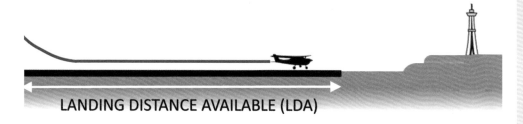

LANDING DISTANCE AVAILABLE (LDA)

13. **(Answer: B)** The definition of a Control Zone (CTR) is: "Controlled airspace extending upwards from the surface of the earth to a specified upper limit".

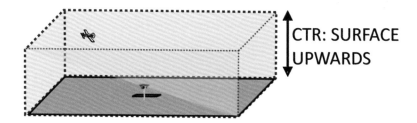

CTR: SURFACE
UPWARDS

14. **(Answer: A)** The Basic Service is an Air Traffic Service provided to give advice and information useful to the safe and efficient conduct of flights. Such items may include weather information, changes in the serviceability of facilities, conditions at aerodromes or general aerial activity information. Traffic Information should not be expected: Outside an ATZ there is no obligation for the controller/FISO to pass Traffic Information. mIn a signal area the symbol on the right indicates that the direction of take-off and mlanding does not necessarily coincide.

Definition	Basic Service is provided to give advice and information useful to the safe and efficient conduct of flights. Such items may include weather information, changes in the serviceability of facilities, conditions at aerodromes or general aerial activity information.
Flight Rules	IFR or VFR flights, but may not be appropriate for flight in IMC
Traffic Information	Traffic Information should not be expected. Pilots are wholly responsible for the avoidance of other traffic
Terrain	Pilots are responsible for terrain clearance at all times
Notes	Unless the pilot has entered into an agreement with a controller to maintain a particular course of action he may change heading, level or route without advising the controller

15. **(Answer: D)** Outside Controlled Airspace certain Air Traffic Control Units are able to provide a Lower Airspace Radar Service to pilots flying in UK uncontrolled airspace up to and including FL 95, within approximately 30 nm of each participating unit. Participating ATSUs are able to provide either a Traffic Service or a Deconfliction Service; both are available at the request of the pilot.

16. **(Answer: C)** In Class D and E airspace the minima for VFR flight are a flight visibility of 5 km and 1500 m horizontally and 1000 feet vertically clear of cloud.

	DISTANCE FROM CLOUD	FLIGHT VISIBILITY
At and Above FL 100 Class C, D, E, F & G	1500 m 1000 ft	8 km
Below Fl 100 Class C, D, E, F & G	1500 m 1000 ft	5 km

Additional low level VFR minima:

AT OR BELOW 3000 FEET AMSL		
CLASS F AND G	Clear of cloud and with the surface in sight	5 km
FOR AIRCRAFT, FLYING AT 140 KNOTS OR LESS		
CLASS C, D and E CLASS F and G	Clear of cloud and with the surface in sight Clear of cloud and with the surface in sight	5 km
FOR HELICOPTERS		
CLASS C, D and E CLASS F and G	Clear of cloud and with the surface in sight Clear of cloud and with the surface in sight and at a speed which is reasonable with regard to the visibility	1500 m 1500 m

17. **(Answer: B)** Each contracting state is recognised to have complete sovereignty over the airspace above its territory. It may impose its national law on users of that airspace. A state's territory is the airspace over the country's borders at ground level and the airspace above its territorial waters.

18. **(Answer: A)** A state MAY require aircraft arriving to or departing from its territory to do so through an international or "customs" airport, which has full customs, immigration and health facilities.

19. **(Answer: C)** Aircraft flying within the airspace of another state may only carry radio-transmitting equipment that has been licensed by the aircraft's state of registration. Additionally, the equipment may only be operated by crew members who are licensed to do so by the State in which the aircraft is registered.

20. **(Answer: D)** The Certificate of Registration is not necessary on domestic flights, but shall be carried on international flights.

Private Flight International	Private Flight - within the UK, Channel Islands, Isle of Man
Certificate of Airworthiness	None required
Airworthiness Review Certificate (ARC)	
Certificate of Registration	
Aircraft Radio Licence	
Flight Crew Licences	
Technical/Journey Log	

21. **(Answer: C)** An aircraft is considered to be overtaking when the faster aircraft is closing within 70° of the slower aircraft's centreline.

 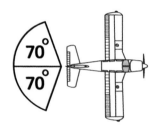

22. **(Answer: A)** Under a Special VFR clearance a pilot is exempt from the "1000 feet rule", that is the need to remain 1000 feet above the highest fixed obstacle within 600 metres of the aircraft. Please note that there is NO exemption from the requirement to alight clear of any congested area.

In the UK Special VFR is a concession offered by ATC to allow aircraft to operate:
- *in a Class A Control Zone or*
- *in any other Control Zone in IMC or at night.*

With a Special VFR clearance, instead of complying with the IFR, which would be required in either of the circumstances above, the pilot follows special instructions given by the controller. A pilot has certain responsibilities when operating on a Special VFR clearance, these are that:

- *He must comply with ATC instructions;*
- *He must remain in flight conditions that enable him to determine his flight path and keep clear of obstacles – in other words remain clear of cloud and in sight of the surface;*
- *He must not enter an ATZ unless permission has been obtained;*
- *He must fly within the limitations of his licence;*
- *The pilot is absolved from the 1000 feet rule, but NO OTHER LOW FLYING RULES – particularly the ability to alight clear.*

23.   **(Answer: A)** A steady red light directed towards an aircraft in flight means: give way to other aircraft and continue circling.

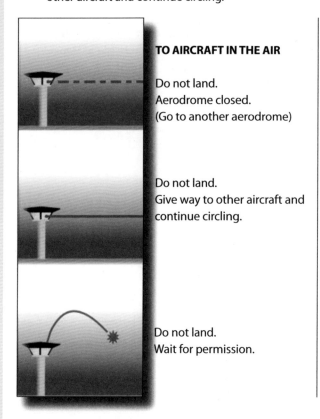

TO AIRCRAFT IN THE AIR

Do not land.
Aerodrome closed.
(Go to another aerodrome)

Do not land.
Give way to other aircraft and
continue circling.

Do not land.
Wait for permission.

TO AIRCRAFT ON THE GROUND

Move clear of the landing area

Stop

24.   **(Answer: A)** Flight Information Service at aerodromes provides information useful to the safe and efficient conduct of flights within an ATZ.

This is an information service NOT a control service. From the information provided it is up to the pilot to decide what, if any, action is required to ensure safe operations. FISOs will use the call sign suffix "Information" for example "Duxford Information", so it will be easy for a pilot to determine the level of service being provided.

25.   **(Answer: D)** The Transition Altitude is the altitude at or below which the vertical position of an aircraft is controlled by reference to altitude i.e. QNH

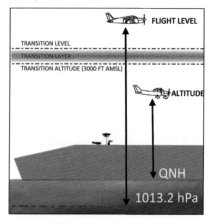

26.   **(Answer: B)** An EASA C of A DOES NOT EXPIRE but must be supported by a current Airworthiness Review Certificate (ARC). The C of A is invalidated if an aircraft is modified, repaired or maintained in a non-approved manner.

27. **(Answer: C)** 3 minutes.

Wake turbulence departure separations:

Lead Aircraft	Following Aircraft	Minimum wake turbulence separation at time aircaft are airbourne	
Heavy	Medium, Small, Light	Departure from the same position	2 minutes
Medium, Small	Light		2 minutes
Heavy (full-length take-off)	Medium, Small, Light	Departure from an intermediated point on the same runway	3 minutes
Medium, Small (full-length take-off)	Light		3 minutes

28. **(Answer: A)** The Pilot-in-Command is the pilot responsible for the operation and safety of an aircraft during flight time.

29. **(Answer: A)** In order to carry passengers the pilot-in-command must have made at least 3 take-offs and landings as the sole manipulator of the controls within the preceding 90 days in the same type or class of aircraft to be flown.

    To carry passengers at night:
    One of the 3 take-offs and landings within the preceding 90 days must have been made at night.

30. **(Answer: D)** The Distress Phase is where an aircraft and its occupants are threatened by grave and/or imminent danger and require immediate assistance.

EMERGENCY PHASE	Definition	Duration
Uncertainty Phase	A situation wherein uncertainty exists as to the safety of an aircraft and its occupants.	Maximum of 30 minutes
Alert Phase	A situation wherein apprehension exists as to the safety of an aircraft and its occupants.	Maximum of one hour.
Distress Phase	A situation wherein there is a reasonable certainty that an aircraft and its occupants are threateneed by grave and imminent danger and require immediate assistance.	Until the aircraft is found and the survivors rescued, or it is clear that there is no longer any chance of so doing.

31. **(Answer: C)** A Traffic Service is available to IFR or VFR flights. If a controller issues either a heading or level that would require flight in IMC, a pilot not qualified to fly in IMC must advise the controller and request alternative instructions.

Definition	The Traffic Service is a surveillance (radar) based ATS where in addition to a Basic Service, the controller provides specific radar derived traffic informaion to assist a pilot in avoiding other traffic.
Flight Rules	IFR or VFR
Traffic Information	**Relevant Traffic Information will be passed** and will be updated if the traffic continues to constitute a definite hazard, or if requested by the pilot. Whether Traffic Information has been passed or not, a pilot is still responsible for collision avoidance.
Terrain	The **pilot is reponsible for terrain clearance**.
Notes	Pilots may operate under their **own navigation or the controller will provide headings** for positioning, sequencing or navigational assistance.

32. **(Answer: D)** At a Government or licensed aerodrome any aircraft is exempt from the low flying regulations if flying in accordance with normal aviation practice for the purpose of: Taking off from, landing at or practising approaches to landing at the aerodrome; or Checking navigational aids or procedures. Any aircraft is exempt from the 500 feet rule when taking off or landing in accordance with normal aviation practice.

33. **(Answer: C)** When a notifiable accident occurs, the aircraft commander must inform:
- *The Chief Inspector of Accidents by the quickest means available and*
- *The local police when the accident has occurred in or over the UK.*

34. **(Answer: B)** By day the air-to-ground signal to indicate that SAR ground signals have been understood is to rock the aircraft's wings. By night the landing lights should be flashed twice, or if the aircraft is not suitably equipped the navigation lights should be switched on and off twice.

35. **(Answer: C)**

36. **(Answer: A)** An accident must be reported if, between the time when anyone boards the aircraft with the intention of flight, until all such persons have disembarked:

- *Anyone is killed or seriously injured while in or on the aircraft or by direct contact with the aircraft including anything that has become detached from it. This includes direct exposure to jet blast but not anything self-inflicted or due to natural causes. It does not include stowaways; or*

- *The aircraft incurs damage or structural failure other than any failure or damage limited to the engine or its accessories. If the damage is only limited to propellers, wingtips, aerials, tyres, brakes, fairings, small dents or small puncture holes it is not reportable. (Unless any of the afore-mentioned adversely affects the aircraft's structural strength, performance or flight characteristics and requires major repair or replacement).*

- *The aircraft is missing or completely inaccessible.*

37. **(Answer: C)** The advice held in a CAA General Aviation Safety Sense leaflet recommends that when flying beyond gliding distance of land life jackets should be worn by all occupants.

38. **(Answer: B)** QNH is the pressure at mean sea level.

- *When set the altimeter will indicate ALTITUDE*
  – the vertical distance above mean sea level.
- *Important for terrain separation as on aeronautical charts, obstacles*
  and the ground are also shown as heights above mean sea level.
- *This setting should be used for any flight away from the circuit.*

39. **(Answer: A)** Medicals are issued in accordance with JAR-FCL 3. JAR-FCL 1 covers Flight Crew Licensing for Aeroplanes and JAR-FCL 2 covers Flight Crew Licensing for Helicopters.

40. **(Answer: B)** Night is the period between the end of evening civil twilight and the beginning of morning civil twilight, or such other period as may be prescribed by the appropriate authority.

NOTE: IN THE UK NIGHT IS DEFINED AS 30 MINUTES AFTER SUNSET UNTIL 30 MINUTES BEFORE SUNRISE.

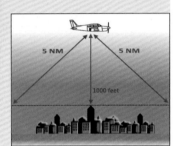

35. Answer C

Under the IFR a pilot must not fly at less than 1000 feet above the highest obstacle within 5 nm of the aircraft

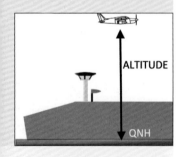

38. Answer B

AIR LAW PAPER 2

1. ICAO recommends that the colour used for taxiway markings should be:
    a. White
    b. Orange
    c. Yellow or white
    d. Yellow

2. In an aerodrome signal area, what is the meaning of the following symbol?
    a. The aerodrome is closed
    b. Sandwiches in the cafe are cut into quarters
    c. The aerodrome is unsafe for the movement of aircraft and landing is prohibited
    d. The state of the manoeuvring area is poor and pilots must exercise caution when landing

3. Runway end lights are:
    a. Fixed unidirectional lights showing red in the direction of the runway
    b. Fixed omnidirectional lights showing red
    c. Fixed unidirectional lights showing green in the direction of the runway
    d. Flashing unidirectional lights showing red in the direction of the runway

4. A JAA PPL is valid for a maximum period of:
    a. 60 months
    b. 48 months
    c. 24 months
    d. 12 months

5. In respect of converging aircraft:
    a. Helicopters give way to aeroplanes
    b. Aeroplanes and helicopters give way to aeroplanes towing a glider
    c. Aeroplanes give way to helicopters and aeroplanes towing a banner
    d. Airships give way to helicopters

6. When two aircraft in the air are approaching head on, or approximately so, and there is danger of a collision, each shall:
    a. Alter heading to the left or right as appropriate
    b. Alter height as appropriate
    c. Alter heading to the left
    d. Alter heading to the right

7. Water contamination on a runway described as "flooded" means that:
    a. The runway is completely covered with standing water
    b. Extensive standing water is visible
    c. Significant patches of standing water are visible
    d. The runway is soaked and cannot be used

8. Each state agrees under the Chicago Convention that:
    a. All aircraft, including those on scheduled services may make flights into or across its territory without prior permission
    b. Only aircraft engaged on scheduled services may make flights into or across its territory without prior permission
    c. All aircraft of other contracting states may cross its territory, provided that one landing is made within the state in question
    d. All aircraft other than those on scheduled services may make flights into or across its territory without prior permission

9. Visual Meteorological Conditions (VMC) minima are defined by ICAO and expressed in terms of:
   a. Visibility, distance from cloud and cloud ceiling
   b. Visibility
   c. Cloud ceiling and runway visual range
   d. Visibility and cloud ceiling

10. A pilot who does not meet international licensing standards in full, but still continues to hold a licence, must have the licence endorsed:
   a. With a special authorisation from the JAA
   b. Showing in which countries he may operate
   c. Showing the ways in which the standards have not been met
   d. With special authorisation from ICAO

11. A pilot suffers a significant injury and is unfit to function as flight crew. The medical certificate:
   a. Remains current
   b. Is deemed suspended
   c. Is deemed suspended if the pilot is unfit to act as a crew member for 20 days
   d. Will have to be renewed at a full initial medical

12. What is the definition of "Pilot-in Command"?
   a. The person flying the aircraft
   b. The person authorising the flight
   c. The most experienced pilot in the aircraft
   d. The pilot responsible for the operation and safety of the aircraft

13. In an aerodrome signal square what is the meaning of a "black ball" suspended from a mast?
   a. Right hand circuit
   b. The direction of take-off and landing are not necessarily the same
   c. Gliding is taking place at the airfield
   d. Left hand circuit

14. A series of white flashes directed from an aerodrome to an aircraft in flight means:
   a. Give way to other aircraft and continue circling
   b. Cleared to land
   c. Land at this aerodrome after receiving a steady green light
   d. Do not land, aerodrome closed

15. If you overtake another aircraft you must alter course:
   a. To the right in the air, to the right on the ground
   b. To the left in the air, to the right on the ground
   c. To the right in the air, to the left on the ground
   d. To the left in the air, to the left on the ground

16. When a "Light" aircraft departs from the same position on the same runway following a "Heavy" aeroplane's departure, the recommended minimum spacing is:
   a. 2 nm
   b. 3 km
   c. 3 minutes
   d. 2 minutes

17. With Standard Pressure Setting (1013.2 hectopascals) set on the altimeter sub-scale an aircraft's vertical position is referred to as:

    a.   Height

    b.   Flight level

    c.   Elevation

    d.   Altitude

18. Operating limitations and information necessary to the safe operation of aircraft are available:

    a.   Only in the pilot's manual

    b.   In the flight manual and on placards and markings

    c.   In the Airworthiness Review Certificate

    d.   Appended to the Certificate of Airworthiness

19. A JAR PPL holder must have a valid Medical Certificate in order to exercise the privileges of the licence. The medical must be either:

    a.   Class 1 or 2

    b.   Class 2 or 3

    c.   Class 2

    d.   An HGV medical certificate or a certificate issued by a GP

20. On the aerodrome manoeuvring area an aircraft is converging with a vehicle which is towing an aircraft. Which must give way?

    a.   The aircraft

    b.   The towing vehicle

    c.   The one which has the other on its left

    d.   The one which has the other on its right

21. In search and rescue operations, what does the following sign mean 'V'?

    a.   Require medical assistance

    b.   Proceeding in the direction indicated

    c.   Request instructions

    d.   Require assistance

22. The transponder code used to indicate an emergency is:

    a.   7700

    b.   7600

    c.   7500

    d.   7000

23. On an aerodrome signal area what does the following symbol mean?

    a.   Take-offs and landings must be in the same direction

    b.   Land with caution

    c.   Gliding in progress at the airfield

    d.   The directions of landing and take-off do not necessarily coincide

24. "The length of the take-off run available plus the length of the clearway, if available" is a definition of the:

    a.   Accelerate/stop distance available (ASDA)

    b.   Take-off run available (TORA)

    c.   Take-off distance available (TODA)

    d.   Emergency distance available (EDA)

25. Under JAR-FCL, a single pilot single-engine class rating is valid for:

    a.   13 months

    b.   2 years

    c.   3 years

    d.   1 year

26. Under the Chicago Convention, when an aircraft lands within another contracting state, the authorities of that country:

    a.   May search the aircraft after notifying the operator in advance

    b.   Have the right to search the aircraft for illegal substances

    c.   Have the right to search the aircraft without causing unreasonable delay

    d.   Have no right to search the aircraft

27. To fly on an international flight, a pilot must hold a licence issued or rendered valid by:

    a.   Any contracting state

    b.   ICAO

    c.   The state where the aircraft is based

    d.   The state of registry of the aircraft

28. Under the Chicago Convention, ensuring compliance with rules and regulations concerning aircraft in flight is the duty of:

    a.   The state over whose territory the flight is taking place

    b.   The state of registry

    c.   ICAO

    d.   The state of registry and the state over whose territory the flight is taking place

29. An Alerting Service is provided:

    a.   Automatically to all aircraft known to any of the Air Traffic Services

    b.   To all aircraft for which there is a current flight plan

    c.   Only by Flight Information Service Officers

    d.   To all aircraft in receipt of an Air Traffic Control service

30. The Transition Altitude is:

    a.   3000 feet AMSL

    b.   Altitude above which vertical position is controlled by reference to SPS

    c.   Altitude at and below which vertical position is controlled by reference to QNH

    d.   A level below which QNH must be used

31. What is the definition of "Air Traffic"?

    a.   All aircraft in flight within an FIR

    b.   All aircraft in flight or on the manoeuvring area of an aerodrome

    c.   All aircraft in flight or on the manoeuvring area or apron of an aerodrome

    d.   All aircraft on the manoeuvring area or apron of an aerodrome

32. The minimum medical requirement to allow a student pilot training for the issue of a JAR-FCL PPL(A) to fly solo is a:

    a.   Class 1 Medical Certificate

    b.   Class 2 Medical Certificate

    c.   Class 3 Medical Certificate

    d.   Declaration from their GP

33. An aircraft Weight Schedule must be prepared by the operator and preserved:

    a.   For six months after the next weighing

    b.   For nine months after the next weighing

    c.   For twelve months after the next weighing

    d.   Until the next weighing

34. The absolute minimum flight visibility required to fly outside controlled airspace by a PPL (A) holder who has neither an IR nor an IMC rating is (UK) :

   a.   1000 m
   b.   3 km
   c.   5 km
   d.   1500 m

35. Whilst flying at night you see the green navigation light of another flying machine at a similar level on a steady relative bearing of 310:

   a.   There is a risk of collision, you should maintain heading and speed
   b.   There is a risk of collision, you should climb or descend
   c.   There is a risk of collision, you should turn right
   d.   There is no risk of collision

36. A PPL holder who becomes aware of the need for a surgical operation must:

   a.   Undergo treatment and need not seek the advice of an Authorised Medical Examiner
   b.   Seek the advice of the Authority or an AME without undue delay
   c.   Seek the advice of his GP without undue delay
   d.   Seek the advice of the hospital concerned

37. Which of the following would be classed as an aircraft accident?

   a.   During landing the propeller tips are slightly damaged
   b.   An engine failure in the circuit. Damage is confined to the engine and the aircraft makes a successful forced landing on the runway.
   c.   A person is seriously injured on the apron by the wingtip of a taxiing aircraft
   d.   An aircraft under tow damages another parked aircraft

38. Within a Control Zone with no access lanes on a SVFR clearance ATC provide (UK):

   a.   Separation from other SVFR traffic and obstacle clearance
   b.   Neither separation from other SVFR traffic nor obstacle clearance
   c.   Obstacle clearance, but separation is the pilot's responsibility
   d.   Separation from other SVFR traffic, obstacle clearance is the pilot's responsibility

39. Before carrying passengers a PPL(A) holder shall have made 3 take-offs and 3 landings within:

   a.   The preceding 45 days
   b.   The preceding 90 days
   c.   The preceding calendar month
   d.   The preceding 60 days

40. VFR traffic in Class D airspace may expect:

   a.   Separation from all other aircraft
   b.   Traffic information on VFR flights and separation from IFR aircraft
   c.   Traffic information on all other flights
   d.   Traffic information on IFR flights and separation from VFR flights

---

END OF LAW PAPER 2

No.	A	B	C	D
1				X
2			X	
3	X			
4	X			
5		X		
6				X
7		X		
8				X
9	X			
10			X	
11		X		
12				X
13		X		
14			X	
15			X	
16				X
17		X		
18		X		
19	X			
20	X			
21				X
22	X			
23				X
24			X	
25		X		
26			X	
27				X
28				X
29	X			
30			X	
31		X		
32		X		
33	X			
34		X		
35	X			
36		X		
37			X	
38				X
39		X		
40			X	

CORRECT ANSWERS: PERCENTAGES										
30	31	32	33	34	35	36	37	38	39	40
75%	77%	80%	82%	85%	87%	90%	92%	95%	97%	100%

1. **(Answer: D)** ICAO recommends that taxiway markings are yellow.

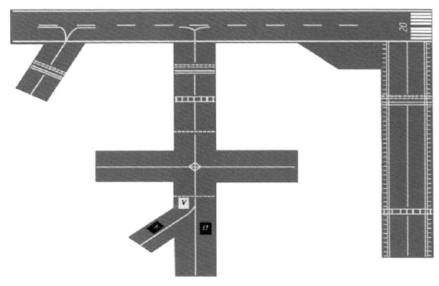

Aerodrome unsafe landing prohibited

Must exercise caution

Land in emergency only

2. **(Answer: C)** A red square with two yellow diagonal stripes placed in the aerodrome signal area indicates that the aerodrome is unsafe and landing is prohibited. Similar signals are: Meaning that the state of the manoeuvring area is poor, pilots must exercise caution, land in emergency only.

3. **(Answer: A)** Runway end lights are fixed unidirectional lights showing red in the direction of the runway shown in red. Green Lights are the Runway threshold lights.

3. **Answer A**

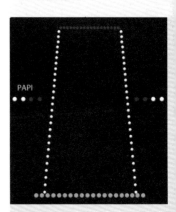

4. **(Answer: A)** A JAA PPL is valid for 5 years (60 months) from the date of issue.

5. **(Answer: B)** When aircraft are converging in the air:
   - *Flying machines must give way to airships, gliders and balloons*
   - *Airships must give way to gliders and balloons*
   - *Gliders must give way to balloons*

   Try to remember this order: Powered aircraft, airships, gliders and balloons. That is the order of priority when aircraft are converging, and whatever you are flying you give way to everything listed after you in the order. Powered aircraft must also give way to aircraft which are towing other aircraft or objects.

6. **(Answer D)** When two aircraft are approaching head on, or approximately so, and there is danger of collision, each must alter heading to the right.

6. **Answer D**

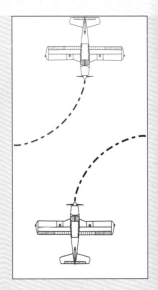

7. **(Answer: B)** "Flooded" means that extensive standing water is visible.

   WATER CONTAMINATION ON RUNWAYS:
Damp:	The surface shows a change in colour due to moisture.
Wet:	The surface is soaked but there is no standing water.
Water patches:	Significant standing water is visible.
Flooded:	Extensive standing water is visible.

   The runway surface is assessed and reported to pilots in thirds – for example it may be described as being "wet/wet/damp".

8. **(Answer: D)** For non-scheduled flights each state will allow aircraft from other states to fly into or through its airspace, and to land within its borders without prior permission; note though that scheduled flights do require permission to overfly another State. However states reserve the right to require any overflying aircraft to land or to follow prescribed routes in airspace where navigation facilities are inadequate or terrain is difficult.

9. **(Answer: A)** Visual Meteorological Conditions (VMC) are expressed in terms of visibility, distance from cloud and ceiling, equal to or better than the specified minima.

10. **(Answer: C)** A pilot who does not meet international licensing standards in full, but still continues to hold a licence, must have the licence endorsed detailing the ways in which the conditions have not been satisfied.

11. **(Answer: B)** A pilot who experiences:
    - *Significant personal injury making him/her unfit to act as flight crew*
    - *Illness involving incapacity for 21 days or more*
    - *Or pregnancy.*

    Must inform the Authority in writing of the injury or pregnancy, and in the case of illness as soon as 21 days have elapsed. The medical certificate is deemed suspended upon the occurrence of such an injury or the confirmation of pregnancy or once the 21 days have elapsed in the case of illness.

12. **(Answer: D)** The pilot-in-command is the person responsible for the operation and safety of the aircraft, and for the safety of all persons on board during the flight.

13. **(Answer: B)** In the signal area, a black ball suspended from a mast means that the directions of take-off and landing are not necessarily the same. *(see picture opposite)*

14. **(Answer: C)** A series of white flashes directed from an aerodrome to an aircraft in flight means: land at this aerodrome after receiving a steady green light.

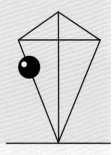

13. Answer B

TO AIRCRAFT IN THE AIR	TO AIRCRAFT ON THE GROUND
Cleared to land. If pilot is satisfied that no collision risk exists.	Cleared for take-off. If pilot is satisfied that no collision risk exists.
Return to this aerodrome and wait for permission to land.	Cleared to taxi on the manoeuvring area. If pilot is satisfied that no collision risk exists.
Land at this aerodrome after receiving a steady green light.	Return to starting point on the aerodrome.

15. **(Answer: C)** Overtaking in the air: The aircraft being overtaken has the right of way, and the overtaking aircraft, whether climbing, descending or in level flight, will keep out of the way by altering course to the right. The overtaking aircraft must not pass over, under or in front of the other aircraft, unless passing well clear and must take account of wake turbulence. A glider overtaking another glider may alter course in either direction.

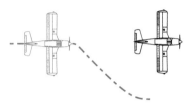

In the Air turn RIGHT
To Overtake

Overtaking on the ground: A flying machine which is being overtaken shall have the right of way and the overtaking flying machine shall keep out of the way by altering its course to the left until the other flying machine has been passed and is clear. Interestingly, the ICAO rule concerning overtaking on the ground makes no mention as to the direction the overtaking aircraft must turn, implying that the overtaking aircraft may pass to either side.

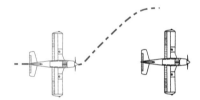

On the Ground turn LEFT
To Overtake

16. **(Answer: D)** 2 minutes.

Wake turbulence departure separations:

Lead Aircraft	Following Aircraft	Minimum wake turbulence separation at time aircraft are airborne	
Heavy	Meduim, Small Light	Departure from the same position	2 Minutes
Medium, Small	Light		2 Minutes
Heavy (full length take-off)	Medium, Small, Light	Departure from an intermediate point on the same runway	3 Minutes
Medium, Small (full length take-off)	Light		3 Minutes

- *The heavier the aircraft and the more slowly it is flying, the stronger the vortex.*
- *Vortices are especially persistent in calm conditions*
- *Vortices are generated by fixed-wing aircraft when the nose wheel lifts off the runway on take-off and continue until the nose wheel touches down on landing.*

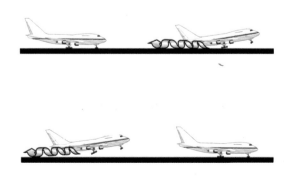

16. ANSWER D

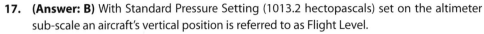

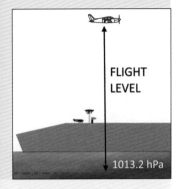

17. Answer B

SPS is usually used at high level when terrain separation is not the most significant issue and traffic separation is the main concern.

17. **(Answer: B)** With Standard Pressure Setting (1013.2 hectopascals) set on the altimeter sub-scale an aircraft's vertical position is referred to as Flight Level.

18. **(Answer: B)** The flight manual forms part of the C of A and specifies requirements, procedures and limitations relating to the operation of the aircraft. ICAO Annex 8: Each aircraft shall be provided with a Flight manual, placards or other documents describing any limitations within which the aircraft is considered airworthy, and any information necessary for the safe operation of the aircraft.

19. **(Answer: A)** A JAR PPL holder must have a valid Medical Certificate in order to exercise the privileges of the licence. The medical must be either Class 1 or Class 2.

20. **(Answer: A)** The aircraft must give way. If ATC have not instructed otherwise the right of way on the ground goes to:
   • *Aircraft taking off or landing,*
   • *Vehicles involved in towing*
   • *Aircraft*
   • *Vehicles.*

21. **(Answer: D)** In search and rescue operations V means "require assistance".

   Standard Ground-to-Air Visual SAR Signals

V	**Require Assistance**
X	**Require Medical Assistance**
→	**Proceeding in this direction**
Y	**Yes or Affirmative**
N	**No or Negative**

22. **(Answer: A)** The special purpose transponder codes are:
   7700 = emergency
   7600 = radio failure
   7500 = unlawful interference

23. Answer D

23. **(Answer: D)** In a signal area the following symbol indicates that the direction of take-off and landing does not necessarily coincide.

24. **(Answer: C)** The Take-off distance available (TODA) is the length of the take-off run available plus the length of any associated clearway.

   A clearway is a defined rectangular area of ground or water under the control of the appropriate authority, prepared as a suitable area over which an aeroplane may make an initial portion of its climb to a specified height.

24. Answer C

TAKE-OFF RUN AVAILABLE (TORA)   CLEARWAY

TAKE-OFF DISTANCE AVAILABLE (TODA)

25. **(Answer: B)** According to JAR-FCL a single pilot single-engine class rating is valid for 2 years.

26. **(Answer: C)** Each State has the right to search aircraft from another state on landing or before departure, and to inspect documentation without causing unnecessary delay.

27. **(Answer: D)** The pilot of every aircraft engaged in international navigation shall have licences or certificates of competence issued or rendered valid by the State in which the aircraft is registered.

28. **(Answer: D)** Both the State in which the aircraft is registered and the State within whose airspace a flight takes place are responsible for ensuring that the appropriate rules and regulations are adhered to.

29. **(Answer: A)** An Alerting Service is automatically provided to all aircraft known to any of the Air Traffic Services. It means that the ground station will ensure that the appropriate organisations are alerted to aircraft in need of search and rescue aid and assistance is given to those organisations as required.

30. **(Answer: C)** The Transition Altitude is the altitude at or below which the vertical position of an aircraft is controlled by reference to altitude i.e. QNH

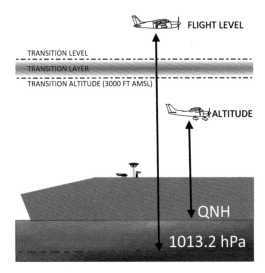

30. ANSWER C

31. **(Answer: B)** "Air Traffic" is defined as all aircraft in flight or operating on the manoeuvring area of aerodromes.

32. **Answer: B)** A Class 2 medical certificate is required for the JAR-FCL PPL.

33. **(Answer: A)** When a new Weight Schedule is prepared the previous Weight Schedule must be preserved for a period of six months. ANO Article 23.

34. **(Answer: B)** This question is about the privileges accorded to a Private Pilot, set out in the ANO Schedule 7. This states that unless a pilot has obtained either an Instrument Rating (IR) or an Instrument Meteorological Conditions Rating (IMCR), he may not fly as pilot-in-command:
    i.   *When outside controlled airspace in a flight visibility of less than 3 km.*
    ii. *On a Special VFR flight in a Control Zone in a flight visibility of less than 10 km except on a route or in an ATZ notified for the purpose.*
    iii. *Out of sight of the surface.*
    iv. *Or as co-pilot, of an aircraft in Class D and E airspace in circumstances that require compliance with the IFR.*

35. Answer A

Remember:

RED to RED = SAFE

GREEN to GREEN = SAFE

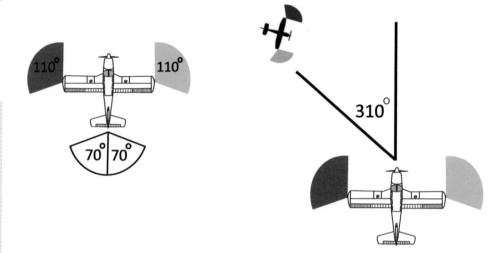

35. **(Answer: A)** There is a risk of collision, you have the right of way (your aircraft is on the right) and so you should maintain heading and speed.

36. **(Answer: B)** Licence holders or student pilots shall not exercise the privileges of their licences, related ratings or authorisations at any time when they are aware of any decrease in their medical fitness which might render them unable to safely exercise those privileges. They shall without undue delay seek the advice of the authority or AME when they become aware of the need for:

    - *A hospital or clinic admission for more than 12 hours*
    - *A surgical operation or invasive procedure*
    - *The regular use of medication*
    - *The regular use of correcting lenses*

37. **(Answer: C)** An accident must be reported if, between the time when anyone boards the aircraft with the intention of flight, until all such persons have disembarked:

    - *Anyone is killed or seriously injured while in or on the aircraft or by direct contact with the aircraft including anything that has become detached from it. This includes direct exposure to jet blast but not anything self-inflicted or due to natural causes. It does not include stowaways; or*
    - *The aircraft incurs damage or structural failure other than any failure or damage limited to the engine or its accessories. If the damage is only limited to propellers, wingtips, aerials, tyres, brakes, fairings, small dents or small puncture holes, it is not reportable. (Unless any of the afore-mentioned adversely affects the aircraft's structural strength, performance or flight characteristics and requires major repair or replacement).*
    - *The aircraft is missing or completely inaccessible.*

38. **(Answer: D)** On a Special VFR clearance outside any notified access lanes or areas, ATC will provide separation between aircraft operating SVFR. The pilot is responsible for obstacle clearance. Under SVFR the pilot's responsibilities are:

    - *He must comply with ATC instructions;*
    - *He must remain in flight conditions that enable him to determine his flight path and keep clear of obstacles – in other words remain clear of cloud and in sight of the surface;*
    - *He must not enter an ATZ unless permission has been obtained;*
    - *He must fly within the limitations of his license.*
    - *The pilot is absolved from the 1000 feet rule, but NO OTHER LOW FLYING RULES – particularly the ability to alight clear.*

39. **(Answer: B)** Currency: To carry passengers a pilot must have made at least 3 take-offs and landings as the sole manipulator of the controls within the preceding 90 days in the same type or class of aircraft.

40. **(Answer: C)** VFR aircraft in Class D airspace will receive traffic information on both IFR and other VFR aircraft. It is the responsibility of the pilot operating VFR to then see and avoid other traffic.

CLASS D	
FLIGHT RULES	IFR and VFR
REQUIREMENTS	ATC clearance before entry. Comply with ATC instructions
ATC SERVICE	(a) Separate IFR flights from other IFR flights; (b) Pass traffic information to IFR flights on VFR flights and give traffic avoidance advice if requested; (c) Pass traffic information to VFR flights on IFR flights and other VFR flights.

END OF EXPLANATIONS PAPER 2

INTENTIONALLY BLANK

AIR LAW PAPER 3

1. This symbol across a taxiway means:

   a. There is one more holding point before the runway

   b. The end of the useable taxiway and the symbol must not be crossed

   c. A holding point which must not be crossed in the direction of the runway without ATC permission

   d. A holding point which must not be crossed in the direction of the taxiway without ATC permission

2. In an aerodrome signal area, a red square with a single yellow diagonal stripe means:

   a. The aerodrome is closed

   b. Landing is prohibited, the aerodrome is unsafe for the movement of aircraft

   c. Sandwiches in the cafe are cut in half

   d. The state of the manoeuvring area is poor and pilots must exercise caution when landing

3. The dimensions of an ATZ surrounding an aerodrome where the longest runway is greater than 1850m are: a circle of ...(i)... in radius extending from the surface to ...(ii)...feet AAL.

   a. i) 2 nm   ii) 2000 ft

   b. i) 2½nm   ii) 2000 ft

   c. i) 5 nm   ii) 3000 ft

   d. i) 2½km   ii) 2000 ft

4. Whilst flying within an ATZ the pilot of an aircraft equipped with a two-way radio must:

   a. Maintain a continuous listening watch on the appropriate frequency and report the aircraft's position and heading on entering and leaving the zone

   b. Report the aircraft's position, intentions and height on entering and leaving the zone

   c. Maintain a continuous listening watch on the appropriate frequency and report the aircraft'sposition and height on entering and leaving the zone

   d. Report the aircraft's position and heading on entering and leaving the zone

5. Where take-offs and landings are not confined to a runway. A pilot taking off shall position so as to leave clear .... any aircraft which is taking off:

   a. On the pilot's left

   b. On the pilot's left, if it is a standard left hand circuit pattern

   c. On the pilot's right

   d. On the pilot's right, if it is a right hand circuit pattern

6. After prolonged holding you find your fuel state is becoming critical. What should you do?

   a. Notify ATC with the phrase "fuel emergency"

   b. Notify ATC with the phrase "fuel priority"

   c. Notify ATC with the phrase "minimum fuel"

   d. Declare an emergency, either MAYDAY or PAN

7. In relation to Search and Rescue a phase wherein there is apprehension as to the safety of an aircraft and its occupants is called the:

   a. Uncertainty Phase

   b. Alert Phase

   c. Emergency Phase

   d. Distress Phase

8. Under the terms of the Chicago convention , in addition to certain others, an aircraft involved in international navigation is required to carry which of the following documents?

   a. Certificate of Registration and crew log books

   b. Journey log book and passports

   c. Certificate of registration, certificate of airworthiness and crew licences

   d. Certificate of airworthiness and crew log books

9.   Under the terms of the Chicago convention, a C of A issued in one contracting state will be recognised as valid by another contracting state if:

   a.   Both are members of the JAA

   b.   There is a bi-lateral agreement between the states

   c.   The C of A is issued in accordance with ICAO standards and requirements

   d.   The C of A is current

10.   Whilst flying at night you see the red navigation light of another flying machine on a steady relative bearing of 030 at a similar level. There is:

   a.   There is a risk of collision, you should maintain heading and speed

   b.   There is no risk of collision

   c.   There is a risk of collision, you should climb or descend

   d.   There is a risk of collision, you should turn right

11.   An aircraft displaying a single red navigation light by night is:

   a.   An airship

   b.   Incorrect

   c.   A glider

   d.   A glider or a free balloon

12.   When an aircraft from a contracting ICAO state lands in the territory of another state, with regard to customs duty:

   a.   Fuel, spare parts and lubricating oils are subject to customs duty

   b.   Spare parts and lubricating oils remaining on board are exempt from customs duty

   c.   Spare parts, but not lubricating oils remaining on board are exempt

   d.   Spare parts and lubricating oils remaining on board are exempt from customs duty as long as the next flight leaves the country in question

13.   An aircraft shall not be flown under simulated instrument flight conditions unless:

   a.   An instructor is on board and ATC have been advised

   b.   The pilot in command holds an instrument rating

   c.   ATC have been informed

   d.   The aircraft has dual controls and a safety pilot occupies the second control seat

14.   A pilot intercepted by another aircraft should try to establish contact with the intercepting aircraft on:

   a.   The frequency currently in use

   b.   The nearest FIS frequency

   c.   121.5 MHz

   d.   The frequency of the nearest aerodrome

15.   ATC has not allocated an approach order, if two or more aircraft are on final approach which has the right of way?

   a.   The one closest to the runway

   b.   The one at the lower altitude

   c.   The one with the greatest altitude

   d.   The one with the fastest approach speed

16.   If you are issued an Air Traffic Control Clearance which you consider to be unsuitable, you should:

   a.   Request an alternative clearance

   b.   Comply with the clearance even though it is unsuitable

   c.   Ignore the clearance and continue as you planned to

   d.   Comply with as much of the clearance as you can

17.   The definition of "alternate aerodrome" is:

    a.   An aerodrome, specified in a flight plan, to be used in case of emergency

    b.   An aerodrome to which the flight will proceed if the first diversion airfield is unavailable

    c.   An aerodrome to which a flight may proceed if it is either impossible or inadvisable to land at the intended destination aerodrome

    d.   A temporary base, if the normal base aerodrome is unusable

18.   Approved limitations within which the aircraft is considered airworthy are contained in:

    a.   The aircraft maintenance documents

    b.   The Pilot's Operating handbook

    c.   The aircraft technical manual

    d.   The flight manual and on cockpit placards and markings

19.   Flying within sight of the surface in Class G at 130 knots below 3000 ft AMSL, the VMC minima are:

    a.   Visibility 1500 m, clear of cloud

    b.   Visibility 5 km, clear of cloud

    c.   Visibility 1500 m, 1500 ft vertically from cloud

    d.   Visibility 5 km, 1000 m horizontally from cloud

20.   ICAO requires that all aircraft operated on VFR flights shall be equipped with at least:

    a.   Attitude indicator, sensitive pressure altimeter, accurate time piece

    b.   Magnetic compass, attitude indicator, sensitive pressure altimeter

    c.   Magnetic compass, accurate time piece, airspeed indicator

    d.   Magnetic compass, attitude indicator, airspeed indicator

21.   A person on the ground is seriously injured after being hit by a component that has become detached from an aircraft in flight. The event is :

    a.   An aircraft incident

    b.   A reportable occurrence

    c.   A crime

    d.   An aircraft accident

22.   On over water flights single engine land planes should carry life rafts when their distance from land suitable for making an emergency landing is more than:

    a.   100 km

    b.   200 km

    c.   100 nm

    d.   200 nm

23.   Controlled airspace extending from the surface of the earth upwards to a specified upper limit is a:

    a.   Control Zone

    b.   Control Area

    c.   Aerodrome Traffic Zone

    d.   Airway

24.   With QNH set on the altimeter subscale, vertical position is reported as:

    a.   Flight level

    b.   Altitude

    c.   Height

    d.   Elevation

25. Water contamination on a runway described as "water patches" means that:

   a.   The runway surface shows a change of colour due to moisture

   b.   The surface is soaked but there is no standing water

   c.   Extensive standing water is visible

   d.   Significant patches of standing water are visible

26. A designated area on an aerodrome provided for aircraft parking, refuelling and the loading and unloading of passengers or cargo, is the:

   a.   Manoeuvring area

   b.   Movement area

   c.   Apron

   d.   Terminal

27. The minimum age at which a student pilot can make a solo flight is:

   a.   16 years

   b.   15 years

   c.   18 years

   d.   17 years

28. A Terminal Control Area (TCA) is a:

   a.   Control Area in the vicinity of major airports handling only arriving flights

   b.   Control Area established at the confluence of ATS routes in the vicinity of one or more major aerodromes

   c.   Control Zone established at the confluence of ATS routes in the vicinity of one or more major aerodromes

   d.   Control Area in the vicinity of major airports handling only departing flights

29. An Air Traffic Control service is provided to all aircraft. IFR flights are separated from each other and receive traffic information on VFR flights. VFR flights receive traffic information on all other flights. What Class of airspace is being described?

   a.   Class A

   b.   Class B

   c.   Class C

   d.   Class D

30. The minimum flight time required for the issue of a JAR-FCL PPL(A)is:

   a.   25 hours

   b.   30 hours

   c.   35 hours

   d.   45 hours

31. Under UK regulations the minimum radio and navigation equipment required to fly VFR in Class D is:

   a.   VHF communications

   b.   VHF communications and transponder

   c.   VHF communications, VOR and transponder

   d.   VHF communications, VOR, DME and transponder

32. In relation to Search and Rescue signals, what is the visual signal used by survivors to indicate "require medical assistance"?

   a.   V

   b.   N

   c.   X

   d.   Y

33. On an international flight a UK registered aircraft must carry a Certificate of Airworthiness issued or rendered valid by:

    a.   EASA

    b.   The JAA

    c.   The UK CAA

    d.   ICAO

34. Which of the following is a method to re-validate a single engine piston class rating?

    a.   Pass a proficiency check flight with a flight examiner within 12 months preceding the expiry date of the rating

    b.   Complete 12 hours of flight time including 6 hours PIC and 12 take-offs and landings, and complete a 1 hour training flight with an instructor within the 12 months preceding the expiry of the rating

    c.   Complete 12 hours of flight time including 6 take-offs and landings, and complete a 2 hour training flight with an instructor within the 6 months preceding the expiry of the rating

    d.   Complete a 2 hour training flight with a flying instructor in 6 months preceding the expiry of the rating

35. To overtake another aircraft on the ground you must (UK):

    a.   Alter course to the left

    b.   Alter course to the right

    c.   Not overtake, but wait for the aircraft ahead to speed up

    d.   Alter course to the left or right

36. To overtake another aircraft in the air you must:

    a.   Alter course to the left

    b.   Alter course to the right

    c.   Fly over or under the other aircraft

    d.   Alter course to the left or right

37. The flight time required for the grant of a licence or rating:

    a.   May be flown in any aircraft deemed airworthy e.g." Permit to Fly" aircraft

    b.   May be flown in any aircraft with a valid C of A

    c.   Must be flown in an aircraft of the same category for which the licence or rating is sought

    d.   May be flown in a different category of aircraft for which the licence or rating is sought

38. On encountering severe weather phenomena that were not included in the forecast you should:

    a.   Report the conditions on landing

    b.   Make a note not to trust the forecast again

    c.   Make a special air-report to air traffic

    d.   Leave the vicinity by the quickest means available

39. If you have caused notice of your intended arrival at an aerodrome, you must ensure that the appropriate authority at that aerodrome are advised of:

    a.   Any change in destination or estimated delay of 45 minutes or more

    b.   Any estimated delay of 30 minutes or more

    c.   Any estimated delay of 60 minutes or more

    d.   Any change in destination or estimated delay of 30 minutes or more

40. When in level flight at altitude 5,000 feet. Given a track of 280°T with a variation of 3W and 15° of port drift an appropriate cruising level would be:

    a.   FL 50

    b.   FL 55

    c.   FL 60

    d.   FL 45

END OF AIR LAW PAPER 3

AIR LAW PAPER 3: ANSWERS

No.	A	B	C	D
1			X	
2				X
3		X		
4			X	
5	X			
6				X
7		X		
8			X	
9			X	
10				X
11				X
12		X		
13				X
14			X	
15		X		
16	X			
17			X	
18				X
19	X			
20			X	
21				X
22			X	
23	X			
24		X		
25				X
26			X	
27	X			
28		X		
29				X
30				X
31	X			
32			X	
33			X	
34		X		
35	X			
36		X		
37			X	
38			X	
39	X			
40				X

CORRECT ANSWERS: PERCENTAGES										
30	31	32	33	34	35	36	37	38	39	40
75%	77%	80%	82%	85%	87%	90%	92%	95%	97%	100%

AIR LAW PAPER 3: EXPLANATIONS

1. **(Answer: C)** A holding point marking consisting of two solid and two broken lines is used to indicate the last holding point before the runway. It must not be crossed when moving towards the runway without permission from ATC.

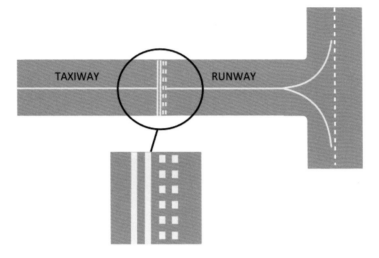

2. **(Answer: D)** A red square with a single yellow diagonal stripe placed in the aerodrome signal area indicates that the state of the manoeuvring area is poor and pilots must exercise special care when landing.

3. **(Answer: B)** 2½nm from the surface to 2,000 feet. ATZs are established around many aerodromes for the protection of traffic operating at that airfield. An ATZ extends from the ground, i.e. aerodrome elevation to 2,000 feet, and is circular.

   The radius of the circle depends on the length of the longest runway at the airfield:
   - *If it is 1850 m or less the radius of the ATZ is 2 nm,*
   - *If greater than 1850 m the radius is 2.5 nm.*

   NOTE: ICAO DOES NOT SPECIFY THE DIMENSIONS OF AN ATZ, THESE ARE DECIDED AND PROMULGATED BY THE NATIONAL AUTHORITIES – THOSE QUOTED HERE ARE FOR THE UK.

   ATZs adopt the classification of the airspace within which they lie.

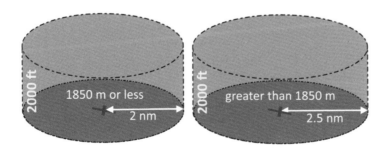

4. **(Answer: C)** Whilst flying within the ATZ the pilot must:

- *Maintain a continuous listening watch on the appropriate frequency, or if this is not possible*
- *Keep watch for visual signals from the ground.*
- *If the aircraft is radio equipped the pilot must report his position and height on*
- *entering and immediately prior to leaving the ATZ.*

Rule 43 of the ANO also states that a pilot may not fly, take off or land within the ATZ unless he either:

- *has permission from the ATCU or*
- *has obtained the information to enable the flight to be conducted safely in the ATZ from the FISO or A/G communication service.*

5. **(Answer: A)** If take-offs and landings are not confined to a runway a flying machine which is about to take off shall take up position and manoeuvre in such a way as to leave clear on its left any aircraft which has already taken off or is about to take off.

6. **(Answer: D)** If after prolonged holding you find your fuel state is becoming critical you should declare an emergency, either a "Mayday" or "Pan Pan" call as appropriate. Any other options are not recognised states of emergency and ATC will simply seek clarification from you as to whether you wish to declare a "Mayday" or "Pan Pan". AIC pink 58 82/2003.

7. **(Answer: B)** The Alert Phase is one wherein apprehension exists as to the safety of an aircraft and its occupants.

Emergency Phase	Definition	Duration
Uncertainty Phase	A situation wherein uncertainty exists as to the safety of an aircraft and its occupants.	Maximum of 30 minutes
Alert Phase	A situation wherein apprehension exists as to the safety of an aircraft and its occupants.	Maximum of one hour
Distress Phase	A situation wherein there is a reasonable certainty that an aircraft and its occupants are threatened by grave and imminent danger and require immediate assistance.	Until the aircraft is found and the survivors rescued. OR It is clear that there is no longer any chance of so doing.

8. **(Answer: C)** An aircraft involved in international navigation is required to carry Certificate of Registration, Certificate of Airworthiness and crew licences

ICAO ARTICLE 29 DOCUMENTS CARRIED IN AIRCRAFT
All aircraft flying internationally shall carry the following documents:

- *Certificate of registration;*
- *Certificate of Airworthiness;*
- *Appropriate licences for each crew member;*
- *Journey logbook;*
- *Appropriate radio licences;*
- *If carrying passengers, a list of their names and places of embarkation (boarding) and destination;*
- *If carrying cargo, a manifest and detailed declarations of cargo.*

9. **(Answer: C) ICAO ARTICLE 33 RECOGNITION OF CERTIFICATES AND LICENCES**

Certificates of Airworthiness and flight crew licences issued by the state in which the aircraft is registered shall be recognised by other contracting states, provided that the requirements for the issue of such certificates and licences meet ICAO standards.

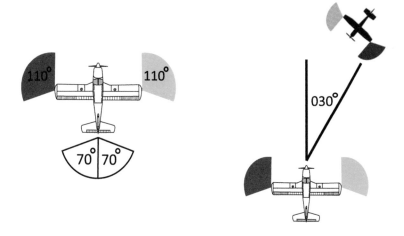

10. **(Answer: D)** A flying machine is on a collision course and has the right of way; you should turn right to give way.

11. **(Answer: D)** By night, a glider may display either the basic navigation lights, or a steady red light visible in all directions. Free balloons are required to show a steady red light visible in all directions.

12. **(Answer: B)** Fuel, lubricating oils, spare parts, regular equipment and aircraft stores retained on board the aircraft are temporarily exempt from customs duty.
     ICAO ARTICLE 24 CUSTOMS DUTY
     Aircraft entering another state's territory shall be admitted temporarily free of duty, subject to the state's customs regulations.
     Fuel, oil, spare parts and regular equipment that are on board an aircraft on arrival in another state, and retained on board on departure, shall be exempt from duty. This does not apply to anything that is unloaded from the aircraft.
     Spare parts imported into a state for use by an aircraft from another state on international operations shall be free of duty.

13. **(Answer: D)** An aircraft may not be flown under simulated instrument conditions, meaning that the pilot is flying with his field of vision artificially restricted, unless the aircraft is fitted with dual controls and a safety pilot is present in the second control seat to provide assistance to the pilot flying the aircraft. Note a student pilot is not able to act as a "safety pilot" for the purpose of this rule. ANO Rule 23.

14. **(Answer: C)** A pilot intercepted by another aircraft should try to establish contact with the intercepting aircraft on 121.5 MHz giving the call sign and the nature of the flight.

15. **(Answer: B)** When ATC has not allocated an approach order, if two or more aircraft are on final approach the lower aircraft has right of way (but it must not cut in front, or overtake another on final approach). Provided that:
     *   *When ATC give an order of priority for landing, aircraft must approach in that order; and*
     *   *You must give way to any aircraft in an emergency*

16. **(Answer: A)** If you are issued an Air Traffic Control Clearance which you consider to be unsuitable, or with which you cannot comply, you should an alternative clearance.

17. **(Answer: C)** Alternate aerodrome: an aerodrome to which an aircraft may proceed if it becomes either impossible or inadvisable to proceed to or land at the intended destination aerodrome.

18. **(Answer: D)** The flight manual forms part of the C of A and specifies requirements, procedures and limitations relating to the operation of the aircraft.

    ICAO Annex 8: Each aircraft shall be provided with a Flight manual, placards or other documents describing any limitations within which the aircraft is considered airworthy, and any information necessary for the safe operation of the aircraft.

19. **(Answer: A)** Flying within sight of the surface in Class G at 130 knots below 3000 ft AMSL, the VMC minima are flight visibility of 1500 m and remaining clear of cloud.

At or Below 3000 ft AMSL		
Class F & G	Clear of cloud and with the surface in sight	5 km
For Aircraft, Flying at 140 knots or less		
Class C, D & E	Clear of cloud and with the surface in sight	5 km
Class F & G	Clear of cloud and with the surface in sight	1500 m

20. **(Answer: C) ICAO ANNEX 6.**

    All aeroplanes operated as VFR flights shall be equipped with:

    •   *A magnetic compass*

    •   *An accurate time piece*

    •   *A sensitive pressure altimeter*

    •   *An airspeed indicator*

    •   *Any additional equipment prescribed by its Authority.*

21. **(Answer: D)** An accident must be reported if, between the time when anyone boards the aircraft with the intention of flight, until all such persons have disembarked:

    •   *Anyone is killed or seriously injured while in or on the aircraft or by direct contact with the aircraft including anything that has become detached from it. This includes direct exposure to jet blast but not anything self-inflicted or due to natural causes. It does not include stowaways; or*

    •   *The aircraft incurs damage or structural failure other than any failure or damage limited to the engine or its accessories. If the damage is only limited to propellers, wingtips, aerials, tyres, brakes, fairings, small dents or small puncture holes, it is not reportable. (Unless any of the afore-mentioned adversely affects the aircraft's structural strength, performance or flight characteristics and requires major repair or replacement).*

    •   *The aircraft is missing or completely inaccessible.*

22. **(Answer: C)** All aeroplanes on extended open water flights shall be equipped with one life jacket, or suitable floatation device, for each person on board, when the flight will be over water and more than 50 nm from land suitable for an emergency landing.

    Life rafts capable of carrying all persons on board when the flight will be over water and more than 100 nm from land suitable for an emergency landing for a single engine aircraft, or 200 nm in the case of a multi engine aircraft.

23. **(Answer: A)** The definition of a Control Zone (CTR) is "Controlled airspace extending upwards from the surface of the earth to a specified upper limit".

A Control Area (CTA) is airspace of defined dimensions which extends upwards from a specified altitude or flight level to an upper limit, usually a Flight Level.

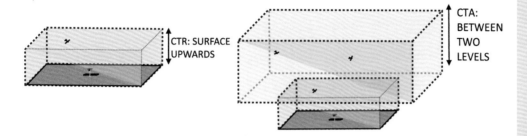

24. **(Answer: B)** With QNH set vertical position is reported at an "altitude".

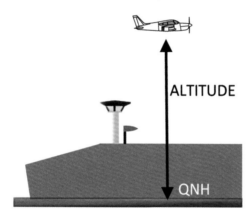

25. **(Answer: D)** "Water patches" means that significant standing water is visible.

WATER CONTAMINATION ON RUNWAYS:

Damp:	The surface shows a change in colour due to moisture.
Wet:	The surface is soaked but there is no standing water.
Water-patches:	Significant standing water is visible.
Flooded:	Extensive standing water is visible.

The runway surface is assessed and reported to pilots in thirds – for example it may be described as being "wet/wet/damp".

26. **(Answer: C)** An apron is a paved area on an aerodrome used for aircraft parking, loading and unloading of passengers, mail or cargo, and refuelling.

27. **(Answer: A)** 16 years is the minimum age at which a student pilot can make a solo flight.

28. **(Answer: B)** A Terminal Control Area (TCA) or Terminal Manoeuvring Area (TMA) is a Control Area established at the confluence of ATS routes in the vicinity of one or more major aerodromes.

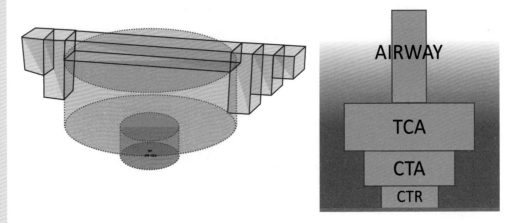

29. **(Answer: D)** Class D Airspace.

CLASS D	
FLIGHT RULES	IFR and VFR
REQUIREMENTS	ATC clearance before entry. Comply with ATC instructions
ATC SERVICE	(a) Separate IFR flights from other IFR flights; (b) Pass traffic information to IFR flights on VFR flights and give traffic avoidance advice if requested; (c) Pass traffic information to VFR flights on IFR flights and other VFR flights.

30. **(Answer: D)** An applicant for a PPL(A) shall have completed at least 45 hours flight time.

31. **(Answer: A)** The minimum radio and navigation equipment required to fly VFR in Class D is equipment for VHF communications. Any pilot wishing to enter controlled airspace must obtain permission and comply with any clearance issued. Whilst within controlled airspace a continuous listening watch must be maintained on the appropriate frequency. Note: ATC may authorise otherwise to accommodate non-radio aircraft, in this case special arrangements will be made by telephone with the pilot concerned before departure.

32. **(Answer: C)** "X" is the visual signal to be used by survivors during Search and Rescue operations to indicate "require medical assistance".

    Standard Ground-to-Air Visual SAR Signals

V	**Require Assistance**
X	**Require Medical Assistance**
→	**Proceeding in this direction**
Y	**Yes or Affirmative**
N	**No or Negative**

33. **(Answer: C) ICAO ARTICLE 31 CERTIFICATE OF AIRWORTHINESS**

    All aircraft operating internationally shall be provided with a Certificate of Airworthiness issued or rendered valid by the State in which it is registered.

34. (Answer: B) An SEP Certificate of Test is valid for 24 months, it can be revalidated by:

    a.   Passing a Proficiency Check with a flight examiner within a period of 3 months preceding the date of expiry, or

    b.   A Certificate of Revalidation relating to experience. Within the 12 months preceding expiry you must have:

        i.   *Logged at least 12 hours flight time (a minimum of 6 as pilot in command)*
        ii.   *12 take-offs and landings; and*
        iii.   *A 1-hour training flight with a flight instructor (recorded and signed in the applicant's log book) If the 24 months (but no more than 5 years) are exceeded without a Certificate of Revalidation, in order to renew the privileges a Proficiency Check with an examiner must be undertaken in order to renew.*

35. (Answer: A) Overtaking on the Ground: A flying machine which is being overtaken shall have the right of way and the overtaking flying machine shall keep out of the way by altering its course to the left until that other flying machine has been passed and is clear. The ICAO rule concerning overtaking on the ground makes no mention as to the direction the overtaking aircraft must turn, implying that the overtaking aircraft may pass to either side.

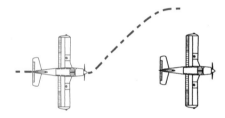

COLLISION AVOIDANCE SUMMARY: ON THE GROUND

GENERAL RIGHT OF WAY	1. Aircraft taking off or landing 2. Vehicles involved in towing 3. Aircraft 4. Vehicles
TWO AIRCRAFT HEAD ON	Each turn **RIGHT**
TWO AIRCRAFT CONVERGING	The one which has the other on its right shall give way. If you are *"on the right you're in the right"*
OVERTAKING	Aircraft being overtaken has right of way. Overtaking aircraft alter course to **LEFT**

36. (Answer: B) Overtaking in the Air: The aircraft being overtaken has the right of way, and the overtaking aircraft, whether climbing, descending or in level flight, will keep out of the way by altering course to the right. The overtaking aircraft must not pass over, under or in front of the other aircraft, unless passing well clear and must take account of wake turbulence. A glider overtaking another glider may alter course in either direction.

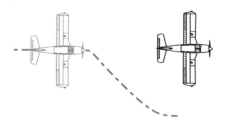

COLLISION AVOIDANCE SUMMARY: IN THE AIR

GENERAL RIGHT OF WAY	Give way to anything below you in the order: 1. Flying machines 2. Airships 3. Gliders 4. Balloons
TWO AIRCRAFT HEAD ON	Each turn **RIGHT**
TWO AIRCRAFT CONVERGING	The one which has the other on its right shall give way. If you are *"on the right you're in the right"*
OVERTAKING	Aircraft being overtaken has right of way. Overtaking aircraft alter course to **LEFT**

NOTE: WITH REGARD TO COLLISION AVOIDANCE ICAO USES SLIGHTLY DIFFERENT WORDING, AND REFERS TO HEADING RATHER THAN COURSE.

37. **(Answer: C)** Flight time to be credited for a licence or rating shall have been flown in the same category of aircraft for which the rating is sought; unless otherwise specified in JAR-FCL.

38. **(Answer: C)** ANO Rule 4 The commander of an aircraft must report as soon as possible any hazardous flight conditions encountered, providing details pertinent to the safety of other aircraft. The quickest means would normally be by radio to the Air Traffic Services.

Special aircraft observations are required as special air-reports for any of the following:

- *Severe icing*
- *Severe turbulence*
- *Severe mountain waves*
- *Thunderstorms*
- *Volcanic ash clouds or pre-eruption volcanic activity.*

Special aircraft observations may be reported if, in the opinion of the pilot in command, conditions are encountered which may affect the safety of other aircraft.

39. **(Answer: A)** ANO Rule 17 If the commander of an aircraft has caused notice of the intended arrival of the aircraft at an aerodrome to be given to the Air Traffic Control Unit or other authority at that aerodrome, he shall ensure that the unit or authority is informed as quickly as possible of:

- *any change of intended destination; and*
- *any estimated delay in arrival of 45 minutes or more.*

40. **(Answer: D)** FL 45 is the most appropriate quadrantal cruising level

Given: Cruising altitude 5,000 feet Track 280°T Variation 3W Drift 15°P

Ignore the drift as this is irrelevant. The magnetic track is 283°M and this is what the quadrantal level is based upon. It puts the aircraft within the sector of 270°M to 359°M which means selecting an even flight level plus five hundred feet. Hence FL 45 is the closest, the next available would be FL 65.

ANO RULE 34
When in level flight above 3,000 feet, or the appropriate transition altitude, whichever is higher and below 19,500 feet, the aircraft must be flown at a flight level appropriate to its magnetic track. Unless flying:
- *in conformity with instructions given by an air traffic control unit;*
- *in accordance with notified en-route holding patterns; or*
- *in accordance with aerodrome holding procedures.*

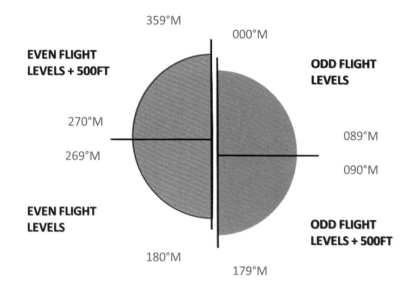

END OF EXPLANATIONS PAPER 3

INTENTIONALLY BLANK

AIR LAW & OPERATIONAL PROCEDURES PAPER 4

1. Each state agrees under the Chicago Convention that:
   a. All aircraft, including those on scheduled services may make flights into or across its territory without prior permission
   b. All aircraft other than those on scheduled services may make flights into or across its territory without prior permission
   c. Only aircraft engaged on scheduled services may make flights into or across its territory without prior permission
   d. All aircraft of other contracting states may cross its territory, provided one landing is made within the state in question

2. Under the Chicago Convention, when an aircraft lands within another contracting state the authorities of that country:
   a. May search the aircraft after notifying the operator in advance
   b. Have the right to search the aircraft for illegal substances
   c. Have no right to search the aircraft
   d. Have the right to search the aircraft without causing unreasonable delay

3. ICAO recognises that, with respect to airspace sovereignty, each contracting state:
   a. Has complete sovereignty over the airspace above its territory
   b. Shares sovereignty with any neighbours having a land border
   c. Must reach regional agreement as to airspace sovereignty
   d. Has no right to sovereignty to the airspace above its territory

4. With regard to the Chicago Convention, when an aircraft enters its territory a contracting state:
   a. Must require it to land at a customs airport
   b. May require it to land at a port of entry
   c. May require it to land at a customs airport
   d. May require it to land at an immigration airport

5. Aerodrome signs that carry mandatory instructions are coloured:
   a. Black script on a red background
   b. Black script on a yellow background
   c. White script on a red background
   d. Red script on a white background

6. In the signals area, a rectangular green flag flown from a mast means:
   a. Left-hand circuits
   b. The direction of take-off and landing does not necessarily coincide
   c. Right-hand circuits
   d. Go

7. In the signals area a white dumb-bell means:
   a. Gliders and aeroplanes need ATC permission to move on the surface
   b. On the ground gliders and aeroplanes shall move only on paved, metalled or hard surfaces
   c. On the ground gliders and aeroplanes shall avoid moving on paved, metalled or hard surfaces
   d. Aeroplanes must take off on the hard runway

8. On an aerodrome the position at which a pilot can report to ATC or other aerodrome authority is marked by:

a. A black board carrying a yellow "C"
b. A red board carrying a white "A"
c. A yellow board carrying a black "A"
d. A yellow board carrying a black "C"

9. Except for helicopters or when aircraft are taking off or landing at a licensed or government aerodrome, you must not fly over the congested area of any city, town or settlement below a height which would enable the aircraft to:

a. Alight clear of the congested area in the event of a power unit failure or below 1000 ft above the highest fixed obstacle within 600 m of the aircraft. Whichever is the higher.
b. Alight safely within the congested area or below 1000 ft above the highest fixed obstacle within 600 m of the aircraft. Whichever is the higher.
c. Alight safely within the congested area or below 1000 ft above the highest fixed obstacle within 5 nm of the aircraft. Whichever is the higher.
d. Alight clear of the congested area in the event of a power unit failure or below 1000 ft above the highest fixed obstacle within 5 nm of the aircraft. Whichever is the higher.

10. The following are possible objectives of the Air Traffic Services:

1. To prevent collisions between aircraft in the air.

2. To assist in preventing collisions between aircraft moving on the apron and the manoeuvring area.

3. To expedite and maintain an orderly flow of traffic.

4. To notify the appropriate organisations of aircraft in need of search and rescue aid, and to assist such organisations as required.

5. To provide information useful to the safe and efficient conduct of flight.

6. To assist in preventing collisions between aircraft and obstructions on the manoeuvring area.

The correct objectives are:
a. 1, 2, 5 and 6
b. 1, 2, 3, 4, 5 and 6
c. 1, 3, 4 and 5
d. 1, 2, 3, 4 and 5

11. The Transition Layer is the airspace between:
a. Mean sea level and the transition altitude
b. The transition level and mean sea level
c. The transition altitude and the transition layer
d. 3000 feet and the transition level

12. An aircraft operating on a Special VFR clearance is exempt from (UK):
a. The "500 feet rule"
b. The "1000 feet rule"
c. The need to "land clear a the congested area"
d. Both the "500 feet rule" and the "1000 feet rule"

13. A Special VFR clearance enables a pilot to:

    a.   Fly with lower weather minima

    b.   Cross an airway without needing a valid IR

    c.   Fly within a Control Zone in circumstances normally requiring an IFR clearance

    d.   Enter a Control Zone without clearance

14. A PPL receiving a Special VFR clearance must maintain a flight visibility of:

    a.   10 km and remain clear of cloud and in sight of the surface

    b.   5 km and remain clear of cloud and in sight of the surface

    c.   10 nm and remain clear of cloud and in sight of the surface

    d.   5 nm and remain clear of cloud and in sight of the surface

15. An aircraft in the UK flying in sight of the surface and following a road, railway, canal, coastline or any other line of landmarks shall keep them on its (....i....) unless (....ii....):

    a.   i) Right ii) within controlled airspace in accordance with ATC instructions

    b.   i) Right ii) otherwise instructed by a FISO

    c.   i) Left ii) otherwise instructed by a FISO

    d.   i) Left ii) within controlled airspace in accordance with ATC instructions

16. A PPL with no additional ratings is in receipt of a Deconfliction Service, ATC instruct the pilot to climb to altitude 4,000 feet. Complying with this instruction would mean the pilot entering cloud. The pilot should:

    a.   Maintain his present level and advise the controller why

    b.   Acknowledge the instruction, but not comply with it

    c.   Comply with the instruction and fly on instruments

    d.   Ignore the instruction

17. If the commander of an aircraft has caused notice of the intended arrival of the aircraft at an aerodrome to be given to the air traffic control unit or other authority at that aerodrome, he shall ensure that the unit or authority is informed as quickly as possible of:

    a.   Any estimated delay in arrival of 30 minutes or more.

    b.   Any estimated delay in arrival of 60 minutes or more.

    c.   Any change of intended destination

    d.   Any change of intended destination; and any estimated delay in arrival of 45 minutes or more.

18. When transiting a MATZ the vertical position of an aircraft is normally controlled by reference to:

    a.   Standard Pressure Setting 1013 hPa

    b.   QFE at the military aerodrome

    c.   QNH at the military aerodrome

    d.   Regional QNH

19. What is the difference between these two different runway threshold markings?

    a.   They are both permanently thresholds. In (i) the pre-threshold is unfit for the movement of aircraft and (ii) the pre-threshold may be used for taxi and take off but not for landing.

    b.   They are both permanently thresholds. In (i) the pre-threshold is unfit for the movement of aircraft and (ii) the pre-threshold may be used.

    c.   They are both temporarily thresholds. In (i) the pre-threshold is unfit for the movement of aircraft and (ii) the pre-threshold may be used for taxi and take off but not for landing.

    d.   They are both temporarily thresholds. In (i) the pre-threshold is unfit for the movement of aircraft and (ii) the pre-threshold may be used.

19. i

19. ii

20. Before entering an active ATZ, or manoeuvring on the surface of the aerodrome a pilot must:

    a. Inform the tower of his intentions

    b. Make two way radio contact with the authority in charge at the aerodrome

    c. Obtain the information from the ATC, FISO or air/ground station to enable the flight to continue safely

    d. Obtain either permission from ATC, or information from the FISO or air/ground station to enable the flight to continue safely

21. A flight plan must be filed for any flight that will cross the UK FIR boundary, but in which of the following circumstances is it advisable to file a flight plan?

    a. For any flight within controlled airspace

    b. For any flight requesting a Deconfliction Service

    c. For any flight more than 5 nm from the UK coastline

    d. For any flight more than 10 nm from the UK coastline

22. With a Regional QNH set on the altimeter sub-scale, the altimeter will:

    a. Accurately indicate height above the ground

    b. Over-read the actual altitude above mean sea level

    c. Accurately indicate altitude above mean sea level

    d. Under-read the actual altitude above mean sea level

23. When flying beneath a Terminal Control Area, or Terminal Manoeuvring Area, what altimeter sub-scale setting should be used?

    a. The appropriate Regional QNH

    b. The QNH of an aerodrome situated beneath the TMA

    c. The QFE of an aerodrome situated beneath the TMA

    d. The lowest between either the Regional QNH or the QNH of an aerodrome beneath the TMA

24. Unless flying within controlled airspace in accordance with ATC instructions, the pilot of an aircraft following a line feature such as a road, railway or coastline should:

    a. Fly with the feature to the left of the aircraft

    b. Fly with the feature to the right of the aircraft

    c. Fly directly above the feature

    d. Keep the feature visible but fly to either convenient side

25. In the aerodrome signal area a black ball suspended from a mast has the same meaning as which of the following signals?

    a. A red square with a yellow cross

    b. A white "T"

    c. A white "T" with a white disc at the head of the "T" in line with the shaft

    d. A red square with a yellow diagonal stripe

26. The provisions of the ANO apply to:

    a. All UK registered aircraft

    b. All aircraft in the UK and to all UK registered aircraft wherever they may be

    c. Only to UK registered aircraft when flying in the UK

    d. All UK registered aircraft when flying in the airspace of another JAA contracting state

27. When may the UK rules of the air and the provisions of the ANO be departed from?

    a. To expedite a routing at any time

    b. When flying outside the boundaries of the UK FIR

    c. To avoid immediate danger or to comply with the law of another country within whose airspace the aircraft is flying

    d. To comply with an ATC instruction

28. You wish to file a flight plan for a flight from an aerodrome that does not have an air traffic service reporting office. You should:

    a. When airborne call the nearest radar unit to file the details

    b. Telephone the details to the destination airfield

    c. When airborne make radio contact with the FIS frequency and file the details

    d. Submit the details either by telephone or by radio to the parent unit designated to serve the departure aerodrome

29. Having filed a flight plan, should a delay be incurred after how long must a DLA message be sent?

    a. 30 minutes

    b. 45 minutes

    c. 60 minutes

    d. 2 hours

30. Should a licence holder wish to transfer his licence from one JAA member state to another JAA member state, it will be permitted provided that:

    a. The licence holder has a work permit valid for the new state

    b. The licence holder resides in the new state for more than 90 days but less than 185 days per year

    c. The licence holder can show "normal residency" in the new state

    d. There are no provisions and the switch can be made at any time

31. Under certain circumstances and subject to complying with specific requirements, a PPL holder may fly as pilot in command for the purpose of aerial work. Two examples are:

    a. Glider towing and parachute dropping

    b. Aerial photography and glider towing

    c. Pleasure flights and crop spraying

    d. Banner towing and glider towing

32. A Military Aerodrome Traffic Zone (MATZ) may be established around UK military aerodromes. They extend from the surface up to 3,000 feet and have a radius of 5 nm. One or more stubs aligned with the final approach path(s) may also be present, the dimensions of the stubs are:

    a. Between 2,000 and 3,000 feet, extending 5 nm from the MATZ boundary with a width of 4 nm

    b. Between 1,000 and 3,000 feet, extending 4 nm from the MATZ boundary with a width of 5 nm

    c. Between 1,000 and 2,000 feet, extending 4 nm from the MATZ boundary with a width of 5 nm

    d. Between 1,000 and 3,000 feet, extending 5 nm from the MATZ boundary with a width of 4 nm

33. This symbol painted across a taxiway denotes:

    a. An instrument CAT I/II/III holding point where there is one more holding point before the runway

    b. The end of the useable taxiway and must not be crossed

    c. A holding point which must not be crossed in the direction of the runway without ATC permission

    d. A holding point which must not be crossed in the direction of the taxiway without ATC permission

Question 33

34. Which of the following would constitute an aircraft accident?

    a. A person is slightly hurt by a panel falling from an aircraft in flight

    b. A main tyre bursts on take off

    c. An engineer positioning the aircraft to a hangar taxis into a building and causes extensive damage to the aircraft

    d. The pilot was forced to ditch and the aircraft has now sunk

35. On the aerodrome manoeuvring area an aircraft is converging with a vehicle which is towing an aircraft. Which must give way?

    a.   The towing vehicle

    b.   The aircraft

    c.   The one which has the other on its left

    d.   The one which has the other on its right

36. Flying within sight of the surface in Class G at 130 knots below 3000 ft AMSL, the VMC minima are:

    a.   Visibility 5 km, clear of cloud

    b.   Visibility 1500 m, 1500 ft vertically from cloud

    c.   Visibility 1500 m, clear of cloud

    d.   Visibility 5 km, 1000 m horizontally from cloud

37. To carry passengers the pilot-in-command must have made, as the sole manipulator of the controls, at least:

    a.   One take-off and landing in the same type or class to be flown within the preceding 30 days

    b.   Three take-offs and landings within the preceding 90 days

    c.   Three take-offs and landings in the same type or class to be flown within the preceding 90 days

    d.   One take-off and landing in the same type or class to be flown within the preceding 28 days

38. What is the difference between a Control Zone and a Control Area?

    a.   Control Areas are always Class A airspace, Control Zones can be other classes

    b.   A pilot requires an ATC clearance to transit through a Control Area

    c.   Control Areas extend from the surface upwards to a specified upper limit, Control Zones extend between two specified levels.

    d.   Control Areas extend between two specified levels, Control Zones extend from the surface upwards to a specified upper limit

39. A flashing red light directed from an aerodrome to an aircraft in flight means:

    a.   Do not land. Give way to other aircraft and continue circling

    b.   Do not land. Airfield closed

    c.   Wait for permission to land

    d.   Position downwind

40. The purpose of a Basic Service is to:

    a.   Separate aircraft outside controlled airspace

    b.   Provide information useful to the safe and efficient conduct of flight

    c.   Give warnings of traffic using radar derived information, but the avoidance of such traffic is the pilot's responsibility

    d.   Deconflict aircraft outside controlled airspace, but the avoidance of such traffic is the pilot's responsibility

---

END OF AIR LAW PAPER 4

INTENTIONALLY BLANK

AIR LAW & OPS PAPER 4: ANSWERS

	A	B	C	D
1.		X		
2.				X
3.	X			
4.			X	
5.			X	
6.			X	
7.		X		
8.				X
9.	X			
10.		X		
11.			X	
12.		X		
13.			X	
14.	X			
15				X
16.	X			
17.				X
18.		X		
19.	X			
20.				X
21.				X
22.				X
23.		X		
24.	X			
25.			X	
26.		X		
27.			X	
28.				X
29.	X			
30.			X	
31.	X			
32.				X
33.	X			
34.				X
35.		X		
36.			X	
37.			X	
38.				X
39.		X		
40.		X		

CORRECT ANSWERS: PERCENTAGES										
30	31	32	33	34	35	36	37	38	39	40
75%	77%	80%	82%	85%	87%	90%	92%	95%	97%	100%

1. **(Answer: B)** For non-scheduled flights each state will allow aircraft from other states to fly into or through its airspace, and to land within its borders without prior permission; note though that scheduled flights do require permission to overfly another State. However states do reserve the right to require any over-flying aircraft to land or to follow prescribed routes in airspace where navigation facilities are inadequate or terrain is difficult.

2. **(Answer: D)** Each state has the right to search aircraft from another state on landing or before departure and to inspect documentation without causing unnecessary delay.

3. **(Answer: A)** Each contracting state is recognised to have complete sovereignty over the airspace above its territory. It may impose its national law on users of that airspace. A state's territory is the airspace over the country's borders at ground level and the airspace above its territorial waters.

4. **(Answer: C)** A state may require aircraft arriving to or departing from its territory to do so through an international or "customs" airport, which has full customs, immigration and health facilities.

5. **(Answer: C)** ICAO Annex 14 states that mandatory instruction signs at aerodromes shall consist of an inscription in white on a red background.

 NO ENTRY

 Intermediate Taxi-Holding Position (ITHP)
- Protects a priority route.

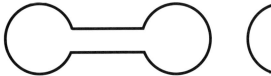 **Visual Runway Taxi-Holding Position (RTHP)**
- This sign might also be used for the CATI hold, if it is co-located with the visual hold.

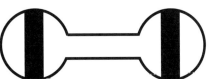 **CAT I RTHP**
- Where a visual hold is established closer to the runway.

6. **(Answer: C)** In the signals area, a rectangular green flag flown from a mast means that right-hand circuits are in force.

7. **(Answer: B)** A white dumb-bell indicates that the movement of aeroplanes and gliders on the ground shall be confined to paved, metalled or similar hard surfaces. The addition of black stripes in each circle of the dumb-bell means that aeroplanes and gliders must take off and land on a runway, but movement on the ground is not confined to hard surfaces.

8. Answer D

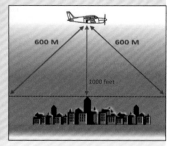

9. Answer A

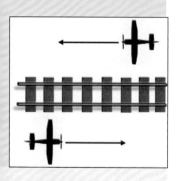

15. Answer D

8.   **(Answer: D)** On an aerodrome the position at which a pilot can report to ATC or other aerodrome authority is marked by a yellow board bearing a black "**C**".

9.   **(Answer: A)** Except for helicopters or when aircraft are taking off or landing at a licensed or government aerodrome, you must not fly over the congested area of any city town or settlement below a height which would enable the aircraft to alight clear of the congested area in the event of a power unit failure or below 1000 ft above the highest fixed obstacle within 600 m of the aircraft. Whichever is the higher.

10.   **(Answer: B)** The primary objectives of the Air Traffic Services are:

 • *To prevent collisions between aircraft in the air.*
 • *To assist in preventing collisions between aircraft moving on the apron and the manoeuvring area.*
 • *To assist in preventing collisions between aircraft and obstructions on the manoeuvring area.*
 • *To expedite and maintain an orderly flow of traffic.*
 • *To notify the appropriate organisations of aircraft in need of search and rescue aid, and to assist such organisations as required.*
 • *To provide information useful to the safe and efficient conduct of flight.*

11.   **(Answer: C)** The Transition Layer is the airspace between the transition altitude and the transition level.

12.   **(Answer: B)** Under a Special VFR clearance a pilot is exempt from the "1000 feet rule", that is the need to remain 1000 feet above the highest fixed obstacle within 600 metres of the aircraft (see question 9 above). Please note that there is NO exemption from the requirement to alight clear of any congested area.

13.   **(Answer: C)** A Special VFR clearance enables a pilot to fly within a Control Zone in circumstances normally requiring an IFR clearance. Special VFR clearances are only permitted within control ZONES, usually at the request of the pilot. SVFR is a concession offered by ATC, which allows an aircraft to operate within a control zone which is Class A or in any other control zone in IMC or at night, without requiring compliance with the Instrument Flight Rules. Instead pilots will comply with instructions given by the Air Traffic Control Unit.

14.   **(Answer: A)** A PPL holder (with no additional ratings) receiving a Special VFR clearance must have a flight visibility of 10 km or more, and remain clear of cloud and in sight of the surface.

15.   **(Answer: D)** An aircraft in the UK flying in sight of the surface and following a road, railway, canal, coastline or any other line of landmarks shall keep them on its left unless flying within controlled airspace and in accordance instructions from the appropriate ATCU.

16.   **(Answer: A)** Although a Deconfliction Service is available to aircraft operating VFR outside controlled airspace it may not be suitable for pilots not qualified to fly in IMC. In providing the service a controller will aim to guide the aircraft to maintain a specified distance either vertically or laterally from other traffic. The deconfliction minima that the controller is trying to achieve are 5 nm or 3,000 feet against unknown traffic; this is reduced to 3 nm and 1000 feet should the intentions of the other traffic be known. The controller will issue headings and/or levels to achieve the minima; the pilot is expected to comply with the instructions or advise the controller if it is not possible.

17. **(Answer: D)** If the commander of an aircraft has caused notice of the intended arrival of the aircraft at an aerodrome to be given to the Air Traffic Control unit or other authority at that aerodrome, he shall ensure that the unit or authority is informed as quickly as possible of any change of intended destination; and any estimated delay in arrival of 45 minutes or more. ANO Rule 17.

18. **(Answer: B)** When transiting a MATZ the vertical position of an aircraft is normally controlled by reference to the QFE at the military aerodrome.

19. **(Answer: A)** These are permanently displaced threshold markings. In (i) the pre-threshold is unfit for the movement of aircraft and (ii) the pre-threshold may be used for taxi and take off but not for landing.

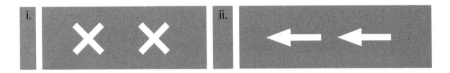

These are temporarily displaced threshold markings with the same meaning.

20. **(Answer: D)** ANO Rule 45 states that: An aircraft must not enter an ATZ, or manoeuvre on the aerodrome, unless the pilot-in-command has obtained either:

    • *permission from ATC, or*
    • *where there is no ATC unit established, information from the FISO or A/G station to enable the flight to continue safely.*

21. **(Answer: D)** A full flight plan is filed using the FPL form, an abbreviated flight plan is the term given to the limited information required to obtain a clearance for a portion of flight, for instance crossing a control zone. Abbreviated flight plans may be filed either by telephone prior to departure or by radio when airborne.

    A flight plan **may** be filed for any flight.

    A flight plan **must** be filed in the following circumstances:
    • *For all IFR flights within controlled airspace*
    • *For all VFR flights within Class C and D airspace*
    • *When the pilot wants to receive an Air Traffic Advisory Service (Class F airspace)*
    • *For all flights which will cross a UK international FIR boundary*
    • *For any flight where the destination is more than 40 km from the aerodrome of departure and the aircraft's MTWA exceeds 5700 kg*

    It is **advisable** to file a flight plan if the flight involves flying:
    • *Over the sea, more than 10 nm from the UK coastline*
    • *Over sparsely populated areas where Search and Rescue operations would be difficult*
    • *Into an area where SAR operations are in progress. In this case the plan should include the expected times of entering and leaving the area and the details must also be passed to the appropriate ACC. The ACC will notify Kinloss ARCC.*

22. **(Answer: D)** The UK is divided into 20 Altimeter Setting Regions (ASRs). The Regional Pressure Setting, or Regional QNH, is the lowest forecast QNH within each region. As this is the lowest QNH value expected within the region when the Regional QNH is set you will either be at, or slightly higher, than the altitude indicated. With the altimeter under-reading the true altitude terrain clearance is assured.

    The RPS are updated each hour and are valid for H+1 to H+2.

23. **(Answer: B)** Below the transition altitude when flying beneath a Terminal Control Area, or Terminal Manoeuvring Area, the altimeter sub-scale should be set to the QNH of an aerodrome situated beneath the TMA.

24. **(Answer: A)** ANO Rule 16. An aircraft in the UK flying in sight of the surface and following a road, railway, canal, coastline or any other line of landmarks shall keep them on its left.

    This has two advantages:
    * *You can see the feature on your side of the aircraft; and*
    * *Opposite direction traffic, provided that the pilot is obeying the rule, will be on the other side of the line feature.*

    The Right-hand traffic rule does not apply to an aircraft flying in controlled airspace in accordance with instructions given by the appropriate ATCU. *(See question 15 for diagram)*

25. **(Answer: C)** A black ball suspended from a mast and a white "T" with a white disc at the head of the "T" in line with the shaft have the same meaning – that the direction of take-off and landing does not necessarily coincide.

26. **(Answer: B)** UK Rules of the Air apply to:
    * *All aircraft in the UK (including offshore installations, where the low flying regulations may need to be taken into account), and*
    * *To all UK registered aircraft wherever they may be.*

27. **(Answer: C)** The only time that the rules may be departed from is when:
    * *avoiding immediate danger*
    * *when complying with the laws of another country within whose airspace we are flying.*

    If a departure is made for safety reasons the circumstances, must be reported afterwards to the competent authority:
    * *within 10 days*
    * *in writing to the Authority of the country in whose territory the departure from the rules took place*

28. **(Answer: D)** A flight plan filed before departure should be submitted to the Air Traffic Services reporting office at the departure aerodrome. Where no such unit exists the plan should be submitted by phone or fax, or failing this by radio, to the unit designated to serve the departure aerodrome. (ICAO Doc 4444)

    NOTE: IN THE UK THERE IS AN ADDITIONAL INTERNET SERVICE CALLED AFPEX (ASSISTED FLIGHT PLANNING EXCHANGE) AT **WWW.FLIGHTPLANNINGONLINE.CO.UK**

29. **(Answer: A)** ICAO requires that a delay message (DLA) must be sent if the estimated off block time is more than 30 minutes later than that already shown in the flight plan. The pilot must advise the departure aerodrome ATSU or parent AFTN unit so that a DLA message can be sent.

30. **(Answer: C)** If a licence holder wishes to transfer the licence to another JAA member state he will have to show "normal residency". This is the place where he resides and/or works for more than 185 days each year.

31. **(Answer: A)** A PPL may fly for the purpose of aerial work which consists of:
    - *Towing a glider in flight; or*
    - *A flight for the purpose of dropping parachutists*

    In either case the aircraft must be owned, or operated under arrangements entered into by a club of which the licence holder and any person carried in the aircraft or in any glider towed by the aircraft are members.

32. **(Answer: D)** A Military Aerodrome Traffic Zone (MATZ) may be established around UK military aerodromes. They extend from the surface up to 3,000 feet and have a radius of 5 nm. One or more stubs aligned with the final approach path(s) may also be present extending between 1,000 and 3,000 feet, extending 5 nm from the MATZ boundary with a width of 4 nm.

    Technically a MATZ is unregulated airspace, so there is no legal requirement to obtain permission to enter. However civil pilots wishing to penetrate the MATZ are strongly advised to contact the military controller. Within the MATZ is a normal ATZ and the usual ATZ procedures must be observed.

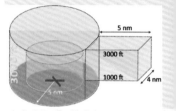

Question 32

33. **(Answer: A)** It is a Runway Taxi- Holding Point identifying a Category I/II or III hold where a visual/Category I hold is provided closer to the runway.

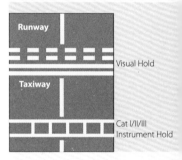

Question 33

34. **(Answer: D)** In this case the aircraft is completely inaccessible. Although answer "C" sounds like a serious incident, because there was no intention to fly the aircraft, it does not constitute a reportable accident.

    An accident must be reported if, between the time when anyone boards the aircraft with the intention of flight, until all such persons have disembarked:

    - *Anyone is killed or seriously injured while in or on the aircraft or by direct contact with the aircraft including anything that has become detached from it. This includes direct exposure to jet blast but not anything self-inflicted or due to natural causes. It does not include stowaways; or*
    - *The aircraft incurs damage or structural failure other than any failure or damage limited to the engine or its accessories. If the damage is only limited to propellers, wingtips, aerials, tyres, brakes, fairings, small dents or small puncture holes, it is not reportable. (Unless any of the afore-mentioned adversely affects the aircraft's structural strength, performance or flight characteristics and requires major repair or replacement).*
    - *The aircraft is missing or completely inaccessible.*

35. **(Answer: B)** The aircraft. If ATC have not instructed otherwise the right of way on the ground goes to:
    1. Aircraft taking off or landing,
    2. Vehicles involved in towing
    3. Aircraft
    4. Vehicles

36. **(Answer: C)** Flying within sight of the surface in Class G airspace at 130 knots below 3000 ft AMSL, the VMC minima are flight visibility of 1500 m and remaining clear of cloud.

At or Below 3000 ft AMSL		
Class F & G	Clear of cloud and with the surface in sight	5 km
For Aircraft, Flying at 140 knots or less		
Class C, D & E	Clear of cloud and with the surface in sight	5 km
Class F & G	Clear of cloud and with the surface in sight	1500 m

37. **(Answer: C)** In order to carry passengers the pilot-in-command must have made at least 3 take-offs and landings as the sole manipulator of the controls within the preceding 90 days in the same type or class of aircraft to be flown.

    To carry passengers at night:
    One of the 3 take-offs and landings within the preceding 90 days must have been made at night.

38. **(Answer: D)** A Control Area or CTA is airspace of defined dimensions which extends upwards from a specified altitude or flight level to an upper limit, usually a Flight Level.

    The definition of a Control Zone is "Controlled airspace extending upwards from the surface of the earth to a specified upper limit".

39. **(Answer: B)** A flashing red light directed from an aerodrome to an aircraft in flight means "Do not land. Aerodrome closed".

40. **(Answer: B)** The Basic Service is an Air Traffic Service provided to give advice and information useful to the safe and efficient conduct of flights. Such items may include weather information, changes in the serviceability of facilities, conditions at aerodromes or general aerial activity information.

    - *The service is available to IFR or VFR flights, but may not be appropriate for flight in IMC.*
    - *Traffic Information should not be expected. Outside an ATZ there is no obligation for the controller/FISO to pass Traffic Information.*

END OF EXPLANATIONS PAPER 4

SUMMARY OF AIR TRAFFIC SERVICES

WITHIN CONTROLLED AIRSPACE:

A RADAR CONTROL SERVICE is provided. VFR aircraft must comply with ATC instructions or REQUEST an alternative clearance. I.e. You cannot deviate from the instructions given without first obtaining permission from the controller.

AIR TRAFFIC SERVICES OUTSIDE CONTROLLED AIRSPACE (ATSOCAS):

A pilot is at all times responsible for terrain clearance and collision avoidance, the following services are available to help a pilot discharge his collision avoidance responsibilities. Unless an agreement has been entered into, you may alter course and level as you wish.

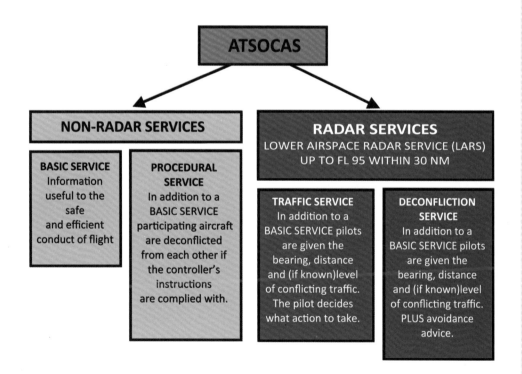

INTENTIONALLY BLANK

PART 2: METEOROLOGY

The Meteorology examination consists of 20 questions; the time allowed is one hour.

The pass mark is 75%.

Each question is multiple choice with four possible answers A, B, C and D. You should indicate your chosen answer by placing a cross in the appropriate box on the answer sheet.

Blank answer sheets are to be found at the end of this publication, these may be photocopied.

INTENTIONALLY BLANK

METEOROLOGY PAPER 1

1. Light aircraft operate in a division of the atmosphere called the:
   a. Tropopause
   b. Troposphere
   c. Stratosphere
   d. Stratopause

2. Water vapour:
   a. Comprises a large proportion of the atmosphere and is a gas
   b. Is a liquid suspended within clouds
   c. Comprises a small proportion of the atmosphere and is a liquid
   d. Comprises a small proportion of the atmosphere and is a gas

3. Assuming no cloud cover, when will the earth will be at its coldest?
   a. Just after sunrise
   b. Dawn
   c. Just after sunset
   d. Midnight

4. The temperature at 3000 feet is plus 11°C and the temperature at 4000 feet is plus 10°C. How would you describe the atmosphere between these levels?
   a. Stable
   b. Unstable
   c. Conditionally unstable
   d. Saturated

5. The temperature at 3000 feet is plus 20°C and the temperature at 4000 feet is plus 15°C. How would you describe the atmosphere between these levels?
   a. Stable
   b. Unstable
   c. Conditionally unstable
   d. Saturated

6. The temperature at 3000 feet is plus 20°C and the temperature at 4000 feet is plus 18°C. How would you describe the atmosphere between these levels?
   a. Stable
   b. Unstable
   c. Conditionally unstable
   d. Saturated

7. Air arriving over the UK in winter which is cold and dry, and which brings clear skies, cold weather and coastal showers would be a:
   a. Tropical Maritime Air mass
   b. Polar Continental Air mass
   c. Tropical Continental Air mass
   d. Polar Maritime Air mass

8. Air moving solely under the influence of the Pressure Gradient Force will tend to move from:
   a. Low pressure to an adjacent area of low pressure
   b. High pressure to an adjacent area of low pressure
   c. High pressure to an adjacent area of high pressure
   d. Low pressure to an adjacent area of high pressure

9.   What type of cloud is likely to form by orographic uplift in unstable air?

   a.   Stratus or layer cloud
   b.   Lenticular cloud with little vertical development
   c.   A widespread sheet of layer cloud with associated drizzle
   d.   Cloud with a great deal of vertical development

10.   Your planned flight is over a mountainous region. There is forecast to be a strong wind blowing across the ridge. Where would you assume to encounter turbulence associated with a rotor zone?

   a.   Immediately above the ridge
   b.   Downwind of the ridge
   c.   Upwind of the ridge
   d.   Below the ridge

11.   The symbol ≡≡≡ on a meteorological chart means:

   a.   Widespread fog
   b.   Freezing fog
   c.   Widespread mist
   d.   Sky obscured

12.   This symbol on a forecast chart means:

   a.   Severe turbulence
   b.   Hail
   c.   Severe icing
   d.   Severe icing and turbulence

13. Hail will fall from which type of cloud?

   a.   NS
   b.   CB
   c.   ST
   d.   SC

14.   Within the "warm sector" of a typical low pressure frontal system the weather most likely to be experienced is:

   a.   Low cloud, drizzle and poor visibility
   b.   Cumuliform cloud and good visibility
   c.   Heavy rain
   d.   Thunderstorms

15.   In a cumulonimbus (CB) cloud where would you expect to find severe icing?

   a.   Above 10,000 feet
   b.   In the cloud with air temperatures between 0° and -20°C
   c.   In the anvil
   d.   In the vicinity of the gust front

16.   You are flying in rain, above the freezing level, within the cold sector underneath a warm front. What type of icing are you most likely to encounter?

   a.   Hoar frost
   b.   Rime ice
   c.   Clear or rain ice
   d.   A mix of all of the above

17. A warm front is approaching your aerodrome, what is the correct order of cloud types you will you see pass?

    a.   Cirrostratus, cirrus, altocumulus, cumulonimbus
    b.   Stratus, nimbostratus, altostratus, cirrostratus
    c.   Cirrus, cirrocumulus, altocumulus, nimbocumulus
    d.   Cirrus, cirrostratus, altostratus, nimbostratus, stratus

18. The Form 214, UK Low Level Spot Wind Chart, is issued every .... (i).... hours and is valid for .... (ii).... hours:

    a.   i) 6   ii) 6
    b.   i) 6   ii) 8
    c.   i) 8   ii) 12
    d.   i) 6   ii) 12

19. Unstable air is characterised by:

    a.   Cumuliform cloud and poor visibility
    b.   Layer cloud with poor visibility
    c.   Layer cloud with good visibility
    d.   Cumuliform cloud with good visibility

20. A TREND is included at the end of the METAR or surface actual, the TREND is a forecast valid for:

    a.   1 hour after the time of the observation
    b.   2 hours after the time of the observation
    c.   2 hours after the observation is issued
    d.   1 hour after the observation is issued

END OF METEOROLOGY PAPER 1

METEOROLOGY PAPER 1: ANSWERS

No.	A	B	C	D
1		X		
2				X
3	X			
4	X			
5		X		
6			X	
7		X		
8		X		
9				X
10		X		
11	X			
12			X	
13		X		
14	X			
15		X		
16			X	
17				X
18	X			
19				X
20		X		

CORRECT ANSWERS: PERCENTAGES					
15	16	17	18	19	20
87%	90%	92%	95%	97%	100%

1. **(Answer: B)** The troposphere is the lowest layer in the atmosphere. It is where practically all "weather" occurs and is the region where all light aircraft operate.

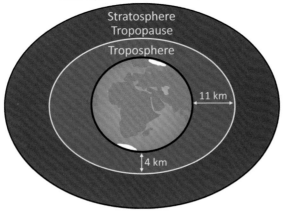

2. **(Answer: D)** Water vapour comprises only a small proportion of the atmosphere and is a gas. The actual amount of water vapour is variable up to a maximum value of around 4%.

3. **(Answer: A)** Solar heating takes place by day only, but terrestrial re-radiation continues both day and night. Without cloud cover, the earth's surface will warm during the day, reaching a maximum by around mid-afternoon. It will cool by night reaching a minimum just after dawn.

    An overcast day will have a lower maximum temperature, as cloud will block and reduce incoming solar radiation. Conversely cloud cover by night will absorb and re-radiate terrestrial radiation back to the surface acting as a "blanket" and reducing heat loss.

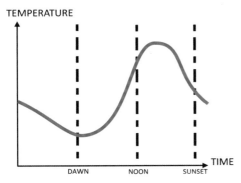

DIURNAL TEMPERATURE
VARIATION: CLEAR SKY

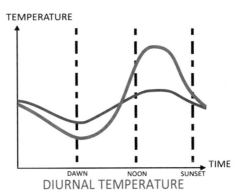

DIURNAL TEMPERATURE
VARIATION: OVERCAST

4.   **(Answer: A)** Upper air temperatures are regularly observed and are referred to as the environmental or ambient air temperatures. The Environmental Lapse Rate (ELR) is the actual observed rate of decrease of temperature with increase in height at a particular time and place.

Air displaced within this environment will change temperature at either the Dry Adiabatic Lapse Rate (DALR) or the Saturated Adiabatic Lapse Rate (SALR) depending on its water vapour content. The term adiabatic means that there is no heat exchange with the environment, temperature changes are due to changes in pressure. On ascent pressure reduces, consequently the air expands and cools.

The DALR is the rate of cooling with ascent or warming with descent of UNSATURATED air when displaced vertically. The Dry Adiabatic Lapse Rate is 3°C per 1000 feet.

The Saturated Adiabatic Lapse Rate (SALR) is the rate of cooling with ascent or warming with descent of SATURATED air, which can be considered to be 1.5°C per 1000 feet.

In this question we are given temperatures of plus 11°C at 3000 feet and plus 10°C at 4000 feet, therefore the Environmental Lapse Rate (ELR) is 1°C per 1000 feet. We need to compare this rate to the DALR and the SALR to decide how a displaced parcel of air will behave.

At 1°C per 1000 feet this ELR is less than 1.5°C/1000 ft. Whether displaced air is cooling at the DALR or SALR it will always be colder and therefore more dense than the surroundings. It will tend to stop rising and return (sink) to its original level. The atmosphere is said to be **STABLE**.

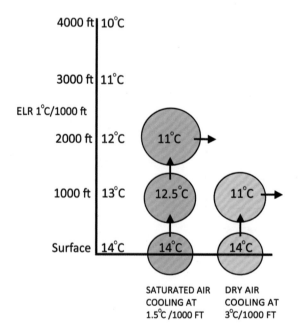

5.   **(Answer: B)** In this question we are told that at 3000 feet it is plus 20°C and the temperature at 4000 feet is plus 15°C, giving an ELR greater than 3°C/1000 ft any displaced parcel of air will always be warmer and less dense than its surroundings. It will therefore continue to rise and the atmosphere is said to be **UNSTABLE**.

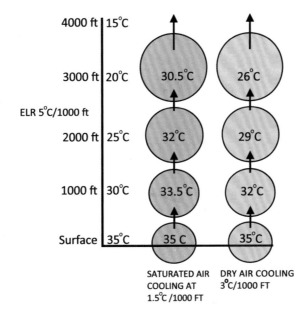

6.   **(Answer: C)** With the temperature at 3000 feet at plus 20°C and the temperature at 4000 feet plus 18°C the ELR lies between 1.5 and 3°C/1000 ft. The atmosphere is **CONDITIONALLY UNSTABLE.**

That is, saturated air is unstable and will continue to rise if displaced; dry air is stable and will tend to return to its original position.

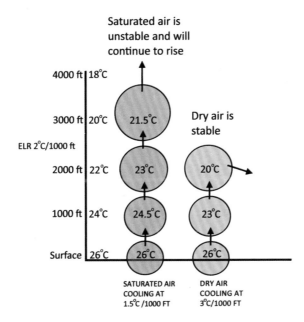

With a surface temperature of 26°C and an ELR of 2°C/1000 ft, at 2000 feet the ambient air temperature is 22°C. Dry air forced to rise will cool at 3°C/1000 ft, at 2000 feet will be 20°C, colder than its surroundings and it will stop rising. Saturated air will cool at 1.5°C/1000 ft, so at 2000 feet it will be 23°C, therefore warmer than its surroundings and will continue to rise.

7.   **(Answer: B)** A Polar Continental Air mass originates in Russia or Scandinavia. It is cold and dry and generally brings good visibility and clear skies. In winter the air can pick up enough moisture from the relatively warm North Sea to trigger convective clouds and showers on the east coast.

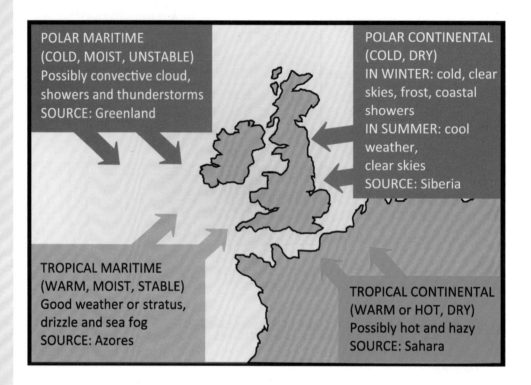

8.   **(Answer: B)** The Pressure Gradient Force is the means by which air in the atmosphere starts to move. It acts to move air from high pressure areas to low pressure areas.

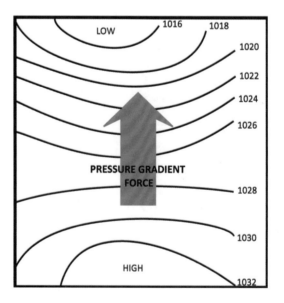

9. **(Answer: D)** Stable air forced to rise over a mountain would lead to status, stratocumulus or lenticular cloud. Unstable air would lead to cumulus or cumulonimbus.

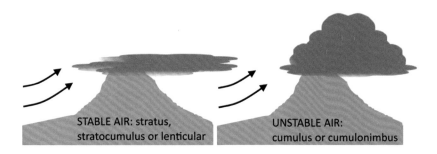

STABLE AIR: stratus, stratocumulus or lenticular

UNSTABLE AIR: cumulus or cumulonimbus

10. **(Answer: B)** Severe turbulence is encountered in the "rotor" which may form downwind of the ridge. The rotor may be revealed by the presence of roll cloud looking like ragged cumulus, but rolling around its horizontal axis. The first rotor immediately downwind is notorious for being the most ferocious.

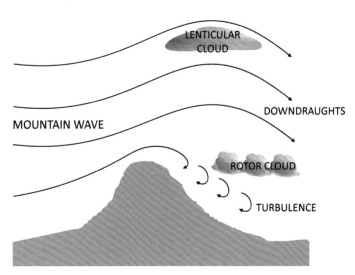

LENTICULAR CLOUD

DOWNDRAUGHTS

MOUNTAIN WAVE

ROTOR CLOUD

TURBULENCE

11. **(Answer: A)** ≡ indicates widespread fog

𝖱	Thunderstorm		" " / " "	Rain	
ϙ	Tropical cyclone		＊	Snow	
⚡	Severe squall line		⊹	Widespread blowing snow	
△	Hail		▽	Shower	
⌒	Moderate turbulence		ς	Severe sand or dust haze	
⋀	Severe turbulence		؟	Widespread sandstorm or duststorm	
⬭	Marked mountain waves		∞	Widespread haze	
⩗	Light aircraft icing		=	Widespread mist	
⩘	Moderate aircraft icing		≡	Widespread fog	
⩙	Severe aircraft icing		≢	Freezing fog	
⌒ᵕ	Freezing precipitation		⌐	Widespread smoke	
•	Drizzle		⛛	Volcanic eruption	

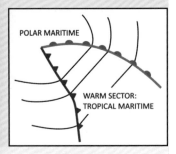

14. Answer A

The warm sector is most likely to be Tropical Maritime air. The warm sector is typified by poor visibility with stratus or stratocumulus cloud often leading to drizzle or light rain.

12. **(Answer: C)** 〖symbol〗 Severe icing *(see page 73 for a list of more symbols).*

13. **(Answer: B)** Hail will only fall from cumulonimbus cloud.

14. **(Answer: A)**

15. **(Answer: B)** Within a thunderstorm icing may be severe at any altitude above the freezing level; severe icing is most likely to be encountered between 0° and -20°C air temperature.

16. **(Answer: C)** Rain or clear ice may form as rain falls through the warm front into the colder air below. If the rain meets an object whose surface is below freezing – an aircraft for example – the rain will freeze on contact. This forms lumps of clear ice which is hard to remove.

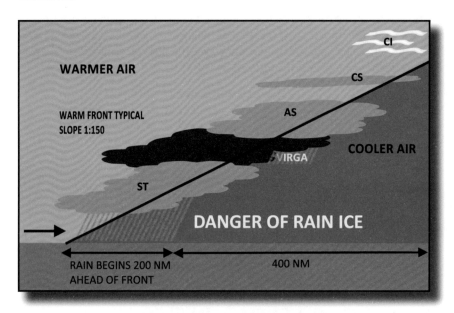

17. **(Answer: D)** For an approaching Warm Front: Cirrus, cirrostratus, altostratus, nimbostratus, stratus is the correct order (see above).

18. **(Answer: A)** Met Forms 214 are issued every 6 hours and are valid for 6 hours :

Issued time:	Valid for flights between:
0000	0300 to 0900
0600	0900 to 1500
1200	1500 to 2100
1800	2100 to 0300

19. **(Answer: D)** If unstable air is made to rise, it will continue to do so even when the original lifting mechanism has been removed. It will cool adiabatically as it rises and when it has cooled below its dewpoint the water vapour will condense. This will lead to cumuliform cloud development. Outside any associated showery precipitation visibility will be good, as strong up draughts will remove a lot of obscuring particles.

20. **(Answer: B)** Trend forecasts are sometimes added to the end of the METAR. They forecast weather changes expected in the 2 hours immediately following the time of the observation.

METEOROLOGY PAPER 2

1. The atmosphere is heated by:
   a. Incoming solar radiation
   b. Re-radiation from cloud
   c. Re-radiation from water vapour and carbon dioxide in the air
   d. Re-radiation from the Earth's surface

2. If air temperature decreases, the relative humidity will
   a. Remain unchanged
   b. Decrease
   c. Increase
   d. Initially decrease and then increase

3. Nearly all weather occurs in the layer of the atmosphere closest to the Earth's surface. This layer is known as the:
   a. Tropopause
   b. Troposphere
   c. Stratosphere
   d. Ionosphere

4. Unstable air arriving over the UK which is both cold and moist would be a:
   a. Tropical Maritime Air mass
   b. Polar Continental Air mass
   c. Tropical Continental Air mass
   d. Polar Maritime Air mass

5. Stable air arriving over the UK which is warm and moist would be a:
   a. Tropical Maritime Air mass
   b. Polar Continental Air mass
   c. Tropical Continental Air mass
   d. Polar Maritime Air mass

6. When relatively warm dry air moves over a water surface, its lower layers will absorb water vapour. The air will become:
   a. Less dense and rise
   b. Less dense and stable
   c. Decrease in humidity because the ocean is warm
   d. More dense and rise

7. What type of cloud may form by orographic uplift in stable air over mountain tops?
   a. Mamatus
   b. Fractus
   c. Castellanus
   d. Lenticularis

8. A lenticular cloud is forecast, what phenomenon would this indicate?
   a. Mountain waves
   b. Föhn wind
   c. Thunderstorm
   d. Cold front

9. Where might you encounter frontal fog?
   a. Behind a warm or occluded front
   b. Behind a cold front
   c. Ahead of a warm or occluded front
   d. Ahead of a cold front

10. Consider an area of low pressure. Where warmer air at the surface is replaced by colder air, the front is known as a:

    a.   Warm front and slopes at approximately 1:50

    b.   Warm front and slopes at approximately 1:150

    c.   Cold front and slopes at approximately 1:50

    d.   Cold front and slopes at approximately 1:150

11. Which of the following would best describe the weather experienced in the UK in winter with an anticyclone?

    a.   Subsiding air will cool adiabatically leading to the formation of cloud. An inversion may form leading to good visibility

    b.   Subsiding air will warm adiabatically dispersing cloud. An inversion may form leading to poor flight visibility

    c.   Rising air cool adiabatically leading to the formation of cloud. An inversion may form leading to good visibility

    d.   Rising air will warm adiabatically dispersing cloud. An inversion may form leading to poor flight visibility

12. Piston engine induction system icing is most likely to be caused by which of the following conditions?

    a.   Warm temperatures, high humidity and low power settings

    b.   Cold temperatures, high humidity and high power settings

    c.   Cold temperatures, high humidity and low power settings

    d.   Warm temperatures, low humidity and high power settings

13. What would the following cloud sequence indicate: cirrus, cirrostratus, alto stratus, nimbostratus?

    a.   The approach of a cold front

    b.   An anticyclone

    c.   The approach of better weather

    d.   The approach of a warm front

14. During their mature stage the hazards associated with thunderstorms or CB clouds may be experienced

    a.   Within the cloud

    b.   Within or below the cloud

    c.   Within approximately 2 nm of the cloud

    d.   Within 10 nm of the cloud

15. You are flying in the UK at a constant altitude and heading with starboard drift. If you do not update the QNH on the altimeter subscale the aircraft would actually be:

    a.   At the altitude indicated on the altimeter

    b.   Higher than indicated on the altimeter

    c.   Lower than indicated on the altimeter

    d.   Better flown on the Regional QNH

16. Your destination airfield has no air traffic services; it is has an airfield elevation of 240 ft AMSL. A nearby airport has a QNH of 1023 hPa. What is the QFE at your destination? (Assume 1 hPA = 30 ft)

    a.   1031

    b.   1016

    c.   1015

    d.   1030

17. Look at the following METAR:
EGLC 291320 24020KT 9999 SCT 055 20/13 Q1026 NOSIG=
What is the meaning of "NOSIG"?

    a.   No significant weather expected within the next 3 hours

    b.   Nothing significant has happened all day

    c.   No significant change is forecast before the next observation is made

    d.   No significant change is forecast during the 2 hours following the observation

18. You are using a Form 215 Forecast Weather Chart.
What does "ISOL 400 M FG LAN D1 TL 09Z" mean?

    a.   Surface visibility in area D1 will be reduced in isolated mist and fog down to 400 over land after 0900 UTC

    b.   Surface visibility in area D1 will be reduced in isolated fog down to 400 metres over land after 0900 UTC

    c.   Surface visibility in area D1 will be reduced in isolated fog down to 400 metres over land until 0900 UTC

    d.   Surface visibility in area D1 will be reduced in widespread fog down to 400 metres over land after 0900 UTC

19. In a TAF the word TEMPO means:

    a.   A temporary variation to the main forecast lasting less than an hour

    b.   Temporary variations that constitute a hazard

    c.   A temporary variation to the main forecast lasting less than an hour, or if recurring, in aggregate less than half of the period indicated.

    d.   A temporary variation to the main forecast lasting in aggregate less than half of the period indicated.

For the following question use Met Form 215 below:

20. You are planning to carry out a precision VFR navigation exercise:

Departing from and returning to Old Sarum with an ETD of 1500. The IAS will be 110 knots and the aircraft is not certified for flight in known icing conditions. The planned flight will remain outside controlled airspace, below 2,000 feet and the route will remain within "Area B".

You are a PPL holder with no Instrument or IMC rating, therefore you must remain clear of cloud, in sight of the surface and maintain a flight visibility of at least 1500 m.
With regard to the Met Form 215 below what is the most sensible course of action?

   a. At the moment the weather is below minima but should improve. Delay for 3 hours
   b. The cloud base is forecast to be 2,000 – 3,000 feet with isolated CBs. Delay until tomorrow
   c. The cloud base is below minima, some flight in IMC may be necessary
   d. The cloud base and visibility are within limits. Take-off as planned

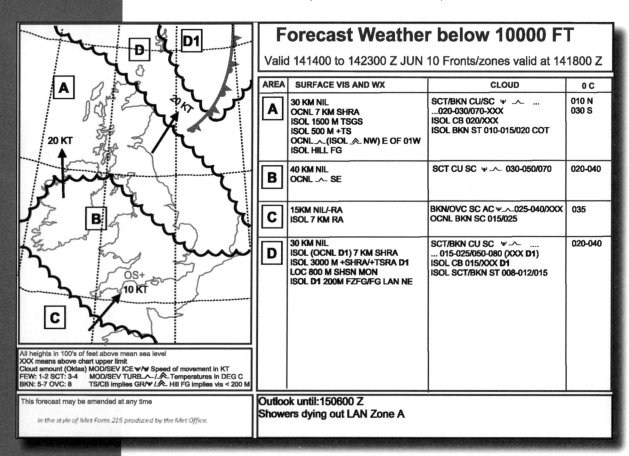

END OF METEOROLOGY PAPER 2

INTENTIONALLY BLANK

No.	A	B	C	D
1				X
2			X	
3		X		
4				X
5	X			
6	X			
7				X
8	X			
9			X	
10			X	
11		X		
12	X			
13				X
14				X
15			X	
16			X	
17				X
18			X	
19			X	
20				X

CORRECT ANSWERS: PERCENTAGES					
15	16	17	18	19	20
87%	90%	92%	95%	97%	100%

METEOROLOGY PAPER 2: EXPLANATIONS

1. **(Answer: D)** Incoming short-wave solar radiation passes through the atmosphere and heats the earth's surface. The earth re-radiates longer wave heat energy which warms the lower layers of the atmosphere.

2. **(Answer: C)** Warm air is able to hold more water vapour that cold air.

   Saturated Air: is air that contains the maximum amount of water vapour possible at that temperature. Relative humidity is the ratio of the actual amount of water vapour present in a particular sample of air compared to the maximum amount of water vapour that the air could hold at its present temperature. Saturated air has a relative humidity of 100%. If the air temperature falls relative humidity will increase.

   Relative Humidity

   The capacity for dry air to absorb water vapour is determined by its temperature and pressure; the more significant factor being the temperature. Warm air is able to hold more water vapour than cold air.

   Dry Air: is air that contains no water vapour at all. This condition will never be encountered in the real world, but it is useful theoretically for the study of meteorology.

   Moist Air: is air that contains some water vapour.

   Saturated Air: is air that contains the maximum amount of water vapour possible at its current temperature and pressure.

   Unsaturated Air: Is air that contains less than the maximum amount of water vapour that it could contain at its current temperature and pressure.

   Relative humidity is an expression of the ratio of the actual amount of water vapour present in a particular sample of air compared to the maximum amount of water vapour that the air could hold at its present temperature.

   $$\text{Relative humidity} = \frac{\text{Mass of water vapour}}{\text{Mass of water vapour for saturation}} \qquad X \qquad \frac{100\%}{1}$$

   Saturated air, which contains the maximum amount of water vapour possible, would have a relative humidity of 100%. As stated earlier warm air can hold more water vapour than cold air – if the temperature falls the air is not able to hold as much water vapour and so its relative humidity will increase.

Temperature	Relative Humidity%					
30°C	16	24	31	45	57	100
20°C	28	42	54	79	100	
15°C	36	53	69	100		
10°C	52	77	100			
5°C	67	100				
0°C	100					
Water Content g/cubic metre	5	7	9	14	17	30

To illustrate this with an example, refer to the graph above. Assume we have at a cubic metre of air containing 9 grammes of water vapour. If the air has a temperature of 30 degrees its relative humidity is 31%, it is roughly holding only a third of the water vapour it possibly could. Cooling this air to 10 degrees increases its relative humidity to 100%, it can hold no more water vapour and is said to be saturated.

The alternative way to saturate air at 30°C is to increase the water content to 30 g/cubic metre. Air that is 100% saturated is said to be at its dewpoint, if air is cooled below its dewpoint it is no longer able to support all the water vapour contained within it – the excess must be shed and will condense as visible water droplets or ice.

3. **(Answer: B)** The troposphere is the lowest layer in the atmosphere. It is where practically all "weather" occurs and is the region where all light aircraft operate.

4. **(Answer: D)** A Polar Maritime air mass originates near Canada or Greenland. At source it is relatively humid, cool and stable. On its passage south the air mass is heated from below by the relatively warmer sea, its moisture content increases and it becomes unstable. On reaching the UK, polar maritime air brings convective clouds and possibly thunderstorms.

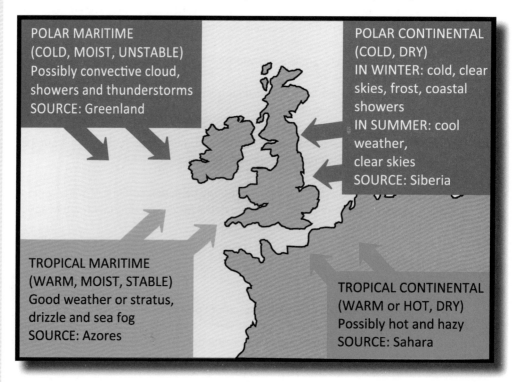

5. **(Answer: A)** A Tropical Maritime Air mass originates in the Azores. Such air is warm and humid. It is also stable on reaching the UK because as it travels north it is cooled from below.

6. **(Answer: A)** Water vapour is less dense than air, when water vapour is added to the air it becomes less dense than its surroundings and will rise.

7. **(Answer: D)** Stable air forced to rise over a mountain would lead to stratus, stratocumulus or lenticular cloud. Unstable air would lead to cumulus or cumulonimbus.

8.   **(Answer: A)** Lenticular cloud forms in a mountain wave. Mountain waves will form when the following conditions are present:

- *A wind speed of 15 knots or more*
- *A wind blowing at right angles (or within 30° of) to the axis of the mountain range*
- *A wind strength which increases with height with little change in direction*
- *A layer of stable air just above the ridge, with less stable air above and below*

Lenticular cloud may form in the "crests" of the waves.

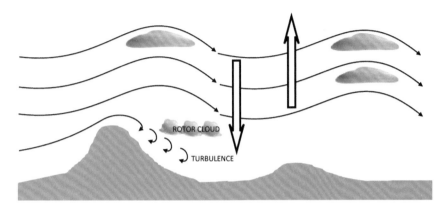

9.   **(Answer: C)** Frontal fog forms due to the evaporation of raindrops falling through the cold air ahead of a warm or occluded front:

- *Water re-condenses under the ST or NS cloud*
- *At times condensation will occur at ground level*
- *Belt of fog*
- *Up to 100 nm wide*

The fog belt will move along with the front just ahead of its surface position

10.   **(Answer: C)** Seen from the surface, when warm air is replaced by colder air the front is called a Cold Front. The slope between the air masses is typically quite steep, around 1:50.

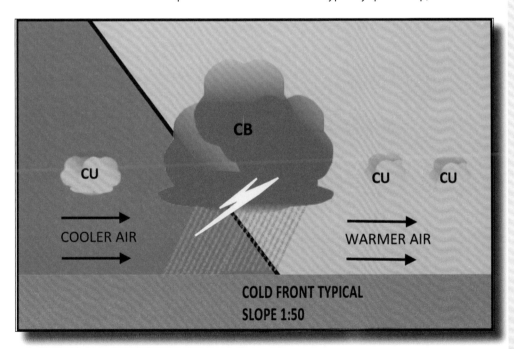

11. **(Answer: B)** Subsiding air in an anticyclone will warm as it descends and cloud will tend to disperse. The air may warm sufficiently to create an inversion which may trap smoke, haze and dust below it. This often happens in the UK in winter leading to poor flight visibility and generally "gloomy" days.

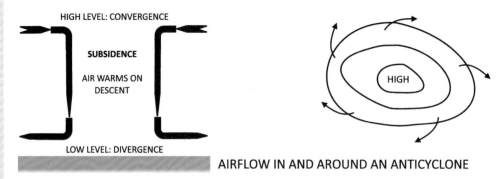

AIRFLOW IN AND AROUND AN ANTICYCLONE

12. **(Answer: A)** Ice can form in the carburettor and induction system in moist air even with outside air temperatures as high as 30°C. Adiabatic cooling occurs when the air expands as it passes through the venturi into the carburettor and also when the fuel evaporates (absorbing latent heat) – the combined effect is that even warm air can have its temperature decreased below zero. If the air is moist enough ice will form.

   Throttle icing is more likely at low power settings because the venturi effect is greater and the small opening could be blocked with just a small amount of ice.

13. **(Answer: D)** As a warm front passes an observer on the ground would see a gradually lowering stratiform cloud base. First cirrus, then a lowering base of cirrostratus, altostratus and nimbostratus.

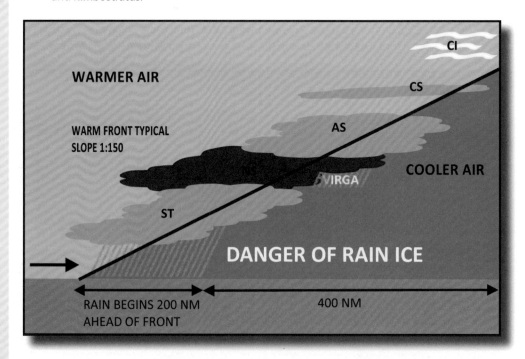

14. **(Answer: D)** The dangers presented by thunderstorms are not just found within or below the cloud. Thunderstorms should be avoided by at least 10 nm. See AIC PINK 81/2004

15. **(Answer: C)** Buys Ballot's Law states that: in the northern hemisphere if you stand with your back to the wind, low pressure will be to your left"

In this question the aircraft is experiencing starboard drift i.e. the wind is coming from the left. Therefore, you are flying towards an area of low pressure, where the QNH will be lower. If the subscale setting is not updated the altimeter will over read, i.e. you will be lower than you think you are. Remember "high to low – lookout below".

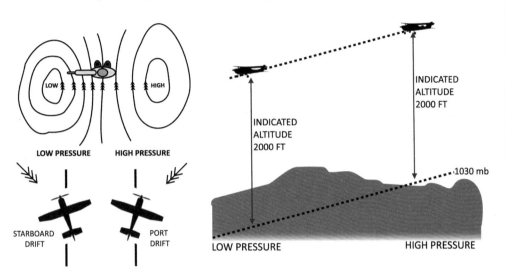

16. **(Answer: C)** We are given a local QNH (pressure at mean sea level)of 1023 hPa, and an airfield elevation (height of the airfield above mean sea level) of 240 ft.

We are also told to accept that 1 hPa equals 30 feet.
The elevation of 240 ft equates to 8 hPa. Hence:
QFE = 1023 – 8 = 1015 hPa
Bear in mind that pressure always reduces with height which is why the 8 hPa is subtracted.

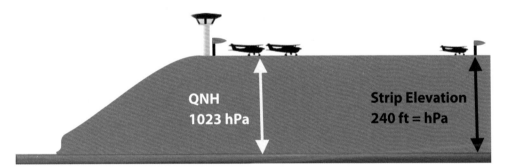

18. **(Answer: C)** "ISOL 400 M FG LAN D1 TL 09Z" decodes as:

ISOL = isolated (affecting less than 25% of the area concerned)
400 M = visibility 400 metres
FG = fog
LAN = inland (or overland)
TL= until
09Z = 0900 Zulu

19. **(Answer: C)** TEMPO = A temporary variation to the main forecast lasting less than an hour, or if recurring, in aggregate less than half of the period indicated.

20. **(Answer: D)** The departure aerodrome and intended route are within Area B.

The forecast for Area B is for visibility 40 km with no significant weather. There may be occasional moderate turbulence in the South East of the area.

Cloud will be scattered (3-4 Oktas) with a base between 3,000 and 5,000 feet.
The freezing level is between 2,000 and 4,000 feet.

As the flight is planned to remain below 2,000 feet, take off when ready!

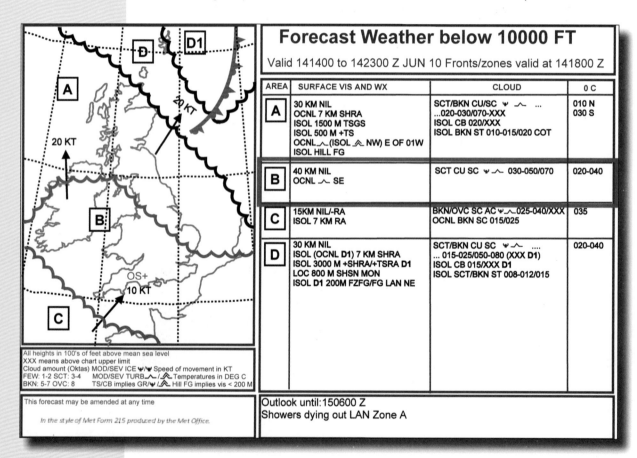

END OF EXPLANATIONS PAPER 2

1. The phrase "visibility forward of an aircraft in flight" is a definition for:

    a. Surface visibility

    b. RVR

    c. Vertical visibility

    d. Flight visibility

2. The symbol on a forecast chart means:

    a. Severe turbulence

    b. Hail

    c. Severe icing

    d. Severe icing and turbulence

3. What is the major hazard to flight presented by an occluded front?

    a. Fog

    b. Strong up draughts

    c. Heavy rain or snow

    d. Thunderstorm activity hidden by stratus cloud

4. When air moves under the influence of the pressure gradient force towards an area of low pressure it is deflected by the Coriolis effect. Consequently in the northern hemisphere the air flow at 2000ft would be:

    a. Deflected left and flow roughly parallel to the isobars

    b. Deflected left and flow roughly perpendicular to the isobars

    c. Deflected right and flow roughly perpendicular to the isobars

    d. Deflected right and flow roughly parallel to the isobars

5. Stable air arriving over the UK which is hot and dry would be a:

    a. Tropical Maritime Air mass

    b. Polar Continental Air mass

    c. Tropical Continental Air mass

    d. Polar Maritime Air mass

6. The term for a balanced wind flow around curved isobars is:

    a. Pressure gradient

    b. Geostrophic wind

    c. Gradient wind

    d. Coriolis wind

7. Which weather system is most likely to lead to thunderstorm activity?

    a. Cold front

    b. Occluded front

    c. Warm front

    d. A col

8. You are flying in the UK towards an area of low pressure. What wind do you expect?

    a. A headwind

    b. A tailwind

    c. Drift to the left (port)

    d. Drift to the right (starboard)

9. What conditions favour the formation of radiation fog?

    a. High relative humidity, light wind and clear sky

    b. High relative humidity, light wind and overcast sky

    c. High relative humidity, no wind and clear sky

    d. Low relative humidity, light wind and clear sky

10. The conditions favourable to a CB cloud developing, are:

    a.   A deep layer of stable air

    b.   A deep layer of unstable air and low relative humidity

    c.   A trigger action, moist air and a deep layer of instability

    d.   A trigger action, moist air and a deep layer of stability

11. Assuming an equal pressure gradient, a warm front travels at:

    a.   ⅓ of the speed of the cold front

    b.   ⅔ of the speed of the cold front

    c.   ¾ of the speed of the cold front

    d.   ½ of the speed of the cold front

12. In the UK, on the passage of a warm front the wind would:

    a.   Veer

    b.   Back

    c.   Remain unchanged

    d.   Increase

13. It is midnight at an aerodrome in the centre of England. The surface wind is 120/05 KT. What would the 2000 ft wind be?

    a.   080/20 KT

    b.   030/25 KT

    c.   160/20 KT

    d.   160/10 KT

14. In the UK low level winds around a depression blow:

    a.   In a clockwise direction

    b.   In an anti clockwise direction

    c.   Parallel to the isobars

    d.   Perpendicular to the isobars

15. In the UK low level winds around an anticyclone blow:

    a.   Perpendicular to the isobars

    b.   In a clockwise direction

    c.   In an anti clockwise direction

    d.   Parallel to the isobars

16. What notice should you give to a forecasting office if you require a Special Forecast for a flight of over 500 nm?

    a.   Four hours

    b.   Two hours

    c.   Three hours

    d.   Five hours

17. A METAR is:

    a.   A forecast for a specific aerodrome

    b.   A routine weather report, or surface actual, for a specific aerodrome

    c.   A forecast of weather conditions for the next two hours

    d.   A routine weather report for a group of aerodromes

Refer to Met Form 215 below to answer the next three questions:

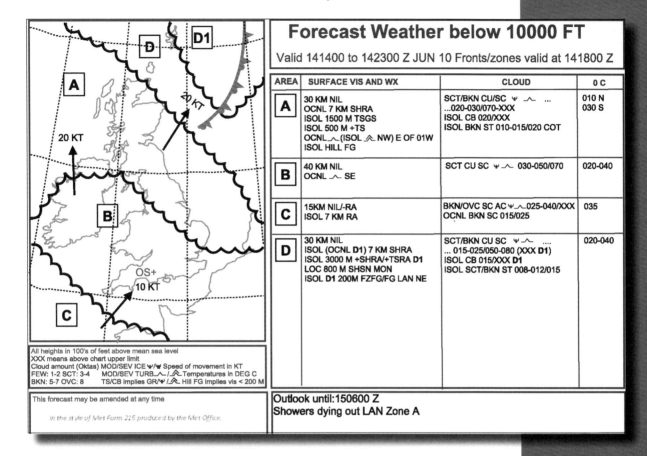

18. Identify the feature in the top right hand corner of the chart in Area D1.

    a.   A warm frontal system

    b.   A cold frontal system

    c.   A stationary frontal system

    d.   An occluded frontal system

19. What is the height of the 0° isotherm in area B?

    a.   20,000 – 40,000 feet

    b.   2,000 – 4,000 feet

    c.   200 – 400 feet

    d.   0000 – 1500 feet

20. In area D1 what does "ISOL 200 M FZFG/FG LAN NE" mean?

    a.   In area D1 the visibility will be reduced to 200 metres by freezing fog or fog over land

    b.   Overland in the SW of area D1 it will be foggy

    c.   Isolated freezing fog or fog will reduce the visibility in area D1 to 200 metres

    d.   Surface visibility in area D1 will be reduced to 200 metres by freezing fog or fog over land in the north east of the area

---

END OF METEOROLOGY PAPER 3

METEOROLOGY PAPER 3: ANSWERS

No.	A	B	C	D
1				X
2			X	
3				X
4				X
5			X	
6			X	
7	X			
8				X
9	X			
10			X	
11		X		
12	X			
13			X	
14		X		
15		X		
16	X			
17		X		
18				X
19		X		
20				X

CORRECT ANSWERS: PERCENTAGES					
15	16	17	18	19	20
87%	90%	92%	95%	97%	100%

1. **(Answer: D)** Flight visibility is defined as the "visibility forward of an aircraft in flight".

2. **(Answer: C)** Severe icing.

┌⟨	Thunderstorm		" " " "	Rain
↺	Tropical cyclone		✳	Snow
⤳ᵡ	Severe squall line		⊥	Widespread blowing snow
△	Hail		▽	Shower
⌒	Moderate turbulence		⌇	Severe sand or dust haze
⌃	Severe turbulence		⌇	Widespread sandstorm or duststorm
⬭	Marked mountain waves		∞	Widespread haze
⤵	Light aircraft icing		═	Widespread mist
⤸	Moderate aircraft icing		≡	Widespread fog
⤸	Severe aircraft icing		⩥	Freezing fog
⤳	Freezing precipitation		⌐	Widespread smoke
•	Drizzle		⌂	Volcanic eruption

3. **(Answer: D)** The cloud associated with an occluded front is often a combination of the cloud associated with the individual warm and cold fronts. One particular hazard is that stratiform cloud from the warm front could conceal cumulus or cumulonimbus cloud from the cold front.

    There are two types of occluded front depending upon whether the warm or the cold front remains at the surface; the relative temperatures of the three airmasses involved will govern how a frontal system occludes. Broadly speaking a cold occlusion is more common in summer, and a warm occlusion in winter.

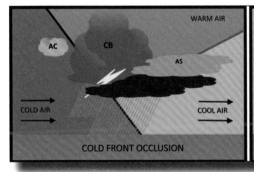

COLD FRONT OCCLUSION

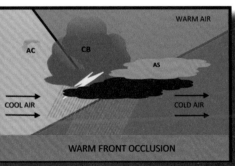

WARM FRONT OCCLUSION

4.   **(Answer: D)** Initial air movement is under the influence of the pressure gradient force (PGF), from high to low pressure. Once the air starts to move the Coriolis effect (or geostrophic force, GF), due to the rotation of the earth, acts at 90° to the PGF. The wind at 2000 ft is the flow of air when the PGF and the GF are in equilibrium. This is also known as the Geostrophic wind and blows parallel to straight isobars.

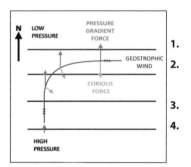

1.   The PGF starts air moving High to Low pressure
2.   The Coriolis Force deflects the moving air RIGHT in the Northern Hemisphere.
3.   Curved path will continue until PGF=GF
4.   Balanced wind flow parallel to isobars: Geostrophic wind

5.   **(Answer: C)** A Tropical Continental Air mass originates in southern Europe or north Africa. It is hot and dry; it tends to be stable on reaching the UK due to cooling from below on its passage north.

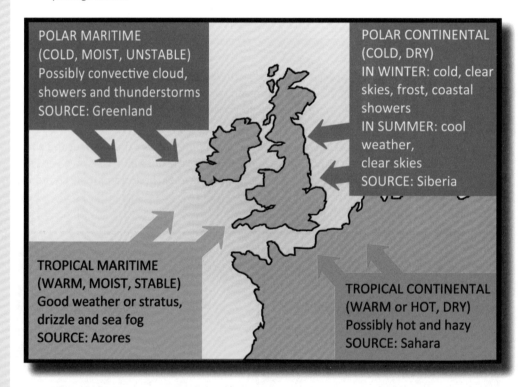

6.   **(Answer: C)** Gradient wind is the term for a balanced wind flow around curved isobars. It is assumed to blow at 2,000 feet.

      The following explanation considers only the Northern Hemisphere.

      In order for the wind to follow the curved pattern of isobars another force must act upon the airflow. This force is the Cyclostrophic Force. Cyclostrophic Force can be thought of as similar to Centripetal force in that it acts towards the centre of the turn - it will either augment or reduce the Pressure Gradient Force making the airflow follow a curved path.

Around a low pressure depression the Cyclostrophic Force acts in the same direction as the Pressure Gradient Force: **PGF + CF = GF**

Around a high pressure anticyclone the Cyclostrophic Force acts in the same direction as the Geostrophic Force: **GF + CF = PGF**

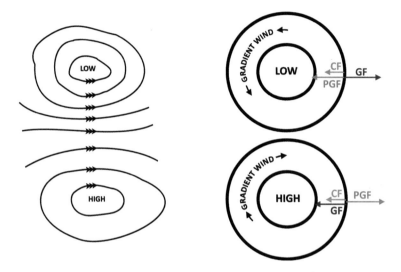

Around a depression, the PGF supplies the CF, so there is less PGF to be balanced by the GF. As a result of this the wind speed around a low will be LESS than around a high given the same pressure gradient, shown by the spacing of isobars.

7. **(Answer: A)** A cold front is most likely to have thunderstorm activity, as the warm sector air is forced to rise by the wedge of cold air under-cutting it. Warm fronts are associated with layer cloud.

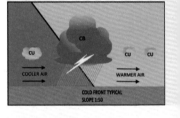

7. Answer A

8. **(Answer: D)** Buys Ballot's Law states that: "in the northern hemisphere if you stand with your back to the wind, low pressure will be to your left" Flying towards low pressure will lead to starboard drift.

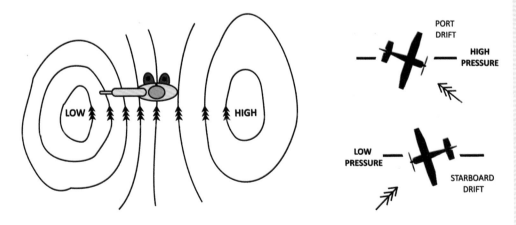

9. **(Answer: A)** Radiation fog only forms over a land surface when air in contact with the surface is cooled below its dewpoint. Condensation will take place and fog will form. This is most likely when:

- *the air Is moist (high relative humidity),*
- *there are clear skies (maximum radiative cooling) and*
- *there is a light wind 2-8 KT (to mix the lowest levels of the air)*

10. **(Answer: C)** The conditions necessary for thunderstorms to develop are: a trigger action to start the air rising, a deep layer of instability so that the air will continue to rise and a high moisture content.

11. **(Answer: B)** A warm front travels at approximately ⅔ the speed of the cold front. Hence the reason that frontal systems often occlude as the warm front is caught up by the cold front.

12. **(Answer: A)** On the passage of a warm front, the surface wind will veer, i.e. alter in a clockwise direction.

13. **(Answer: C)** By night there is no solar radiation and therefore no thermal mixing. Compared to the 2000 ft wind the surface wind will have decreased in speed by 15-20 KT and be backed by 40°. This is due to a weakened Coriolis force because of the speed reduction.

    Given a surface wind of 120/05 KT, the 2000 ft wind is likely to be 160/20 KT.

14. **(Answer: B)** Air flows into a depression from an area of high pressure. Wind is deflected to the right in the northern hemisphere due to the Coriolis effect, leading to an anti-clockwise flow around a depression. See illustrations below and left, marked for answer 15.

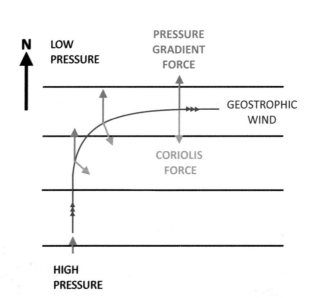

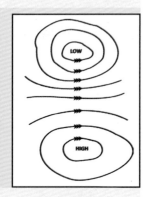

12. Answer A

15. Answer B

15. **(Answer: B)** In the Northern Hemisphere when air flows out of an area of high pressure the wind is deflected to the right due to the Coriolis effect, leading to a clockwise air flow around an anticyclone.

16. **(Answer: A)** A Special Forecast for a particular flight may be requested from a forecast office. At least 2 hours notice is required and this increases to at least 4 hours notice if the flight is over 500 nm.

17. **(Answer: B)** A METAR is a routine weather report for a particular aerodrome. These may also be referred to as a Surface Actual (SA). They are produced at the time of the meteorological observation which is usually at minutes 20 and 50.

18. **(Answer: D)** An occluded front.

WARM FRONT   COLD FRONT   OCCLUDED FRONT

19. **(Answer: B)** The third column on the right hand side gives the altitude of the 0°C isotherm, or freezing level. Levels are printed in hundreds, hence 020-040 represents 2,000 – 4,000 feet.

AREA	SURFACE VIS AND WX	CLOUD	0 C
B	40 KM NIL OCNL ⌒ SE	SCT CU SC ☰ ⌒ 030-050/070	020-040

20. **(Answer: D)** "ISOL 200 M FZFG/FG LAN NE"

ISOL = isolated (affecting less than 25% of the area concerned)
200 M = visibility 200 metres
FZFG = freezing fog
FG = fog
LAN = inland or overland
NE = north east or north-easterly

END OF EXPLANATIONS PAPER 3

INTENTIONALLY BLANK

METEOROLOGY PAPER 4

1. A thunderstorm is always a hazard, but it presents the most danger to low flying aircraft during which stage of its life cycle?

   a. Mature stage
   b. Dissipating stage
   c. Cumulus stage
   d. Adult stage

2. Within the "cold sector" of a typical low pressure frontal system the weather most likely to be experienced, is:

   a. Generally good visibility with scattered cumulus cloud
   b. Good visibility below overcast layer cloud
   c. Poor visibility below overcast layer cloud
   d. Poor visibility below scattered or broken layer cloud

3. Within the "warm sector" of a typical low pressure frontal system the weather most likely to be experienced, is:

   a. Low cloud, drizzle and poor visibility
   b. Cumuliform cloud and good visibility
   c. Heavy rain
   d. Thunderstorms

4. On a Forecast weather chart the symbol means:

   a. Mountain waves
   b. Windshear
   c. Lightning
   d. Thunderstorm(s)

5. On a Forecast weather chart the symbol mean:

   a. Mountain waves
   b. Windshear
   c. Lightning
   d. Hail

6. When water evaporates:

   a. Water vapour is formed and latent heat is absorbed
   b. Water vapour is formed and latent heat is released
   c. Ice is formed and latent heat is absorbed
   d. Ice is formed and latent heat is released

7. It is day and the wind at 1000 ft over an inland aerodrome is 230/15 KT. What is your estimate for the surface wind velocity?

   a. 250/08 KT
   b. 220/10 KT
   c. 210/12 KT
   d. 210/10 KT

8. It is 1400 at an inland aerodrome; the sky is clear. The surface wind is 200/25 KT. What is the 2000 ft wind likely to be?

   a. 225/35 KT
   b. 180/35 KT
   c. 220/45 KT
   d. 240/40 KT

9. London or Scottish "VOLMET" is a VHF service. It is:

    a. A facility for pilots to volunteer meteorological information

    b. Composed entirely of pilot reports

    c. A continuous broadcast of actual weather conditions at selected aerodromes

    d. A continuous broadcast of forecast weather conditions at selected aerodromes

10. A fog that can develop over land or sea by both day and night, is:

    a. Sea smoke

    b. Radiation fog

    c. Frontal fog

    d. Advection fog

11. A cold front passage is characterised by:

    a. Wind backing, temperature rising and dewpoint rising

    b. Wind veering, temperature falling and dewpoint rising

    c. Wind veering, temperature falling and dewpoint falling

    d. Wind backing, temperature falling and dewpoint falling

12. Compared to the daytime values, the surface wind at night will:

    a. Veer and decrease

    b. Veer and increase

    c. Back and increase

    d. Back and decrease

13. Refer to Form 214 at the end of this paper (Attachment 1) : What values best represent the i) wind velocity and direction and ii) temperature at 2,000 ft in position 50° N 02°30 E?

    a. i) 070/20   ii) -3°C

    b. i) 070/20   ii) -5°C

    c. i)130/10   ii) -3°C

    d. i)050/05   ii) -5°C

14. CAVOK is often used in a TAF or METAR, which is the most correct description:

    a. Visibility 25 km or more, no cloud, no CB and no weather

    b. Visibility 10 km or more, no cloud below 5,000 feet, no significant weather

    c. Visibility 10 km or more, no cloud below 5,000 feet AAL (or MSA, if higher), no significant weather at or in the vicinity of the aerodrome

    d. Visibility 5 km or more, no cloud below 10,000 feet, no CB, no significant weather

15. When using a Met Form 215, what is implied by TS or CB?

    a. Hail, moderate turbulence and moderate icing

    b. Severe icing and severe turbulence

    c. Hail and slight icing

    d. Hail, severe icing and severe turbulence

16. In a TAF you read: BECMG 1520 9999. What does it mean?

    a. Becoming between 1500 and 2000 UTC visibility 10 km or better

    b. Becoming by 1520 UTC visibility 10 km or better

    c. Gradually the visibility will improve

    d. Between 1520 and midnight UTC visibility over 9 km

17. In relation to sea breezes, which statement is correct?

    a.   By day the surface wind will be on shore

    b.   By day the surface wind will flow parallel to the coast

    c.   By night the surface wind will be on shore

    d.   By night the surface wind will flow parallel to the coast

18. Advection fog is caused by:

    a.   Moist air in contact with the ground cooling below its dewpoint on a clear, cloudless night

    b.   Warm, moist air flowing over a much colder surface which cools the air below its dewpoint

    c.   Moist air being mixed by strong wind until it is below its dewpoint

    d.   Warm, moist air cooling over night in light wind to below its dewpoint.

19. METAR EGGW 231620 36009KT 7000 BKN018 07/01 Q1021 BECMG 33516KT 5000 OVC009 What is the surface wind direction and speed at the time of the report?

    a.   From the north west at 16 KT

    b.   From the south east at 16 KT

    c.   From the north at 9 KT

    d.   From the south at 9 KT

20. Even in cloudless conditions icing may be a hazard. What types of icing might you find?

    a.   Rain and cloudy ice

    b.   Clear and rain ice

    c.   Hoar frost and carburettor ice

    d.   Rime ice and hoar frost

END OF METEOROLOGY PAPER 4

ATTACHMENT 1. Meteorology Paper 4

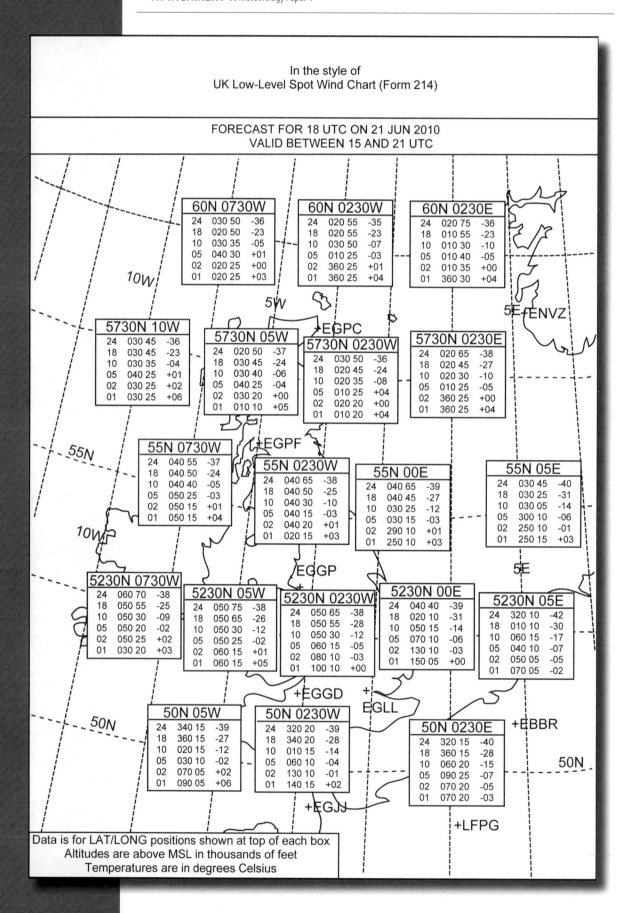

In the style of
UK Low-Level Spot Wind Chart (Form 214)

FORECAST FOR 18 UTC ON 21 JUN 2010
VALID BETWEEN 15 AND 21 UTC

60N 0730W

24	030 50	-36
18	020 50	-23
10	030 35	-05
05	040 30	+01
02	020 25	+00
01	020 25	+03

60N 0230W

24	020 55	-35
18	020 55	-23
10	030 50	-07
05	010 25	-03
02	360 25	+01
01	360 25	+04

60N 0230E

24	020 75	-36
18	010 55	-23
10	010 30	-10
05	010 40	-05
02	010 35	+00
01	360 30	+04

5730N 10W

24	030 45	-36
18	030 45	-23
10	030 35	-04
05	040 25	+01
02	030 25	+02
01	030 25	+06

5730N 05W

24	020 50	-37
18	030 45	-24
10	030 40	-06
05	040 25	-04
02	030 20	+00
01	010 10	+05

5730N 0230W

24	030 50	-36
18	020 45	-24
10	020 35	-08
05	010 25	+04
02	020 20	+00
01	010 20	+04

5730N 0230E

24	020 65	-38
18	020 45	-27
10	020 30	-10
05	010 25	-05
02	360 25	+00
01	360 25	+04

55N 0730W

24	040 55	-37
18	040 50	-24
10	040 40	-05
05	050 25	-03
02	050 15	+01
01	050 15	+04

55N 0230W

24	040 65	-38
18	040 50	-25
10	040 30	-10
05	040 15	-03
02	040 20	+01
01	020 15	+03

55N 00E

24	040 65	-39
18	040 45	-27
10	030 25	-12
05	030 15	-03
02	290 10	+01
01	250 10	+03

55N 05E

24	030 45	-40
18	030 25	-31
10	030 05	-14
05	300 10	-06
02	250 10	-01
01	250 15	+03

5230N 0730W

24	060 70	-38
18	050 55	-25
10	050 30	-09
05	050 20	-02
02	050 25	+02
01	030 20	+03

5230N 05W

24	050 75	-38
18	050 65	-26
10	050 30	-12
05	050 25	-02
02	060 15	+01
01	060 15	+05

5230N 0230W

24	050 65	-38
18	050 55	-28
10	050 30	-12
05	060 15	-05
02	080 10	-03
01	100 10	+00

5230N 00E

24	040 40	-39
18	020 10	-31
10	050 15	-14
05	070 10	-06
02	130 10	-03
01	150 05	+00

5230N 05E

24	320 10	-42
18	010 10	-30
10	060 15	-17
05	040 10	-07
02	050 05	-05
01	070 05	-02

50N 05W

24	340 15	-39
18	360 15	-27
10	020 15	-12
05	030 10	-02
02	070 05	+02
01	090 05	+06

50N 0230W

24	320 20	-39
18	340 20	-28
10	010 15	-14
05	060 10	-04
02	130 10	-01
01	140 15	+02

50N 0230E

24	320 15	-40
18	360 15	-28
10	060 20	-15
05	090 25	-07
02	070 20	-05
01	070 20	-03

Data is for LAT/LONG positions shown at top of each box
Altitudes are above MSL in thousands of feet
Temperatures are in degrees Celsius

INTENTIONALLY BLANK

No.	A	B	C	D
1	X			
2	X			
3	X			
4				X
5				X
6	X			
7			X	
8	X			
9			X	
10				X
11			X	
12				X
13		X		
14			X	
15				X
16	X			
17	X			
18		X		
19			X	
20			X	

CORRECT ANSWERS: PERCENTAGES					
15	16	17	18	19	20
87%	90%	92%	95%	97%	100%

1. **(Answer: A)** The Mature Stage of a thunderstorm has strong up and down draughts meaning violent windshear. In addition there may also be severe icing, severe turbulence, lightning and heavy rain or hail present.

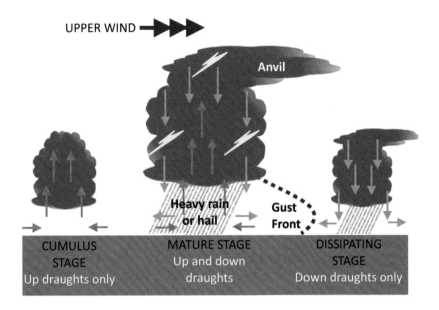

2. **(Answer: A)** The cold sector is most likely to be Polar Maritime air. This will be unstable and give rise to cumuliform cloud. However visibility will be good.

3. **(Answer: A)** The warm sector is most likely to be Tropical Maritime air. The warm sector is typified by poor visibility with stratus or stratocumulus cloud often leading to drizzle or light rain.

4. **(Answer: D)** ⎡⚡ means thunderstorm(s)

5. **(Answer: D)** Δ represents hail

6. **(Answer: A)** Evaporation forms water vapour and latent heat is absorbed. When water changes state latent heat is either absorbed or given off:

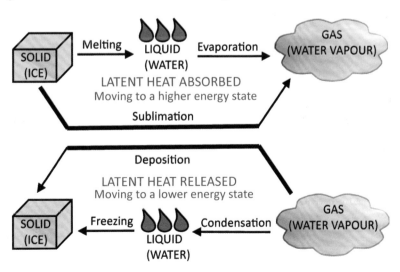

7. **(Answer: C)** The rule of thumb is by day the surface wind is 30° backed and 40% slower than the 2000 ft free stream wind. For this question assume the 1000 ft wind is roughly half those values; hence a 1000 ft wind of 230/15 KT would give:

    Surface wind direction 15° backed = 215
    Surface wind direction = 20% of 15 KT= 3 KT
    15 - 3 = 12 KT
    Nearest answer: **210/12 KT**

8. **(Answer: A)** Under clear skies there will be a lot of thermal turbulence leading to a deep friction layer.

    The surface wind speed will be roughly 40% slower than the 2000 ft wind. The slower speed will mean the Coriolis effect is less and so the wind at the surface will back by approximately 30°
    Given: surface wind 200/25 KT
    2000 ft wind speed = 35 KT (40% of 25 KT is 10 KT)
    2000 ft wind direction = veer by approximately 30° = 230°
    Nearest answer: **225/35 KT**

9. **(Answer: C)** VOLMET continuously broadcasts actual weather reports for selected aerodromes on a discreet VHF frequency. Any trend will also be included and it is updated every half hour.

10. **(Answer: D)** Warm moist air moving over a colder land or sea surface is the trigger enabling advection fog to form. Cooling of the lower layers by the cold surface leads to condensation, resulting in fog forming by day or night. Note: also unlike radiation fog wind speed is irrelevant.

11. **(Answer: C)** When a cold front passes the wind will veer and decrease in strength. By definition a cold front means that cold air is replacing warm air at the surface – so the temperature will drop. Additionally, a lot of moisture will have been lost during frontal precipitation, hence the dewpoint will fall. (see facing page)

12. **(Answer: D)** During the day thermal turbulence leads to a mixing of the surface wind with the faster moving free stream air above. This leads to daytime surface winds being closer to the 2000 ft wind. By night the direction will back and the speed decrease.

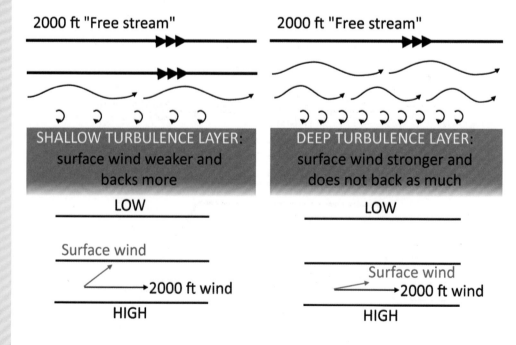

13. **(Answer: B)** Wind velocity: 070/20 KT Temperature: minus 5°C at 2,000 ft in position 50° N 02°30 E

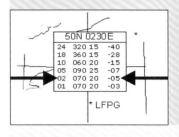

13. Answer B

14. **(Answer: C)** CAVOK means: visibility 10 km or more; no cloud below 5,000 feet AAL or below the minimum sector altitude, whichever is higher and no CB; no significant weather phenomena at or in the vicinity of the aerodrome.

15. **(Answer: D)** When using a Met Form 215 the inclusion of TS or CB in the forecast implies hail, severe icing and severe turbulence. This information is found in a text box to the bottom left of the Form.

> All heights in 100's of feet above mean sea level
> XXX means above chart upper limit
> Cloud amount (Oktas) MOD/SEV ICE ᴪ/ᴪ Speed of movement in KT
> FEW: 1-2 SCT: 3-4   MOD/SEV TURB⌃/⌃ Temperatures in DEG C
> BKN: 5-7 OVC: 8   TS/CB implies GR/ᴪ /⌃ Hill FG implies vis < 200 M

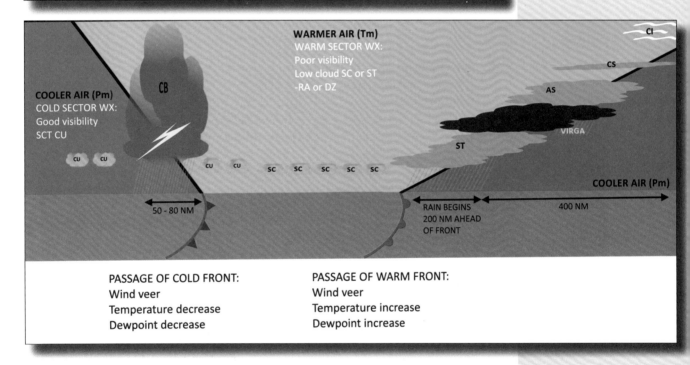

PASSAGE OF COLD FRONT:
Wind veer
Temperature decrease
Dewpoint decrease

PASSAGE OF WARM FRONT:
Wind veer
Temperature increase
Dewpoint increase

16. **(Answer: A)** BECMG 1520 9999 Decodes as:

BECMG	=	becoming
1520	=	the change will start at 1500 and will be complete by 2000 UTC
9999	=	visibility 10 km or more

17. **(Answer: A)** On sunny days the land will heat more quickly than the adjacent sea surface. By midafternoon the air above the land heats up and rises, it is replaced by cooler air from off shore moving in.

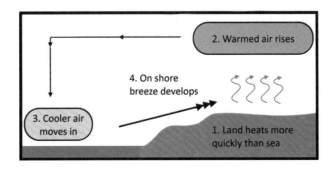

18. **(Answer: B)** Warm moist air moving over a colder land or sea surface is the trigger for advection fog to form. Cooling of the lower layers by the cold surface leads to condensation, resulting in fog forming by day or night. Note: unlike radiation fog both time of day and wind speed are irrelevant.

19. **(Answer: C)** METAR EGGW 231620 36009KT 7000 BKN018 07/01 Q1021 BECMG 33516KT 5000 OVC009

Decodes as:

Airfield:	EGGW = Luton
Time group:	231620 reported on the 23rd at 1620
36009 KT:	Surface wind from 360° True at 9 knots
7000:	Visibility 7 km
BKN018:	Cloud 5 to 7 oktas, base 1,800 feet AAL
07/01:	temperature +7°C, dewpoint +1°C
Q1021:	QNH 1021
BECMG:	becoming during the next 2 hours following the time of the report. Surface wind from 335° True at 16KT, visibility 5 km and cloud 8 oktas at 900 ft AAL

20. **(Answer: C)** Hoar frost can form in clear air when moist air encounters a sub-zero surface. The water vapour in the air sublimates directly from a gas to white crystalline ice on the surface in question.

Carburettor icing may occur without cloud being present. If the air is moist enough the temperature drop within the engine induction system is enough for ice to form. Ice can form in the carburettor and induction system in moist air even with outside air temperatures as high as 30°C. Adiabatic cooling occurs when the air expands as it passes through the venturi into the carburettor and also when the fuel evaporates (absorbing latent heat) – the combined effect is that even warm air can have its temperature decreased below zero. If the air is moist enough ice will form. Throttle icing is more likely at low power settings as the venturi effect is greater.

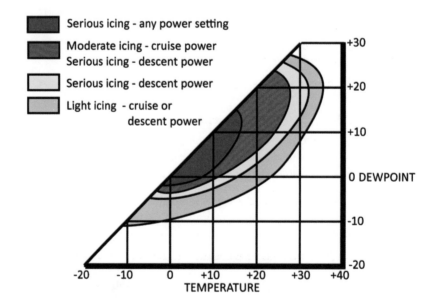

METEOROLOGY PAPER 5

1. What weather is associated with a Polar Maritime air mass over the UK?

    a. Clear skies, good visibility and warm temperatures
    b. Showers, convective clouds and possibly thunder storms
    c. Fog or drizzle
    d. Clear skies, good visibility and cold temperatures

2. The gradient wind is a moderate to strong Westerly. There is a line of hills with a North-South axis. Hazardous conditions are most likely to be found:

    a. When flying towards the hills from the west
    b. When flying towards the hills from the east
    c. There is no danger present
    d. When flying parallel to the hills and to their west

3. Where is rain ice possible?

    a. Below the freezing level in the cold air ahead of a warm front
    b. Above the freezing level in the warm air ahead of a warm front
    c. Above the freezing level in the cold air ahead of a warm front
    d. Below the freezing level in the warm air ahead of a warm front

4. You are flying at night; the moon is setting in the West. In which direction will the visibility be greatest?

    a. To the south
    b. To the west
    c. It will be the same in all directions
    d. To the east

5. You are flying below cloud in rain, the OAT is +8°C. The main icing risk is:

    a. Impact icing
    b. Rain ice
    c. Carburettor icing
    d. Rime icing

6. Drizzle is associated with which type of cloud?

    a. ST
    b. NS
    c. CB
    d. SC

7. Refer to Met Paper 5 Illustration 1. What values best represent the i) wind velocity and direction and ii) temperature at 2,000 ft in position 52° 30 N 0°E/W?

    a. i) 080/10   ii) -3°C
    b. i) 290/10   ii) +1°C
    c. i)130/10   ii) -3°C
    d. i)150/05   ii) +00°C

8. Refer to Met Paper 5 Illustration 1. What values best represent the wind velocity at 2,000 ft in position 52°30 N 02°30 W?

    a. 080/10
    b. 060/15
    c. 070/10
    d. 080/15

MET PAPER 5 Illustration 1

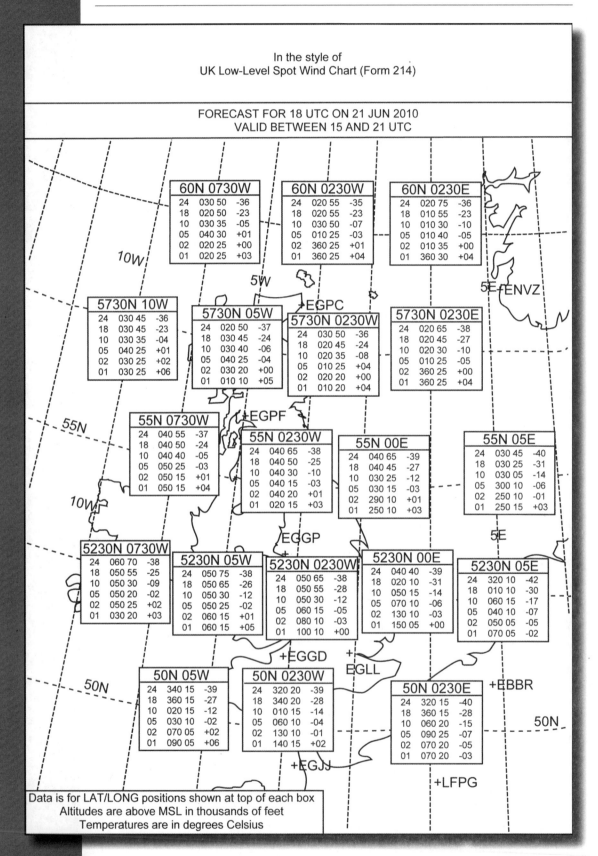

In the style of
UK Low-Level Spot Wind Chart (Form 214)

FORECAST FOR 18 UTC ON 21 JUN 2010
VALID BETWEEN 15 AND 21 UTC

Forecast Weather below 10000 FT

Valid 090900 to 091700 Z FEB 12 Fronts/zones valid at 091200 Z

AREA	SURFACE VIS AND WX	CLOUD	0 C
A	15 KM NIL OCNL 7 KM RA ISOL 5000 M FZRA ⚡ TL 11Z ISOL 3000 M RADZ/BR OCNL 700 M SN MON ISOL 200 M FZFG TL 09Z	BKN/OVC AC/AC 080/XXX SCT/BKN (OVC FRONT) CU/SC... ... ⚡ ⌒ 010-025/080 ISOL (EMBD MAINLY FRONT) ... ... CB 020	000 - 010
B	25 KM NIL ISOL (OCLN B1) 6 KM SHRA/-SHSN ISOL 1500 M SHSN MON AND B1 ISOL ⌒ S TL 13Z	BKN CU ⚡ ⌒ 015-030/040-090	010-015 005-015 B1
C	20 KM NIL OCNL 1300 M SHSN ISOL 500 M +SHSN MAINLY E	SCT/BKN CU SC ⚡ ⌒ 015-030/... ...080/XXX OCNL CB 010/015/XXX	000-010
D	15 KM NIL OCNL 1500 M SHSN ISOL 500 M +SHSN/+TSSN OCNL HILL FG	SCT/BKN CU SC ⚡ ⌒ ... ... 010-02O/080 OCNL CB 010-015/XXX	000-010

Outlook until:100000 Z
Showers dying out LAN Zone B

All heights in 100's of feet above mean sea level
XXX means above chart upper limit
Cloud amount (Oktas) MOD/SEV ICE ⚡/⚡ Speed of movement in KT
FEW: 1-2 SCT: 3-4   MOD/SEV TURB ⌒ / ⌒ Temperatures in DEG C
BKN: 5-7 OVC: 8   TS/CB implies GR/⚡ /⌒ Hill FG implies vis < 200 M

This forecast may be amended at any time

In the style of Met Form 215 produced by the Met Office.

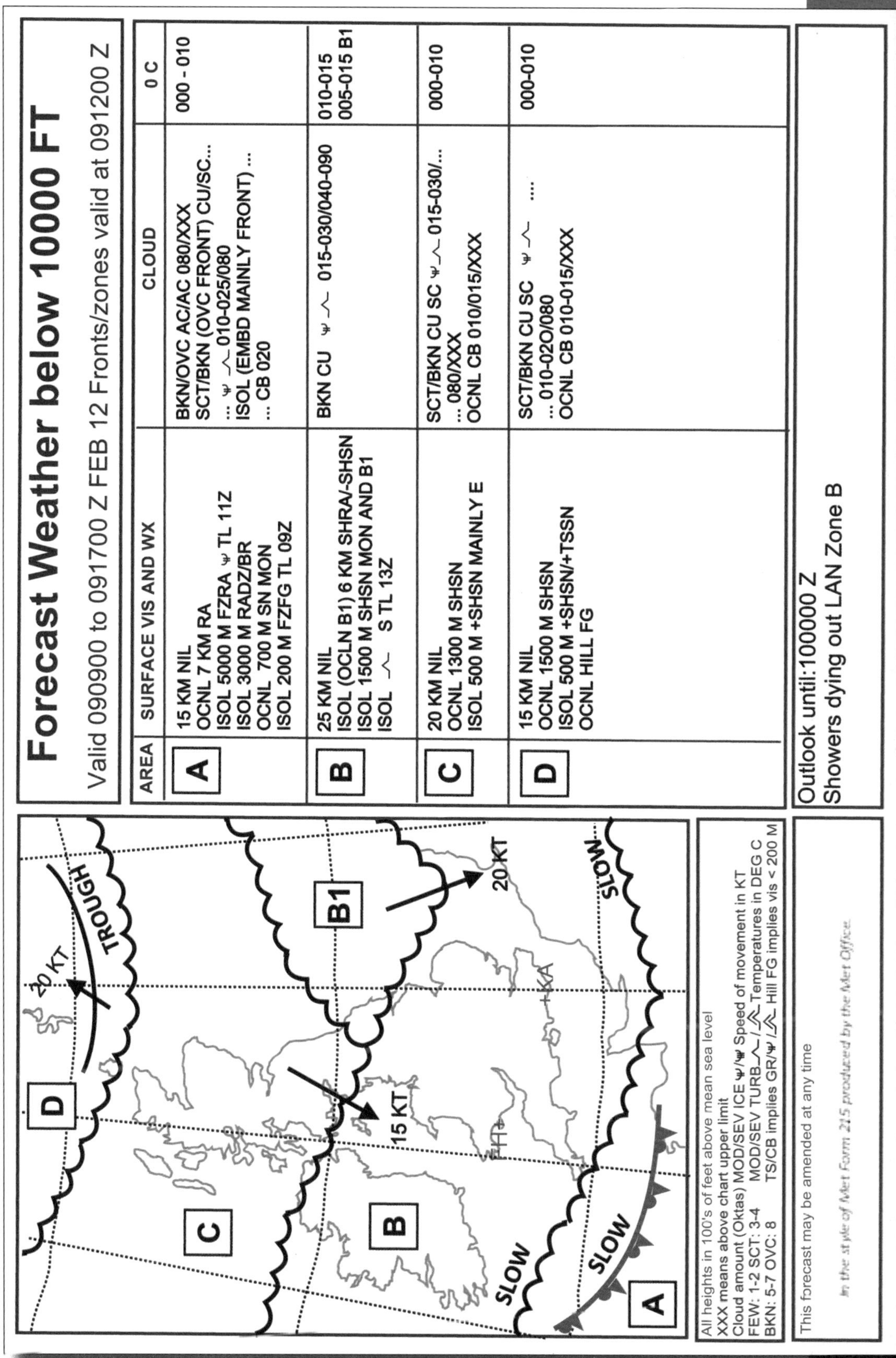

9. Refer to the Met 215 form above (Met Paper 5 Illustration 2). Regarding the Trough in area D, which statement is the MOST correct?

    a. It is not moving

    b. It is moving slowly eastward

    c. It is moving south-westerly at 15 KTS

    d. It is moving north-east at 20 KTS

10. Refer to the Met 215 form above (Met Paper 5 Illustration 2). In area B1 what is the height of the 0°C isotherm?

    a. 500 – 1500 feet

    b. 5000 – 15000 feet

    c. 2000 – 4000 feet

    d. 200 - 400 feet

11. A flight is planned from Shoreham (EGKA) to Swansea (EGFH). The diversion airfield is Kemble. The flight is to remain outside controlled airspace, and will be operated at a minimum level of 1000 feet AGL.

The pilot holds a PPL with no IMC or Instrument Ratings, and so plans to remain VFR. He must remain clear of cloud, in sight of the surface and assume a flight visibility of 3 km must be maintained.

The aircraft is not cleared for flight in known icing conditions.

ETD: 1200Z. Time en-route: 2 hours 30 minutes.

METAR for departure:
EGKA 1150Z 23016KT 9999 –SHRA SCT 019 BKN 040 05/01 Q1002=

TAF for destination:
EGFH 091019 22008KT 9999 SCT030

Given the above and considering Metform 215 (Met Paper 5 llustration 2) what is the most reasonable course of action?

    a. The weather for the departure airfield and destination are suitable to carry out the flight. It may be necessary to avoid isolated showers en-route. Proceed with caution.

    b. Departure and destination conditions are acceptable. However moderate icing is expected to the surface in the south of the area until after 1300 UTC. Delay until after 1300 UTC.

    c. Isolated visibility to 6 km in freezing rain with severe icing are forecast en-route until 1200 UTC. Delay until after 1200 UTC.

    d. The weather for departure is suitable, but the forecast at destination is for thunderstorms and heavy rain showers, expected cloud base 1000 feet AMSL. Delay the flight until much later.

Forecast Weather below 10000 FT

Valid 120900 to 121700 Z APR 11 Fronts/zones valid at 121200 Z

AREA	SURFACE VIS AND WX	CLOUD	0 C
A	40 KM NIL ISOL 6 KM SHRA LAN FM 11Z ISOL HILL FG	SCT (ISOL BKN LAN FM 11Z)... ... CU/SC ᛃ ⌒ 030-050/060-XXX	005-020 N 035 S
B	30 KM NIL OCNL 7 KM SHRA ISOL (OCNL TROUGH) 4000 M... ...SHRA/SHGS ISOL 1500 M +TSGS (+TSSN MON)	SCT/BKN (LOC OVC TROUGH)... ... CU SC ᛃ ⌒ 020-030/060-XXX OCNL (ISOL E) CB 020/XXX ISOL BKN ST 010-015/020... ...TROUGH	010-020
C	10 KM NIL WDSPR 4000 M -SN ISOL 1500 M SN ISOL SEA/COT 2000 M FG ISOL 800 M SHSN MON N	BKN/OVC SC ᛃ ⌒ 025-040 BKN ST SC 005-015/025	000-015

Outlook until:130000 Z
Showers dying out inland

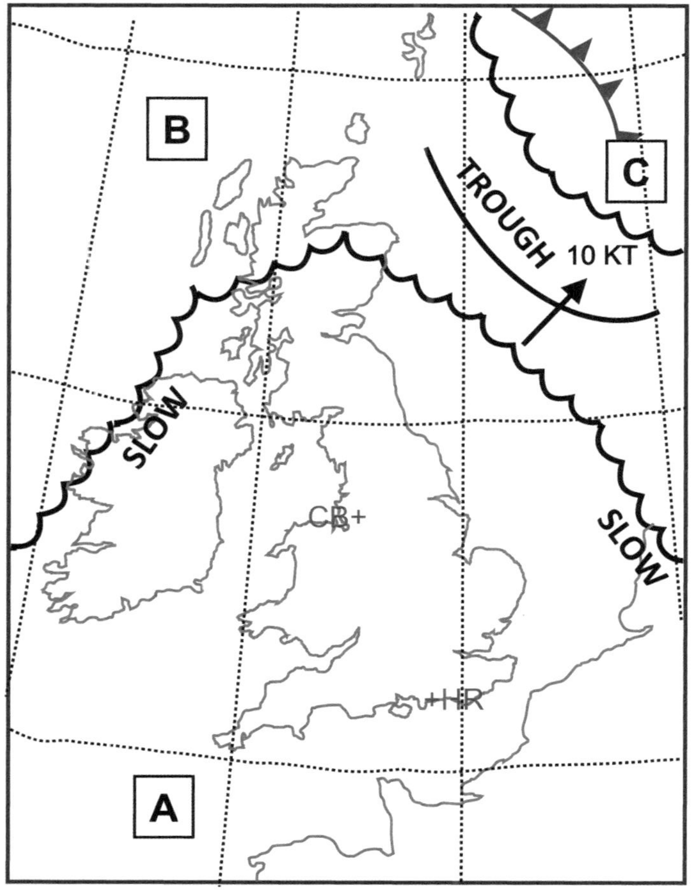

All heights in 100's of feet above mean sea level
XXX means above chart upper limit
Cloud amount (Oktas) MOD/SEV ICE ᛃ/ᛃ Speed of movement in KT
FEW: 1-2 SCT: 3-4   MOD/SEV TURB ⌒/⌒ Temperatures in DEG C
BKN: 5-7 OVC: 8   TS/CB implies GR/ᛃ/⌒ Hill FG implies vis < 200 M

This forecast may be amended at any time

In the style of Met Form 215 produced by the Met Office.

12. A flight is planned from Chichester (Goodwood) (EGHR) to Manchester Barton (EGCB).ETD: 1300Z. Time en-route: 2 hours 30 minutes.

The flight is to remain outside controlled airspace, and will be operated at a minimum level of 1500 feet AGL. The pilot holds a PPL with no IMC or Instrument Ratings and so plans to remain VFR. He must remain clear of cloud, in sight of the surface and assume a flight visibility of 5 km must be maintained. The aircraft is not cleared for flight in known icing conditions.

METAR for departure:
EGHR 121250 03008KT 9999 SCT035 BKN040 15/01 Q1025 NOSIG=

TAF for destination:
EGCB 120900 Z 121019 13012KT CAVOK TEMPO 1517 3000 PROB30 TEMPO 1519 6000 +TSRA SCT020CB

Given the above and considering Met Form 215 (Met Paper 5 Illustration 3) what is the most reasonable course of action?

a. Conditions at the departure airfield are within limits. At the destination thunderstorms are forecast. It is advisable to postpone the flight for at least 24 hours when improvement is likely.

b. Conditions at the departure airfield and for the first half of the flight are within limits. It is less ideal at the destination where CBs will cause a temporary reduction in visibility to 3000 m between 1500 and 1700 UTC. Delaying for two hours would give an ETA of 1730 thus avoiding the reduced visibility.

c. Conditions at the departure airfield and for the first half of the flight within Zone B are well within limits. In Zone A and at the destination a temporary reduction in visibility with CBs to 3,000 feet are forecast between 1500 and 1900 UTC. This is below limits. Together with the predicted TS it is advisable to delay departure until after 1600 UTC, and be ready to avoid isolated thunderstorms en-route. It may be necessary to hold clear of CB activity should a shower be crossing the airfield on arrival; additional holding fuel should be carried.

d. Conditions at the departure airfield and for the first half of the flight within Zone A are well within limits. Conditions at the destination are less favourable with a temporary reduction in visibility to 6000 m between 1500 and 1700 UTC, this is below limits. Together with the predicted isolated TS at and in the vicinity of Barton it is advisable to delay take-off until 1600 UTC. It may be necessary to hold clear of CB activity should a shower be crossing the airfield on arrival, additional holding fuel should be carried.

13. Refer to Met Form 215 (Met Paper 5 Illustration 3). What type of front is shown in areas C?
a. Fast moving
b. Warm
c. Occluded
d. Cold

14. Refer to Met Form 215 (Met Paper 5 Illustration 3). What type of feature is depicted in area B in the North Sea to the East of Scotland? What weather is associated with this feature?
a. It is a trough of high pressure; it brings similar weather to a warm front i.e. layer clouds and rain
b. It is a trough of high pressure and will bring weather similar to an anticyclone, light winds clear skies
c. It is a trough of low pressure, and will bring weather similar to a depression, layer clouds and rain
d. It is a trough of low pressure and will bring weather similar to a cold front, cumulus cloud, possibly CBs and TS.

15. Refer to Met Form 215 (Met Paper 5 Illustration 3). For area C, what does "ISOL 800 M SHSN MON N" mean?

   a. Surface visibility isolated 800 metres with snow showers Monday night
   b. Surface visibility isolated 800 metres with snow showers on mountains to the north of the area
   c. Visibility will be reduced to 800 metres over the mountain tops
   d. Surface visibility isolated 800 in mist with snow storms near the coast

16. Using the two "boxes" below from a Met Form 214, the wind direction, speed and temperature at 3,000 feet at position 50 N 3 30 W is:

   a. 050 degrees 09 knots -2.5°C
   b. 110 degrees 20 knots -3°C
   c. 085 degrees 11 knots -1.5°C
   d. 115 degrees 15 knots -2°C

50N 05W			50N 0230W		
24	340 15	-39	24	320 30	-39
18	360 15	-27	18	340 30	-28
10	020 15	-12	10	010 25	-14
05	040 10	-04	05	070 25	-07
02	070 05	+02	02	130 10	-01
01	090 05	+06	01	140 10	+02

Question 16

17. What are the three conditions necessary for thunderstorms to develop?

   a. A deep layer of stable air, low humidity and orographic lifting
   b. A shallow layer of stable air, high humidity and a trigger action
   c. A deep layer of unstable air, low humidity and orographic lifting
   d. A deep layer of unstable air, high humidity and a trigger action

18. You read the following in a METAR: BECMG FM 1400 –RASH. What does it mean?

   a. From 1400 UTC rain will lessen
   b. Becoming from 1400 UTC moderate rain
   c. Becoming from 1400 UTC slight showers of rain
   d. Becoming from 1400 UTC slight showers of snow

19. Using a Form 215 Forecast Weather Chart.
   What does "OCNL ⌒ (ISOL ⌃ NW) E of 02 W" mean?

   a. Occasional Moderate icing, with isolated severe icing to the north west, east of 02° West
   b. Occasional Moderate icing, with isolated severe turbulence to the north west, east of 02° West
   c. Occasional Moderate turbulence, with isolated severe icing to the north west, east of 02° West
   d. Occasional Moderate turbulence, with isolated severe turbulence to the north west, east of 02° West

20. Your destination airfield has no air traffic services; it is has an airfield elevation of 330 ft amsl. A nearby airport has a QNH of 1030 hPa. What is the QFE at your destination? (Assume 1 hPa = 30 ft)

   a. 1019 hPa
   b. 1041 hPa
   c. 1018 hPa
   d. 1042 hPa

END OF METEOROLOGY PAPER 5

METEOROLOGY PAPER 5: ANSWERS

No.	A	B	C	D
1		X		
2		X		
3			X	
4		X		
5			X	
6	X			
7			X	
8	X			
9				X
10	X			
11	X			
12		X		
13				X
14				X
15		X		
16			X	
17				X
18			X	
19				X
20	X			

CORRECT ANSWERS: PERCENTAGES					
15	16	17	18	19	20
87%	90%	92%	95%	97%	100%

METEOROLOGY PAPER 5: EXPLANATIONS

1. **(Answer: B)** A Polar Maritime air mass originates near Canada or Greenland. At source it is relatively humid, cool and stable. On its passage south the air mass is heated from below by the relatively warmer sea, its moisture content increases and it becomes unstable. On reaching the UK, polar maritime air brings convective clouds and possibly thunderstorms.

2. **(Answer: B)** Where a mountain wave turns down on the lee side of high ground, the down draughts may be greater than the climb performance of a light aircraft. In this question we are told that the mountain range lies north-south and the upper wind is westerly , hence both down draughts and the rotor zone will lie to the east of the range.

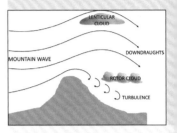

2. ANSWER B

3. **(Answer: C)** Rain ice is possible in the cold air ahead of a warm front when flying above the freezing level.

   Rain falls through the warm front into the colder air below. If the rain meets an object whose surface is below freezing – an aircraft for example – the rain will freeze on contact. This forms lumps of clear ice, which is hard to remove.

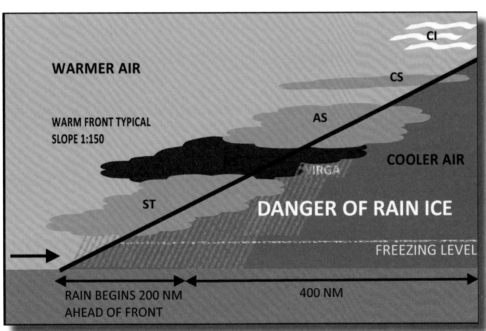

4. **(Answer: B)** At night visual acuity is often better looking towards the moon. Conversely, by day visibility is often worse directly into sun.

5. **(Answer: C)** Ice can form in the carburettor and induction system in moist air even with outside air temperatures as high as 30°C. Adiabatic cooling occurs when the air expands as it passes through the venturi into the carburettor and also when the fuel evaporates (absorbing latent heat) – the combined effect is that even warm air can have its temperature decreased below zero. If the air is moist enough ice will form. Throttle icing is more likely at low power settings, as the venturi effect is greater.

6. **(Answer: A)** Stratus is a layer cloud with little vertical extent and small vertical currents. It is a type of cloud often associated with drizzle.

7. **(Answer: C)** Wind velocity: 130/10 Temperature: minus 3°C

5230N 00E		
24	040 40	-39
18	020 10	-31
10	050 15	-14
05	070 10	-06
02	130 10	-03
01	150 05	+00

7. Answer C

8. **(Answer: A)** Wind velocity: 080/10

5230N 0230W		
24	050 65	-38
18	050 55	-28
10	050 30	-12
05	060 15	-05
02	080 10	-03
01	100 10	+00

8. Answer A

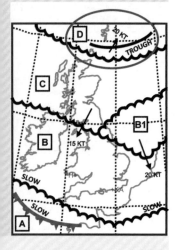

9. Answer A

9. **(Answer: D)** The trough is moving north east at 20 knots.

10. **(Answer: A)** The third column on the right hand side gives the altitude of the 0°C isotherm, or freezing level. Levels are printed in hundreds, hence 005-015 represents 500 – 1,500 feet. *(Refer to Met Paper 5 Illustration 2 on page 109)*

11. **(Answer: A)**

Departure: the METAR is acceptable with visibility greater than 10 km, slight rain showers and 3-4 oktas (scattered) at 1,900 feet.

Destination: the 1000 to 1900 UTC TAF is also suitable with a visibility if 10 km or more and scattered cloud at 3,000 feet.

En-route: from Metform 215 there are isolated showers forecast which may have to be avoided.

Conclusion: Proceed with caution.

12. **(Answer: B)**

Departure METAR:

EGHR 121250 03008KT 9999 SCT035 BKN040 15/01 Q1025 NOSIG=

Decodes as: Timed at 1250 UTC, surface wind 030 degrees 8 knots, visibility greater than 10 km, cloud scattered (3-4 oktas) at 3,500 feet broken (5-7 oktas) 4,000 feet, temperature +15 dewpoint +01 QNH 1025 hectopascals. No significant change expected within the next 2 hours. This is well within limits.

En-route: the Metform 215 Area A shows nothing that would preclude the flight. Isolated showers may be encountered which should be easily avoided.

Destination TAF:

EGCB 120900 Z 121019 13012KT CAVOK TEMPO 1517 3000 PROB30 TEMPO 1519 6000 +TSRA SCT020CB

Decodes as: Issued on the 12th at 0900 UTC forecast for the 12th between 1000 and 1900 UTC.

Surface wind 130 degrees at 12 knots, CAVOK (meaning visibility 10 km or more, no cloud below 5,000 feet AAL or below the minimum sector altitude whichever is the higher, and no significant weather phenomena on or in the vicinity of the aerodrome).

Temporarily between 1500 and 1700 UTC visibility 3000 m.
Between 1500 and 1900 UTC there is a 30% probability of the visibility being 6 km with heavy thunderstorms and rain falling from a scattered (3-4 oktas) layer of cumulonimbus cloud with a base of 2,000 feet.

Conclusion: Therefore, at the original ETA of 1530, the visibility will be below limits at 3000 m. By delaying 2 hours the ETA becomes 1730 UTC which will avoid the temporary reduction in visibility. There will still be a 30% chance of a thunderstorm which we will need to be aware of and hold off if necessary.

13. **(Answer: D)** It is a cold front

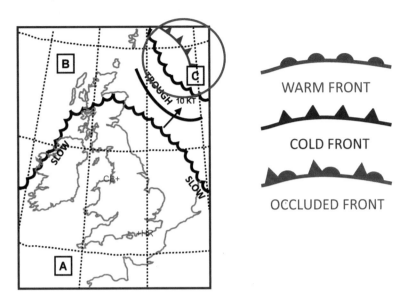

14. **(Answer: D)** A trough is a V-shaped extension from a region of low pressure. Air flows into the area (convergence) and rises; if the air is unstable the weather will be similar to a cold front or a depression with cumuliform cloud, possibly cumulonimbus cloud and thunderstorms.

15. **(Answer: B)** "ISOL 800 M SHSN MON N"

Surface visibility isolated 800 metres with snow showers on mountains to the north of the area.

ISOL	=	isolated (affecting less than 25% of the area concerned)
800 M	=	visibility 800 metres
SH	=	shower
SN	=	snow
MON	=	Above or covering mountains
N	=	north

16. **(Answer: C)** 085 degrees 11 knots -1.5°C

We need to interpolate the figures between the two sets of data provided. Starting first with 50 N 05 W determine the wind at 3,000 feet, by working out what is happening between 2,000 and 5,000 feet. We then need to do the same for 50 N 0230 W.

50N 05W		
24	340 15	-39
18	360 15	-27
10	020 15	-12
05	040 10	-04
02	070 05	+02
01	090 05	+06

50N 0230W		
24	320 30	-39
18	340 30	-28
10	010 25	-14
05	070 25	-07
02	130 10	-01
01	140 10	+02

50N 05W		
5000	040 10	-04
4000	050 09	-02
3000	060 07	+00
2000	070 05	+02

50N 0230W		
5000	070 25	-07
4000	090 20	-05
3000	110 15	-03
2000	130 10	-01

For 50 N 05 W the 3,000 ft wind and temperature are 060 degrees 7 knots and +0°C.
For 50 N 0230 W the 3,000 ft wind and temperature are 110 degrees 15 knots and -3°C.
Now, we are asked for the value at 50 N 03 30 W which is more or less half way between the two longitudes given, so interpolating between the two 3,000 ft figures which we have already calculated, we come up with 085 degrees 11 knots and -1.5°C.

17. **(Answer: D)** For thunderstorms to develop the conditions needed are: a deep layer of unstable air, high humidity and a trigger action
   1. Deep layer of instability, so that when the air starts to rise it will continue upwards
   2. High humidity, to provide the moisture to fuel the storm
   3. Trigger action, to start the air moving upwards. This could be either a front forcing air to rise, a mountain (orographic lifting), strong heating of the air in contact with the surface or heating of the lower layers of a polar airmass moving to lower latitudes.

18. **(Answer: C)** BECMG FM 1400 –SHRA

   Becoming from 1400 UTC slight showers of rain

BECMG	=	becoming
FM	=	from
1400	=	1400 UTC
-	=	slight
SH	=	showers
RA	=	rain

19. **(Answer: D)** "OCNL ⌒ (ISOL ⌃ NW) E of 02W"

   Occasional Moderate turbulence, with isolated severe turbulence to the north west, east of 02° West

OCNL =	occasional (affecting 25 to 50% of the area concerned)
⌒ =	moderate turbulence
ISOL =	isolated (affecting less than 25% of the area concerned)
⌃ =	severe turbulence

20. **(Answer: A)** 1019 hPa

   The elevation of 330 ft translates to 11 hPa. The 11 hPa must be subtracted from the QNH of 1030 hPa (pressure ALWAYS reduces with height) giving us a QFE of 1019 hPa.

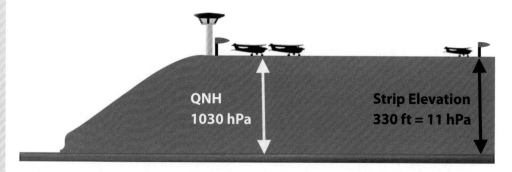

END OF EXPLANATIONS PAPER 5

PART 3: COMMUNICATIONS

The Communications examination consists of 30 questions; the time allowed is 40 minutes.

The pass mark is 75%.

Each question is multiple choice with four possible answers A, B, C and D.

You should indicate your chosen answer by placing a cross in the appropriate box on the answer sheet.

Blank answer sheets are to be found at the end of this publication, these may be photocopied.

INTENTIONALLY BLANK

COMMUNICATIONS PAPER 1

1. The correct pronunciation for transmitting an altitude of 2500 is:

   a. Two fife zero zero

   b. Two fife hundred

   c. Too tousand fife hundred

   d. Too fife zero zero

2. The correct RTF phraseology for frequency 121.275 MHz is:

   a. One two one decimal two seven

   b. One two one two seven five

   c. One two one two seven

   d. One two one decimal two seven five

3. The time 2150 is transmitted by radiotelephony as:

   a. Two one five zero, or five zero

   b. Twenty one fifty

   c. Two one fifty

   d. Ten to ten

4. The word "Roger" has the meaning:

   a. I understand your last transmission

   b. Received and understood

   c. I will comply with your message

   d. I have received all of your last transmission

5. The transponder should be set to which code in the event of an emergency?

   a. 7000

   b. 7500

   c. 7600

   d. 7700

6. Readability 3 means:

   a. Perfectly readable

   b. Unreadable

   c. Readable but with difficulty

   d. Readable now and then

7. A service providing automated airfield and meteorological information for arriving and departing traffic is:

   a. AFIS

   b. ATIS

   c. FIS

   d. APIS

8. Distress is defined as a condition:

   a. Where the pilot considers the aircraft has an emergency

   b. Concerning the safety of an aircraft or other vehicle

   c. Of grave and/or imminent danger and of requiring immediate assistance

   d. Concerning the safety of an aircraft, or some person on board or within sight, and of not requiring immediate assistance

9. A distress call must be preceded by the prefix:

    a.   PAN PAN or MAYDAY transmitted twice

    b.   MAYDAY transmitted once

    c.   MAYDAY transmitted three times

    d.   PAN PAN transmitted three times

10. At what range on a straight in approach could you report "G-AJGV long final"?

    a.   Between 8 nm and 4 nm

    b.   Between 7 nm and 3 nm

    c.   At 10 nm

    d.   Between 9 nm and 5 nm

11. When requesting a MATZ transit, at what range/time (whichever is sooner) must the request be made?

    a.   20 nm or 10 minutes

    b.   15 nm or 5 minutes

    c.   10 nm or 10 minutes

    d.   15 nm or 10 minutes

12. LARS is an ATS surveillance service available to assist pilots flying outside controlled airspace. It is provided up to and including FL.... normally within ...nm of the nominated unit:

    a.   FL 95, 30 nm

    b.   FL 95, 40 nm

    c.   FL 85, 30 nm

    d.   FL 65, 40 nm

13. LARS is an ATS surveillance service available to assist pilots flying outside controlled airspace. The service provided will be ..... or .....:

    a.   Traffic service, Procedural service

    b.   Procedural service, Deconfliction service

    c.   Traffic service, Deconfliction service

    d.   Basic service, Traffic service

14. When may the phrase "take-off" be used by a pilot?

    a.   Only when ready for departure

    b.   Only when acknowledging take-off clearance

    c.   Only ATC may use this phrase

    d.   Only when the power checks are complete

15. The pressure setting 997 hectopascals is transmitted as:

    a.   Pressure nine nine seven

    b.   Nine nine seven

    c.   Nine nine seven pressure setting

    d.   Nine nine seven hectopascals

16. Within UK airspace when clearing an aircraft to a HEIGHT a controller will include the:

    a.   QNH

    b.   Regional pressure setting

    c.   QFE

    d.   Standard pressure setting

17. "STANDBY" means:

    a.   The same as "pass your message"

    b.   Wait and I will call you

    c.   Repeat you last transmission

    d.   Wait and transmit again

18. Aeronautical messages are prioritised. Which of the following is true?

    a.   Flight safety messages are handled before Urgency messages

    b.   Flight regularity messages are handled before VDF messages

    c.   VDF messages are handled before flight safety messages

    d.   Meteorological messages are handled before VDF messages

19. The instruction "SQUAWK IDENT" means:

    a.   Operate the special position identification feature on the transponder

    b.   Set the transponder to standby

    c.   Set the transponder to ON

    d.   Set the transponder to ALT

20. In the UK the three categories of Air Traffic Service are:

    a.   Basic, Traffic and Deconfliction

    b.   ATC, Flight Information Service, Air/Ground Communication Service

    c.   Control, LARS, SVFR

    d.   Radar, Tower, Procedural

21. A Flight Information Service at an aerodrome provides:

    a.   Instructions to aircraft within the ATZ

    b.   Information to aircraft within the ATZ

    c.   Information to aircraft within 15 nm of the aerodrome

    d.   Control of aircraft in the ATZ

22. On your initial call to an ATSU a pilot should pass:

    a.   The aircraft call sign

    b.   Aircraft call sign and type, departure and destination, position, and altitude

    c.   The aircraft call sign, position and heading

    d.   Aircraft call sign and service requested

23. Regarding VDF, a QDM is the:

    a.   Magnetic bearing of the aircraft from the VDF station

    b.   Magnetic heading (in nil wind) to steer to reach the VDF station

    c.   True bearing of the aircraft from the VDF station

    d.   True heading (in nil wind) to steer to reach the VDF station

24. The correct phraseology format to use when requesting a QDM is:

    a.   QDM,QDM, QDM, G-MACK request QDM

    b.   Request QDM G-MACK

    c.   G-MACK request QDM

    d.   G-MACK request QDM G-MACK

25. The accuracy of a Class A VDF bearing is:

    a.   ± 2°

    b.   ± 5°

    c.   ± 10°

    d.   ± 15°

26. A Special VFR clearance enables a pilot to:

    a.   Fly with lower weather minima

    b.   Cross an airway without needing a valid IR

    c.   Fly within a Control Zone in circumstances normally requiring an IFR clearance

    d.   Enter a Control Zone without clearance

27. An Air Traffic Service where a controller passes specific surveillance derived traffic information, but the avoidance of other traffic is the pilot's responsibility, is:

    a.   Basic Service

    b.   Traffic Service

    c.   Deconfliction Service

    d.   Procedural Service

28. After establishing two-way communication and being asked to "pass your message", pilots requiring a LARS should pass:

    a.   A/c call sign, altitude, position, departure and destination, POB

    b.   Aircraft type, intention, departure and destination, route, POB

    c.   A/c call sign and type, departure point and destination, present position, altitude, request or intention

    d.   A/c call sign, present position, next turning point, altitude

29. When using Safetycom, transmissions shall only be made within ....nm of the aerodrome of intended landing, and not above ...... feet AAL or ......feet above circuit height.

    a.   10 nm 3000 feet 1000 feet

    b.   10 nm 2000 feet 1000 feet

    c.   15 nm 2000 feet 1000 feet

    d.   15 nm 3000 feet 1000 feet

30. 121.5 MHz, the Aeronautical Emergency Frequency:

    a.   May be used to practice distress and urgency calls

    b.   May not be used to practice distress and urgency calls

    c.   May be used to practice distress but not urgency calls

    d.   May be used to practice urgency but not distress calls

---

END OF COMMUNICATIONS PAPER 1

INTENTIONALLY BLANK

COMMUNICATIONS PAPER 1: ANSWERS

No.	A	B	C	D
1			X	
2				X
3	X			
4				X
5				X
6			X	
7.		X		
8			X	
9			X	
10	X			
11		X		
12	X			
13			X	
14		X		
15				X
16			X	
17		X		
18			X	
19	X			
20		X		
21		X		
22				X
23		X		
24				X
25	X			
26			X	
27		X		
28			X	
29		X		
30				X

CORRECT ANSWERS: PERCENTAGES							
23	24	25	26	27	28	29	30
76%	80%	83%	86%	90%	93%	96%	100%

COMMUNICATIONS PAPER 1: EXPLANATIONS

1. **(Answer: C)** Altitude 2500 is pronounced **"too tousand fife hundred".**

   When transmitting altitude, height, cloud height, visibility and runway visual range (basically anything measured in feet or metres!) whole hundreds and thousands are transmitted by stating the number of hundreds and thousands followed by the word "HUN-dred" or "TOU-SAND" as applicable. Combinations follow the same rule.

2. **(Answer: D)** The phraseology for 121.275 is "One two one decimal two seven five". If a number contains a decimal point the RTF word DAY-SEE-MAL is inserted at the appropriate point. When transmitting a frequency all six digits must be pronounced. The only exception being where the fifth and sixth number are both zeros, in which case only the first four digits will be pronounced, as in the first case below:

Number	Transmitted as:	Pronounced as:
121.100 MHz	One two one decimal one	Wun too wun dayseemal wun
120.925 MHz	One two zero decimal nine two five	Wun too zero dayseemal niner too fife
132.550 MHz	One three two decimal five five zero	Wun tree too dayseemal fife fife zero

SEE ALSO COMMUNICATION PAPER 2 QUESTION 2 FOR FURTHER DETAILS.

Numeral or Numeral Element	Pronounciation
0	ZERO
1	WUN
2	TOO
3	TREE
4	FOW ER
5	FIFE
6	SIX
7	SEV EN
8	AIT
9	NIN ER
DECIMAL	DAYSEEMAL
HUNDRED	HUNDRED
THOUSAND	TOUSAND

3. **(Answer: A)** Co-ordinated Universal Time (UTC) is to be used at all times; UTC is also known as Zulu and is the same as GMT. Normally when transmitting time only the minutes of the hour are required. If there is a possibility of confusion the hour should be included as well.

Time	Transmitted as:	Pronounced as:
0805	ZERO FIVE (or zero eight zero five)	ZERO FIFE
1300	ONE THREE ZERO ZERO	WUN TREE ZERO ZERO
2258	FIVE EIGHT (or two two five eight)	FIFE AIT

4. **(Answer: D)** "Roger" has the meaning: I have received all of your last transmission. Note: Under no circumstances should this word be used in reply to a question requiring a direct answer in the affirmative (AFFIRM) or negative (NEGATIVE), or to acknowledge any item that must be readback.

5. **(Answer: D)** An emergency is indicated by the transponder code 7700. The following special purpose codes are in use:

   7700: Emergency
   7600: Communications failure
   7500: Unlawful interference (hijack)
   7000: UK conspicuity code
   2000: Entering an FIR, when operating under VFR, from an adjacent region where the operation of transponders has not been required.

6. **(Answer: C)** Readability 3 means readable but with difficulty. *(See table right)*

Readability Scale	Meaning
1	Unreadable
2	Readable now and then
3	Readable but with difficulty
4	Readable
5	Perfectly readable

7.   **(Answer: B)** ATIS, Automatic Terminal Information Service. At busier airports an Automatic Terminal Information Service is broadcast to provide a range of data, usually weather conditions and essential aerodrome information, on a discreet frequency or selected VOR.

Each ATIS message is coded consecutively using the phonetic alphabet. A new message is generated at regular intervals (usually half hourly at the time of the routine meteorological observations at minutes 20 and 50) or whenever a significant change occurs.

Pilots should advise ATC that they have received the latest ATIS:
On Departure – before taxiing
On Arrival – on first contact with the ATSU.

8.   **(Answer: C)** DISTRESS is a condition of being threatened by grave and/or imminent danger, and of requiring immediate assistance. A distress message will take priority over all other messages.

9.   **(Answer: C)** A distress call begins with the word "MAYDAY" spoken three times

10.   **(Answer: A)** "Long final" is between 8 nm and 4 nm.

11.   **(Answer: B)** Civilian traffic wishing to penetrate a MATZ should make contact with the military controller 15 nm or 5 minutes flying time before reaching the zone boundary, whichever is sooner. On the initial call to the military controller the phrase "Request MATZ penetration" must be used, e.g. "Marham Zone, GMJDE request MATZ penetration".

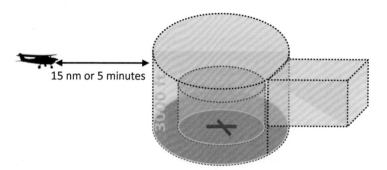

15 nm or 5 minutes

12.   **(Answer: A)** Outside Controlled Airspace certain Air Traffic Service Units are able to provide a Lower Airspace Radar Service to pilots flying in UK uncontrolled airspace up to and including FL 95, within approximately 30 nm of each participating unit.

13.   **(Answer: C)** ATSUs participating in the LARS are able to provide either a Traffic Service or a Deconfliction Service; both are available at the request of the pilot. The controller will inform pilots when they are receiving either a Radar Control Service (within controlled airspace), Traffic Service or Deconfliction Service (outside controlled airspace); and also whenever the level of service changes or terminates. The type of radar service being provided is information that should be read back by the pilot.

14.   **(Answer: B)** The phrase "take-off" may only be used by a pilot to acknowledge take-off clearance. At all other times the word "departure" must be used.

15. **(Answer: D)** The word "hectopascals" must be used when transmitting all pressure settings below 1000, e.g. QNH 994 hectopascals, QFE 987 hectopascals. This is to avoid any confusion with inches of mercury, the datum used in the United States.

16. **(Answer: C)** Height is defined as the vertical distance of a level, point or object considered as a point measured from a specified datum. The datum is normally the highest point on the landing area. With QFE set the aircraft altimeter will indicate height above the aerodrome.

    The phraseology used when referring to vertical position differs depending on the pressure setting in use:

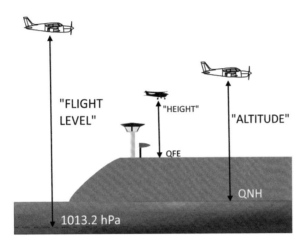

17. **(Answer: B)** Standby means: wait and I will call you. ATC's response to your initial contact call will either be "pass your message" or "standby", the latter simply meaning that the controller is engaged with another task. You should say nothing in response to an instruction to "standby", simply wait and the controller will call you.

18. **(Answer: C)** The Aeronautical Mobile Service handles messages in the following order of priority:

MESSAGE CATEGORY & ORDER OF PRIORITY	RT SIGNAL
1. Distress Calls, Distress Messages and Distress Traffic	**MAYDAY**
2. Urgency Messages	**PAN PAN**
3. Communications relating to Direction Finding (VDF).	
4. Flight Safety Messages.	
5. Meteorological Messages.	
6. Flight regularity Messages	

19. **(Answer: A)** "Squawk ident" means operate the special position identification feature on the transponder. The SPI feature is more usually referred to as the IDENT button. If a controller asks you to squawk "ident" you should press the ident button. This causes a flashing circle to appear around your aircraft's radar return confirming its identity to the controller.

Transponder phraseology:

PHRASE	MEANING
Squawk (code)	Set the code as instructed
Confirm Squawk	Confirm code set on the transponder
Reset (code)	Reselect assigned code
Squawk Ident	Operate the SPI feature
Squawk Mayday	Select emergency
Squawk Standby	Select the standby feature
Squawk Charlie	Select altitude reporting feature
Check altimeter setting and confirm (level)	Check pressure setting and report your level
Stop Squawk Charlie, wrong indication	Deselect pressure altitude reporting transmission as the indication is faulty
Stop Squawk Charlie	Deselect altitude reporting
Confirm (level)	Check and confirm your level. Used to verify the accuracy of the Mode C level information displayed to the controller

20. **(Answer: B)** The UK has three main categories of aeronautical communication service: Air Traffic Control, Flight Information Service, Air/Ground Communication Service.

Air Traffic Control: A controller will issue instructions with which pilots must comply or, if the instruction is not suitable, the pilot must request an alternative clearance.

Flight Information Service: Provides information useful to the safe and efficient conduct of flights in the Aerodrome Traffic Zone. From this information pilots will be able to decide the appropriate course of action to be taken to ensure the safety of flight. Note: on the ground FISOs can issue instructions with which pilots should comply; in the air only information is passed.

Air/Ground: Only limited information is available and all decisions are the pilot's. The level of service is easily identifiable from the call sign used by the ground station.

UNIT	CALL SIGN	SERVICE
Area control centre	CONTROL	ATC
Radar (general)	RADAR	ATC
Approach control	APPROACH	ATC
Approach control radar arrivals	ARRIVAL/DIRECTOR	ATC
Approach control radar departures	DEPARTURE	ATC
Aerodrome control	TOWER	ATC
Surface movement control	GROUND	ATC
Flight information service	INFORMATION	FISO
Air/Ground Communication	RADIO	A/G

21. **(Answer: B)** Flight Information Service at aerodromes is provided for the safe and efficient conduct of flights in the Aerodrome Traffic Zone. From this information pilots will be able to decide the appropriate course of action to be taken to ensure the safety of flight, i.e. the onus is on you, the pilot, to decide. The service is easily identifiable by the call sign suffix "Information".

22. **(Answer: D)** The initial call to an ATS unit should only include the minimum information needed to establish:

    a) the service that an en-route flight requires; or
    b) the clearance/information that a joining or departing flight requires.

    The ATSU will then respond with "Pass Your Message" enabling more detailed information regarding the flight (ADDPAR) to be passed.

23. **(Answer: B)** QDM is: The aircraft's magnetic heading to steer in zero wind to reach the station.

OTHER VDF bearings available:

QDR AIRCRAFT'S MAGNETIC BEARING FROM THE STATION

QTE AIRCRAFT'S TRUE BEARING FROM THE STATION

QUJ AIRCRAFT'S TRUE TRACK TO THE STATION

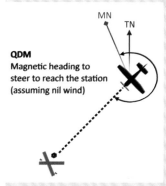

QDM
Magnetic heading to steer to reach the station (assuming nil wind)

24. **(Answer: D)** The correct RTF phraseology format to use when requesting a QDM, is:

    "(Full aircraft call sign) request QDM (full aircraft call sign)"
    For example "G-MACK request QDM G-MACK"

25. **(Answer: A)** A Class A VDF bearing is accurate to +/- 2 degrees

    ACCURACY OF VDF Bearings:
    CLASS A +/- 2 degrees
    CLASS B +/- 5 degrees
    CLASS C +/- 10 degrees
    CLASS D accuracy less than class C

26. **(Answer: C)** A Special VFR clearance enables a pilot to fly within a Control Zone in circumstances normally requiring an IFR clearance. Special VFR clearances are only permitted within control ZONES, usually at the request of the pilot.

    Special VFR is a concession offered by ATC, which allows an aircraft to operate within a control zone which is Class A or in any other control zone in IMC or at night, without requiring compliance with the Instrument Flight Rules. Instead pilots will comply with instructions given by the Air Traffic Control Unit.

27. **(Answer: B)** The Traffic Service is a surveillance (radar) based ATS where in addition to a Basic Service:

    - *The controller provides specific radar derived traffic information to assist a pilot in avoiding other traffic.*
    - *The service is available to IFR or VFR flights at the request of the pilot.*
    - *Relevant Traffic Information will be passed and will be updated if the traffic continues to constitute a definite hazard, or if requested by the pilot.*
    - *Traffic avoidance is ultimately the pilot's responsibility. Whether Traffic Information has been passed or not, a pilot is still responsible for collision avoidance.*

28. **(Answer: C)** When instructed by an ATS Unit to "Pass your message", your reply should contain the following information, ideally in the order specified. ADDPAR is a mnemonic that may be used to keep the details in the correct order until the call becomes second nature:

A	Aircraft Call sign and Type
D	Departure Point
D	Destination
P	Present Position
A	Altitude/Level
R	Request, intentions or additional details (e.g. Flight Rules, Next route point, request—whatever is applicable to the flight)

This call format is appropriate for giving your flight details in many situations including rejoin, obtaining a radar service or basic service, requesting transit of a MATZ or permission to enter a Control Zone.

29. **(Answer: B)** Safetycom is a common frequency introduced for use by aircraft in the vicinity of an airfield or landing site that does not have a notified VHF frequency for radio communications.

    The frequency is 135.475 MHz. Transmissions should only be made on Safetycom when aircraft are below 2000 ft above aerodrome/location elevation or below 1000 ft above promulgated circuit height. Transmissions shall also only be made within 10 nm of the aerodrome or intended landing site.

30. **(Answer: D)** Pilots may simulate emergency incidents (BUT NOT THE STATE OF DISTRESS) on 121.5 MHz to enable them to gain experience of the ATC service available. Before calling, pilots should listen out on the emergency frequency to ensure that no actual or practice incident is already in progress. Simulated emergency calls must be prefixed PRACTICE and should be brief: "Practice Pan, Practice Pan, Practice Pan, London Centre G-BUGA". The emergency controller will then state whether the practice can be accepted.

END OF EXPLANATIONS PAPER 1

---

1. The correct pronunciation for transmitting a height of 3400 is:

   a. Tree fower zero zero
   b. Tree tousand fower hundred
   c. Three thousand four hundred
   d. Three fower zero zero

2. The correct RTF phraseology for frequency 132.700 MHz is:

   a. One three two decimal seven
   b. One three two seven
   c. One three two point seven
   d. One three two decimal seven zero zero

3. The time 0734 is transmitted by radiotelephony as:

   a. Zero seven three four UTC
   b. Seven thirty four, or thirty four
   c. Zero seven three four, or three four
   d. Minute three four

4. You are asked by ATC "are you able to maintain VMC?" a correct reply would contain the phrase:

   a. Wilco
   b. Roger
   c. Affirm or negative
   d. Yes or no

5. Readability 5 means:

   a. Perfectly readable
   b. Unreadable
   c. Readable
   d. Readable now and then

6. The states of emergency are:

   a. Mayday and pan pan
   b. Difficulty and urgency
   c. Distress and urgency
   d. Mayday and distress

7. The correct abbreviation of the call sign "HELAIR GHBAH"

   a. Golf Alpha Hotel
   b. Helair Golf Alpha Hotel
   c. Bravo Alpha Hotel
   d. Helair Alpha Hotel

8. A distress call is preceded by the spoken word "MAYDAY", which is transmitted:

   a. Once
   b. Three times
   c. Twice
   d. Four times

9. Ideally, immediately following "mayday", an aircraft in distress should transmit:

   a. Call sign of the station addressed, time permitting
   b. Nature of the emergency
   c. The aircraft's call sign three times
   d. Altitude and present position

10. When wanting to transit a MATZ a pilot must establish two way communication with the aerodrome controlling the zone by ...(i)..., or ...(ii)... from the boundary whichever is the sooner:

  a.   i) 10 nm   ii) 5 minutes
  b.   i) 10 nm   ii) 10 minutes
  c.   i) 15 nm   ii) 5 minutes
  d.   i) 15 nm   ii) 10 minutes

11. Pilots requesting a MATZ crossing should pass the following information when asked to do so by the military controller:

  a.   Aircraft type, intention, departure and destination, route, POB
  b.   A/c call sign, present position, next turning point, altitude
  c.   A/c call sign, altitude, position, departure and destination, POB
  d.   A/c call sign and type, departure point and destination, present position, altitude, request or intention

12. All messages relating to a climb or descent to a HEIGHT or ALTITUDE should:

  a.   Use the word "TO" followed by the QFE or QNH
  b.   Not use the word "TO"
  c.   Use the word "TO" followed by the word HEIGHT or ALTITUDE
  d.   Use the word "LEVEL" followed by the word HEIGHT or ALTITUDE

13. How should a pilot in an emergency transmit the aircraft's position?

  a.   Present (or last known) position; altitude/flight level; heading
  b.   In relation to the nearest VOR/DME
  c.   Present (or last known) Position
  d.   The last position passed by radar

14. You make an initial call to an ATSU and in reply are told "G-MORG standby", you should:

  a.   Say nothing and wait to be called
  b.   Immediately say "standby G-MORG"
  c.   Say "wilco"
  d.   Call the ATSU again

15. In the Pooley's Flight Guide you read that ALBAN, your intended destination, has an Air/Ground Communication Service. When addressing ALBAN what call sign should you use?

  a.   ALBAN APPROACH
  b.   ALBAN INFORMATION
  c.   ALBAN RADIO
  d.   ALBAN GROUND

16. Regarding VDF, a QDR is the:

  a.   Magnetic bearing of the aircraft from the VDF station
  b.   Magnetic heading (in nil wind) to steer to reach the VDF station
  c.   True bearing of the aircraft from the VDF station
  d.   True heading (in nil wind) to steer to reach the VDF station

17. The accuracy of a Class B VDF bearing is:

  a.   ± 2°
  b.   ± 5°
  c.   ± 10°
  d.   ± 15°

18. The Air Traffic Services available outside controlled airspace, are:

   a.   Flight Information Service, Basic Service, Procedural Service and Traffic Service

   b.   Basic Service, Traffic Information Service, Radar Information Service and Procedural Service

   c.   Basic Service, Traffic Service, Deconfliction Service and Procedural Service

   d.   Basic Service, Radar Traffic Service, Deconfliction Service and Radar Control Service

19. A Special VFR clearance may be issued to allow:

   a.   Flight in a Control Zone in limited visibility

   b.   Flight in an airway without a valid IR

   c.   Aircraft to cross a Control Area without an IFR clearance

   d.   Flight in a Control Zone when it is not possible to comply with the IFR

20. Which of the following is an example of a conditional clearance?

   a.   G-AV after the landing PA28 line up

   b.   G-AV line up after the landing PA28

   c.   G-AV take off at your discretion

   d.   G-AV report final number 2

21. Conditional clearances are only used on an active runway when:

   a.   It is very busy and it is CAVOK

   b.   Aircraft wish to cross the active runway and it is safe

   c.   The aircraft or vehicles concerned are visible to the controller and the pilot. The clearance relates to only one movement

   d.   More than one aircraft is landing

22. You are arriving at an airfield, the FISO is using the call sign suffix "INFORMATION" and tells you: "G-BH, Land at your discretion, surface wind 300/8"

   a.   My discretion, surface wind 300/8 G-BH

   b.   Roger G-BH

   c.   Cleared to land G-BH

   d.   Land at my discretion G-BH

23. In the first instance which frequency should be used for transmitting a MAYDAY?

   a.   121.5 MHz

   b.   The civil or military frequency in use at the time

   c.   The nearest MATZ

   d.   Any local emergency frequency

24. The call sign pre-fix "STUDENT" indicates:

   a.   Training flights

   b.   A student pilot who is lost

   c.   A student pilot flying solo

   d.   A student pilot requiring extra assistance

25. A QNH of 981 hectopascals is transmitted as:

   a.   QNH nine eight one

   b.   Pressure nine eight one

   c.   QNH nine eight one hectopascals

   d.   Nine eight one

26. An Air Traffic Service provided to give advice and information useful for the safe and efficient conduct of flight which may include weather information and general airspace activity, is:

   a.   Basic Service

   b.   Traffic Service

   c.   Deconfliction Service

   d.   Flight Information Service

27. A controller providing, in addition to a Basic Service, specific radar derived traffic information but traffic avoidance is the responsibility of the pilot, is providing what service?

  a. Radar Control Service

  b. Deconfliction Service

  c. Procedural Service

  d. Traffic Service

28. "G-MOJE after departure cleared to zone boundary, via north lane, climb not above altitude 2,500 feet, squawk 4677". What type of message is this?

  a. Take-off clearance

  b. Route clearance

  c. Conditional clearance

  d. Airway joining clearance

29. You are making a standard overhead join, you have flown overhead at 2,000 feet AAL and are commencing your descent to circuit height. What RT call should you make?

  a. "G-HE downwind descending"

  b. "G-HE upwind descending"

  c. "G-HE deadside descending"

  d. "G-HE liveside descending"

30. When reading back an ATC instruction, you should end the message with:

  a. Your aircraft call sign

  b. The ground station call sign

  c. "Over"

  d. "Out"

END OF COMMUNICATIONS PAPER 2

INTENTIONALLY BLANK

	A	B	C	D
1.		X		
2.	X			
3.			X	
4.			X	
5.	X			
6.			X	
7.				X
8.		X		
9.	X			
10.			X	
11.				X
12.			X	
13.	X			
14.	X			
15			X	
16.	X			
17.		X		
18.			X	
19.				X
20.	X			
21.			X	
22.		X		
23.		X		
24.			X	
25.			X	
26.	X			
27.				X
28.		X		
29.			X	
30.	X			

CORRECT ANSWERS: PERCENTAGES							
23	24	25	26	27	28	29	30
76%	80%	83%	86%	90%	93%	96%	100%

Numeral or Numeral Element	Pronounciation
0	ZERO
1	WUN
2	TOO
3	TREE
4	FOW ER
5	FIFE
6	SIX
7	SEV EN
8	AIT
9	NIN ER
DECIMAL	DAYSEEMAL
HUNDRED	HUNDRED
THOUSAND	TOUSAND

1. **(Answer: B)** Note in this question you are asked for the pronunciation. Height 3400 is pronounced "tree tousand fower hundred".

   When transmitting altitude, height, cloud height, visibility and runway visual range (basically anything measured in feet or metres!) whole hundreds and thousands are transmitted by stating the number of hundreds and thousands followed by the word "HUN-dred" or "TOU-SAND" as applicable. Combinations follow the same rule.

2. **(Answer: A)** The phraseology for 132.700 is "One three two decimal seven". If a number contains a decimal point the RTF word DAY-SEE-MAL is inserted at the appropriate point. When transmitting a frequency all six digits must be pronounced. The only exception being where the fifth and sixth number are both zeros, in which case only the first four digits will be pronounced:

Frequency	Transmitted as:	No. of digits to be transmitted
Fifth and sixth digits **BOTH ZERO**		
121.**000** 132.**700**	ONE TWO ONE DECIMAL ZERO ONE THREE TWO DECIMAL SEVEN	4
All six numbers pronounced		
119.055 122.405 133.075 135.725	ONE ONE NINE DECIMAL ZERO FIVE FIVE ONE TWO TWO DECIMAL FOUR ZERO FIVE ONE THREE THREE DECIMAL ZERO SEVEN FIVE ONE THREE FIVE DECIMAL SEVEN TWO FIVE	6
Only the last digit is zero, so all six numbers must be pronounced		
118.050 126.450 131.650	ONE ONE EIGHT DECIMAL ZERO FIVE ZERO ONE TWO SIX DECIMAL FOUR FIVE ZERO ONE THREE ONE DECIMAL SIX FIVE ZERO	6

3. **(Answer: C)** Co-ordinated Universal Time (UTC) is to be used at all times; UTC is also known as Zulu and is the same as GMT. Normally when transmitting time only the minutes of the hour are required. If there is a possibility of confusion the hour should be included as well.

Time	Transmitted as:	Pronounced as:
0805	ZERO FIVE (or zero eight zero five)	ZERO FIFE
1300	ONE THREE ZERO ZERO	WUN TREE ZERO ZERO
2258	FIVE EIGHT (or two two five eight)	FIFE AIT

4. **(Answer: C)** In response to a direct question use "affirm" or "negative" as appropriate. "Roger" only means: I have received all of your last transmission. It does not answer the question!

5. **(Answer: A)** Readability 5 means perfectly readable.

6. **(Answer: C)** Distress and urgency are two states of emergency. They are defined as:

   DISTRESS is a condition of being threatened by grave and/or imminent danger and of requiring immediate assistance. A distress message will take priority over all other messages.

   URGENCY is a condition concerning the safety of an aircraft or other vehicle, or of some other person on board or within sight, but not requiring immediate assistance.

Readability Scale	Meaning
1	Unreadable
2	Readable now and then
3	Readable but with difficulty
4	Readable
5	Perfectly readable

7. **(Answer: D)** The abbreviation of Helair G-HBAH is "Helair Alpha Hotel". Call sign abbreviations follow three patterns:

Full Call Sign		Abbreviated Call Sign
G-AJGV Piper G-MACK* Citation G-HBAH*	**AIRCRAFT REGISTRATION:** The first and the last two characters of the aircraft registration	G-GV Piper CK Citation AH
Either the manufacturer's name or the name of aircraft model may be used to prefix the call sign in place of the first character		
Modernair G-BNPL Britannia G-MORG	The telephony designator of the aircraft operating agency, followed by the last two characters of the registration marking of the aircraft.	Modernair PL Britannia RG
Modernair 012 Monarch 416	**Flight Number:** No abbreviation permitted.	Modernair 012 Monarch 416

8. **(Answer: B)** A distress call begins with the word "MAYDAY" spoken three times.

9. **(Answer: A)** Immediately after "Mayday" the pilot of an aircraft in distress should ideally transmit the call sign of the station being addressed. A distress call begins with the word "MAYDAY" spoken three times; the subsequent information should then be passed ideally in the order below:

MAYDAY MAYDAY MAYDAY	
C	Call sign of station addressed
A	Aircraft call sign
T	Type
N	Nature of the emergency
I	Intentions of pilot-in-command
P	Present (or last known) position; altitude/flight level; heading
P	Pilot qualifications, eg. student pilot; PPL; IMC; IR
O	Other useful information, eg. number on board, fuel endurance

10. **(Answer: C)** Civilian traffic wishing to penetrate a MATZ should make contact with the military controller 15 nm or 5 minutes flying time before reaching the zone boundary, whichever is sooner. On the initial call to the military controller the phrase "Request MATZ penetration" must be used. For example: "Cottesmore Zone G-MORG request MATZ penetration".

11. **(Answer: D)** When instructed an ATS Unit to "Pass your message", your reply should contain the following information, ideally in the order specified. ADDPAR is a mnemonic that may be used to keep the details in the correct order:

A	Aircraft call sign and type
D	Departure point
D	Destination
P	Present Position
A	Altitude/Level
R	Request, intentions or additional details (eg. flight rules, next route point, request—whatever is applicable to the flight)

This call format is appropriate for giving your flight details in many situations including rejoin, obtaining a radar service or basic service, requesting transit of a MATZ or permission to enter a Control Zone.

12. **(Answer: C)** In communications relating to a climb or descent to a height or altitude the word "TO" is used. The word "TO" is to be omitted when referring to Flight Levels. For example:

Golf-Alpha Victor request climb flight level three five

As opposed to:

Golf-Alpha Victor request climb TO altitude three thousand five hundred feet

13. **(Answer: A)** A pilot in an emergency should report his/her position as: Present (or last known) Position; altitude/flight level; and heading. See the full "Mayday" call in the explanation to Question 9 of this paper.

14. **(Answer: A)** Standby means: wait and I will call you. ATC's response your initial contact call will either be "pass your message" or "standby", the latter simply meaning that the controller is engaged with another task. You should say nothing in response to an instruction to "standby", simply wait and the controller will call you.

15. **(Answer: C)** Air/ Ground stations use the call sign suffix "RADIO"

UNIT	CALL SIGN	SERVICE
Area control centre	CONTROL	ATC
Radar (general)	RADAR	ATC
Approach control	APPROACH	ATC
Approach control radar arrivals	ARRIVAL/DIRECTOR	ATC
Approach control radar departures	DEPARTURE	ATC
Aerodrome control	TOWER	ATC
Surface movement control	GROUND	ATC
Flight information service	INFORMATION	FISO
Air/Ground Communication	RADIO	A/G

16. **(Answer: A)** A QDR is the magnetic bearing of the aircraft from the station.

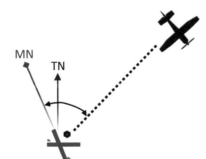

Other VDF bearings available:	
QDM	Magnetic **heading to steer** to reach the station (assuming nil wind)
QTE	Aircraft's **true bearing** from the station
QUJ	Aircraft's **true track** to the station

QDR
Magnetic bearing of the aircraft from the station

17. **(Answer: B)** A Class B VDF bearing is accurate to +/- 5 degrees

ACCURACY OF VDF Bearings:
CLASS A +/- 2 degrees
CLASS B +/- 5 degrees
CLASS C +/- 10 degrees
CLASS D accuracy less than class C

18. **(Answer: C)** The Air Traffic Services available outside controlled airspace are Basic Service, Traffic Service, Deconfliction Service and Procedural Service.

19. **(Answer: D)** A Special VFR clearance may be issued to allow flight in a Control Zone when it is not possible to comply with the IFR. Special VFR clearances are only permitted within control ZONES, usually at the request of the pilot. Special VFR is a concession offered by ATC, which allows an aircraft to operate within a control zone which is Class A or in any other control zone in IMC or at night, without requiring compliance with the Instrument Flight Rules. Instead pilots will comply with instructions given by the Air Traffic Control Unit.

20. **(Answer: A)** It is a Conditional Clearance which may be issued to help the traffic flow. This will relate to one movement only, and if the subject aircraft is landing it must be the next to land. It is vital that the pilot has identified the subject aircraft correctly. If there is any doubt - ask!

    The format or a conditional clearance will be:
    - *Call sign*
    - *The condition*
    - *Identification of the subject of the condition*
    - *The instruction*

21. **(Answer: C)** Conditional clearances will not be used for movements affecting the active runway, except when the aircraft or vehicles concerned are visible to both the controller and pilot. Conditional clearances will relate to one movement only and, in the case of landing traffic, this must be the first aircraft on approach.

22. **(Answer: B)** CAP 413 gives the response "roger G-BH" in response to the transmission "land at your discretion". Practically it may add to the situational awareness of other pilots if you report your intentions, i.e. to land, continue or make a missed approach.

23. **(Answer: B)** The first attempt to transmit an emergency message should be made on the frequency currently in use. If this is not successful the pilot should transmit his/her intention is to change to the Aeronautical Emergency Frequency 121.5 MHz.

24. **(Answer: C)** On initial contact, student pilots who are flying solo shall use the call sign prefix 'STUDENT'. Once acknowledged, it is not normally be necessary for student pilots to use the prefix in subsequent transmissions, unless they feel they are being asked to do something with which they are not familiar.

25. **(Answer: C)** The word "hectopascals" must be used when transmitting all pressure settings below 1000 e.g. QNH 994 hectopascals, QFE 987 hectopascals. This is to avoid any confusion with inches of mercury, the datum used in the United States.

26. **(Answer: A)** The Basic Service is an Air Traffic Service provided to give advice and information useful to the safe and efficient conduct of flights. Such items may include weather information, changes in the serviceability of facilities, conditions at aerodromes or general aerial activity information.

    - *The service is available to IFR or VFR flights, but may not be appropriate for flight in IMC.*
    - *Traffic Information should not be expected. Outside an ATZ there is no obligation for the controller/FISO to pass Traffic Information.*

27. **(Answer: D)** The Traffic Service is a surveillance (radar) based ATS where in addition to a Basic Service:

    - *The controller provides specific radar derived traffic information to assist a pilot in avoiding other traffic.*

- *The service is available to IFR or VFR flights, at the request of the pilot.*
- *Relevant Traffic Information will be passed and will be updated if the traffic continues to constitute a definite hazard, or if requested by the pilot.*
- *Traffic avoidance is ultimately the pilot's responsibility. Whether Traffic Information has been passed or not, a pilot is still responsible for collision avoidance.*

28. **(Answer: B)** "G-MOJE after departure cleared to zone boundary, via north lane, climb not above altitude 2,500 feet, squawk 4677". Is a route clearance.

   Contents of a Clearance
   - Aircraft Identification
   - Clearance Limit
   - Route
   - Level of Flight

   The following may be included:
   - Communication Instructions
   - Any Special Instructions eg. SSR, Approach or Departure Manoeuvres

29. **(Answer: C)** The standard overhead join is a procedure often used at smaller aerodromes. The aircraft is required to:
   a. Overfly the aerodrome at 2000 feet above aerodrome elevation
   b. Determine the circuit direction if not already known (signal square, windsock, other traffic)
   c. Descend on the "dead side" to circuit height:
   d. Join the circuit by crossing the upwind end of the runway at circuit height.
   e. Position downwind

30. **(Answer: A)** To reply to an instruction from the ground first repeat the information, read back or acknowledge the instruction, then say the aircraft call sign.

   Example: **Descend to altitude three thousand feet Golf-Alpha Victor**

END OF EXPLANATIONS PAPER 2

INTENTIONALLY BLANK

1. The correct pronunciation for transmitting an altitude of 14,500, is:

    a. Wun fower thousand five zero zero

    b. Fourteen thousand fife hundred

    c. Wun fower tousand fife hundred

    d. One four tousand five hundred

2. The correct pronunciation for the frequency 129.400 Mhz, is:

    a. One two nine decimal four

    b. Wun too niner dayseemal fower

    c. Wun too niner point four

    d. One two nine decimal four zero zero

3. The time 1130 is pronounced as:

    a. Eleven thirty

    b. Wun wun tree zero, or tree zero

    c. One one three zero, or three zero

    d. Half past eleven

4. The transponder should be set to which code in the event of a radio failure?

    a. 7700

    b. 7600

    c. 7500

    d. 7400

5. The word or phrase used to indicate that you have received an ATC message and will comply with it , is:

    a. Roger

    b. Affirm

    c. Yes

    d. Wilco

6. Readability 4 means:

    a. Perfectly readable

    b. Unreadable

    c. Readable

    d. Readable now and then

7. What does "ATIS" stand for?

    a. Aeronautical Traffic Information Service

    b. Automatic Terminal Information Service

    c. Air Traffic Information Service

    d. Airport Terminal Information Service

8. When may a pilot abbreviate the aircraft RTF call sign?

    a. Only when it has first been abbreviated by the ground station

    b. On the second call to a ground station

    c. When there will be no confusion

    d. If agreed with the ground station before flight

9. Urgency is defined as a condition:

    a. Where the pilot considers the aircraft has an emergency

    b. Concerning the safety of another aircraft or other vehicle requiring immediate assistance

    c. Of grave and/or imminent danger and of requiring immediate assistance

    d. Concerning the safety of an aircraft or other vehicle, or some person on board or within sight, and not requiring immediate assistance

10. The correct radio call to make when you are ready for take-off is:

    a.   Request take- off

    b.   Ready for take-off

    c.   Ready

    d.   Ready for departure

11. The correct content and order of a position report is:

    a.   A/c call sign, position, time, level, next position and ETA

    b.   A/c call sign, route, position, heading and level

    c.   Position, heading, route and ETA

    d.   Position, level, next position and ETA

12. If you are cleared to a HEIGHT of 2500 feet, what pressure setting should be used?

    a.   QNE

    b.   QNH

    c.   QFF

    d.   QFE

13. Following the MAYDAY prefix and the call sign of the station addressed, the correct sequence for the subsequent content of a distress message, is:

    a.   Aircraft call sign, type, the nature of the emergency and position

    b.   Aircraft call sign, type, the nature of the emergency and intention of the commander

    c.   Position, POB, Aircraft call sign, type, and the nature of the emergency

    d.   Aircraft call sign, type, nature of the emergency and POB

14. The instruction "SQUAWK CHARLIE" means:

    a.   Press the IDENT button

    b.   Set the transponder to standby

    c.   Set the transponder to ON

    d.   Set the transponder to ALT

15. You are en route receiving a service from a radar unit, you are asked "G-AJGV Confirm your level", the purpose of this is to:

    a.   Check the altimeter setting you are using

    b.   Check that Mode Charlie is selected

    c.   Verify the accuracy of the Mode C information displayed to the controller

    d.   Check your position

16. In the Pooley's Flight Guide you read that WESTON, your intended destination, has a Flight Information Service. When addressing WESTON what call sign should you use?

    a.   WESTON RADAR

    b.   WESTON RADIO

    c.   WESTON TOWER

    d.   WESTON INFORMATION

17. The correct phraseology format to use when requesting a true bearing, is:

    a.   True bearing true bearing, G-MORG request true bearing G-MORG

    b.   Request QTE G-MORG

    c.   G-MORG request true bearing

    d.   G-MORG request QTE G-MORG

18. A pilot is given an ATC instruction with which he/she cannot comply. ATC should be advised:

    a.   Standby

    b.   Cannot comply

    c.   Unable to comply

    d.   Will not comply

19. The correct format for a conditional clearance, is:

    a.   Call sign, condition, instruction, identification of the subject of the condition

    b.   Call sign, identification of the subject of the condition, condition, instruction

    c.   Call sign, instruction, identification of the subject of the condition, condition

    d.   Call sign, condition, identification of the subject of the condition, instruction

20. A pilot already in communication with either a civil or military ATSU on being confronted with an emergency the pilot should:

    a.   Make a distress call on the frequency in use and keep any allocated squawk

    b.   Select 7700 and change to 121.5 MHz

    c.   Select 7000 and change to 121.5 MHz

    d.   Make a distress call on 121.5 MHz and keep any allocated squawk

21. A Procedural Service is an Air Traffic Service in which:

    a.   Basic Service is not provided, but safety critical information is provided

    b.   In addition to a Basic Service, aircraft participating in the service will be deconflicted as long as the pilots comply with ATC instructions

    c.   In addition to a Basic Service the controller provides specific surveillance derived traffic information

    d.   Basic Service is not provided, but aircraft participating in the service will be deconflicted as long as the pilots comply with instructions

22. "G-MJDE after departure cleared to zone boundary, via north lane, climb not above altitude 2,500 feet, squawk 4677". In relation to this message what is the clearance limit?

    a.   2,500 feet

    b.   The north lane

    c.   The zone boundary

    d.   There is no clearance limit stated

23. After establishing two way communication and being asked to "pass your message", pilots requiring ATSOCAS should pass:

    a.   A/c call sign, present position, next turning point, altitude

    b.   A/c call sign and type, departure point and destination, present position, altitude, request or intention

    c.   Aircraft type, intention, departure and destination, route, POB

    d.   A/c call sign, altitude, position, departure and destination, POB

24. On hearing a distress message a pilot should:

    a.   Immediately attempt to relay

    b.   Maintain radio silence

    c.   Change frequency

    d.   Request a frequency change from ATC

25. You are receiving a Traffic Service and have been asked to report your heading. You have done so twice, and then hear: "G-HH reply not received if you read Thames Radar turn left heading 120 degrees, I say again turn left heading 120 degrees". What may have occurred:

    a.   You have a receiver failure

    b.   You are out of range

    c.   The controller has not been paying attention

    d.   You have a transmitter failure

26. You are departing an airfield. The FISO is using the call sign suffix "INFORMATION" and tells you: "G-BH Take-off at your discretion, surface wind 300/8". A suitable reply is:

    a.   My discretion, surface wind 300/8 G-BH

    b.   Cleared for take-off G-BH

    c.   Roger G-BH

    d.   Taking-off G-BH

27. Which of the following groups must be read back in full?

    a.   All messages from ATC and FIS, but not from Air/Ground

    b.   Level instructions, Headings, VDF information and surface wind

    c.   Clearance to land on or enter an active runway, transponder codes, VDF.

    d.   Frequency changes, pressure settings and visibility

28. As a pilot you may abbreviate your aircraft's radio call sign:

    a.   For all calls except the first

    b.   Only if it has first been abbreviated by the ground station

    c.   When there will be no confusion

    d.   Only when satisfactory two way communication has been established

29. A Special VFR clearance enables a pilot to:

    a.   Fly with lower weather minima

    b.   Cross an airway without needing a valid IR

    c.   Fly within a Control Zone in circumstances normally requiring an IFR clearance

    d.   Enter a Control Zone without clearance

30. LARS is an ATS surveillance service available to assist pilots flying outside controlled airspace. It is provided up to and including FL.... normally within ...nm of the nominated unit. The service provided will be ..... or .....::

    a.   FL 85, 30 nm. Traffic service, Procedural service

    b.   FL 95 40 nm. Procedural service, Deconfliction service

    c.   FL 95, 30 nm. Traffic service, Deconfliction service

    d.   FL 85, 40 nm. Basic service, Traffic service

END OF COMMUNICATIONS PAPER 3

INTENTIONALLY BLANK

COMMUNICATIONS PAPER 3: ANSWERS

	A	B	C	D
1.			X	
2.		X		
3.		X		
4.		X		
5.				X
6.			X	
7.		X		
8.	X			
9.				X
10.				X
11.	X			
12.				X
13.		X		
14.				X
15			X	
16.				X
17.	X			
18.			X	
19.				X
20.	X			
21.		X		
22.			X	
23.		X		
24.		X		
25.				X
26.				X
27.			X	
28.		X		
29.			X	
30.			X	

CORRECT ANSWERS: PERCENTAGES							
23	24	25	26	27	28	29	30
76%	80%	83%	86%	90%	93%	96%	100%

1. **(Answer: C)** Altitude 14,500 is pronounced "wun fower tousand fife hundred". When transmitting altitude, height, cloud height, visibility and runway visual range (basically anything measured in feet or metres!) whole hundreds and thousands are transmitted by stating the number of hundreds and thousands followed by the word "HUN-dred" or "TOU-SAND" as applicable. Combinations follow the same rule.

2. **(Answer: B)** You are asked for the pronunciation for 129.400. It is "Wun too niner dayseemal fower". If a number contains a decimal point the RTF word DAY-SEE-MAL is inserted at the appropriate point. When transmitting a frequency all six digits must be pronounced. The only exception being where the fifth and sixth number are both zeros, in which case only the first four digits will be pronounced. See also communication paper 2, question 2.

3. **(Answer: B)** Note you are asked for the pronunciation, 1130 is spoken as "wun wun tree zero" or "tree zero". Normally when transmitting time only the minutes of the hour are required. If there is a possibility of confusion the hour should be included as well.

4. **(Answer: B)** Radio failure is indicated by the transponder code 7600. The following special purpose codes are in use:
    - **7700:**   Emergency
    - **7600:**   Communications failure
    - **7500:**   Unlawful interference (hijack)
    - **7000:**   UK conspicuity code
    - **2000:**   Entering an FIR, when operating under VFR, from an adjacent region where the operation of transponders has not been required

5. **(Answer: D)** Wilco means: I understand your message and will comply with it (a contraction of "will comply").

6. **(Answer: C)** Readability 4 means "readable". (*See Communications paper 2, question 5 on page 139, for the full readability scale*).

7. **(Answer: B)** ATIS, Automatic Terminal Information Service. At busier airports an Automatic Terminal Information Service is broadcast to provide a range of data, usually weather conditions and essential aerodrome information, on a discreet frequency or selected VOR. Each ATIS message is coded consecutively using the phonetic alphabet. A new message is generated at regular intervals (usually half hourly at the time of the routine meteorological observations at minutes 20 and 50) or whenever a significant change occurs. Pilots should advise ATC that they have received the latest ATIS:

    On Departure – before taxiing

    On Arrival – on first contact with the ATSU.

8. **(Answer: A)** Once satisfactory communication is established, and provided that no confusion is likely, the call sign may be abbreviated. The pilot of an aircraft may only abbreviate the call sign if the relevant aeronautical ground station has abbreviated it first.

9. **(Answer: D)** Urgency is a condition concerning the safety of an aircraft or other vehicle, or of some other person on board or within sight, but not requiring immediate assistance.

10. **(Answer: D)** So that no misunderstanding arises, unless an aircraft is actually being "Cleared for Takeoff", the word "Departure" is to be used by both controllers and pilots.

11. (Answer: A) The standard format for a position report is:

A	Aircraft call sign
P	Position
T	Time
L	Level
N	Next reporting point
E	ETA for the next reporting point

For example: Golf Hotel Bravo Alpha Hotel overhead Bromham 24, estimate Barkway at 46

12. (Answer: D) Height is defined as the vertical distance of a level, point or object considered as a point measured from a specified datum. The datum is normally the highest point on the landing area. With QFE set the aircraft altimeter will indicate height above the aerodrome. The phraseology used when referring to vertical position differs depending on the pressure setting in use:

If QFE is set:	"Height (number) feet"
If QNH is set:	"Height (number) feet"
If standard 1013 hPa is set (SPS):	"Height (number) feet"

13. (Answer: B) The format for a distress call is:

MAYDAY MAYDAY MAYDAY	
C	Call sign of station addressed
A	Aircraft call sign
T	Type
N	Nature of the emergency
I	Intentions of pilot-in-command
P	Present (or last known) position; altitude/flight level; heading
P	Pilot qualifications, eg. student pilot; PPL; IMC; IR
O	Other useful information, eg. number on board, fuel endurance

14. (Answer: D) "Squawk Charlie" means select the ALT setting on the transponder

TRANSPONDER MODE SELECTION	
OFF	The transponder is totally off
STANDBY	The transponder is ready for use but not actually transmitting
ON	The transponder will reply to an interrogation signal, using the four-digit code set in the control panel.
ALT	As for "ON", plus your altitude or flight level will also be displayed on the controller's radar screen. This is known as Mode Charlie.
IDENT	If a controller asks you to squawk "ident" you should press the ident button. This causes a flashing circle to appear around your aircraft's radar return. "Ident" is also known as the SPI (special position identification) feature.

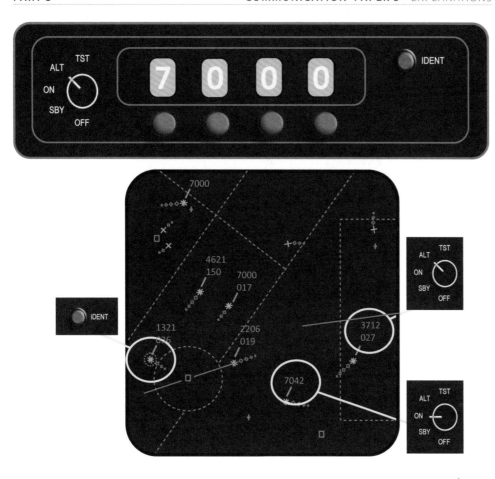

15. **(Answer: C)** "Confirm your level" is used to verify the accuracy of the level information displayed to the controller.

Transponder Phraseology:	
PHRASE	**MEANING**
Squawk (code)	Set the code as instructed
Confirm Squawk	Confirm code set on the transponder
Reset (code)	Reselect assignment code
Squawk Ident	Operate the SPI feature
Squawk Mayday	Select emergency
Squawk Standby	Select the standby feature
Squawk Charlie	Select altitude reporting feature
Check altimeter setting and confirm (level)	Check pressure setting and report your level
Stop Squawk Charlie, wrong indication	Deselect pressure altitude reporting transmission as the indication is faulty
Stop Squawk Charlie	Deselect altitude reporting
Confirm (level)	Check and confirm your level. Used to verify the accuracy of the Mode C level information displayed to the controller

16. **(Answer: D)** A Flight Information Service at an aerodrome uses the call sign suffix "INFORMATION".

17. **(Answer: A)** The correct RTF phraseology format to use when requesting a true bearing, is: **"True bearing true bearing, G-MORG request true bearing G-MORG".** Notice that this phraseology is different to that used when requesting other bearing information, which should follow the format: (Full call sign) request QDM/QDR (Full call sign)

18. **(Answer: C)** "UNABLE TO COMPLY" is the phrase to use when you are given an ATC instruction which you cannot carry out.

19. **(Answer: D)** The format for a conditional clearance will be:
    - Call sign
    - The condition
    - Identification of the subject of the condition
    - The instruction

    For example: **"G-HHAV hold position AFTER the landing Boeing 737 line up and wait runway 26"**

20. **(Answer: A)** The first attempt to transmit an emergency message should be made on the frequency currently in use. If this is not successful the pilot should transmit his/her intention is to change to the Aeronautical Emergency Frequency 121.5 MHz.

    A pilot already in communication with a civil or military ATSU should maintain any SSR code setting previously assigned by ATC (other than the Conspicuity Code 7000) until instructions are received to change the code setting.

21. **(Answer: B)** A Procedural Service is an ATS where, in addition to the provision of a Basic Service, the controller provides vertical, lateral, longitudinal and time instructions, which if complied with will achieve the deconfliction minima against other aircraft participating in the Procedural Service.

    A Procedural Service is most commonly found at ATC Units without surveillance radar equipment at airfields with notified instrument procedures for approach, holding and departure. Pilots flying in the vicinity of aerodromes having instrument approaches outside controlled airspace are encouraged to establish RTF contact with the appropriate ATC Unit.

    Since the service does not involve radar derived information, and as traffic does not legally need to be in contact with a procedural unit in Class F and G airspace, you should be aware that there is a high likelihood of encountering conflicting traffic without any warnings from ATC.

22. **(Answer: C)** Clearance Limit: The point to which an aircraft is granted an Air Traffic Control clearance. In this case the clearance limit is the zone boundary.

    A clearance may vary in complexity from a detailed description of the route and levels to be flown (at busier airports condensed to standard instrument departures) to a brief landing clearance. Clearances are required for any flight, or portion of flight for which an Air Traffic Control or an Air Traffic advisory service is provided.

23. **(Answer: B)** When instructed by an ATS Unit to "Pass your message", your reply should contain the following information, ideally in the order specified. ADDPAR is a mnemonic that may be used to keep the details in the correct order:

A	Aircraft call sign and type
D	Departure point
D	Destination
P	Present Position
A	Altitude/Level
R	Request, intentions or additional details (eg. flight rules, next route point, request—whatever is applicable to the flight)

24. **(Answer: B)** Transmissions from aircraft in distress have priority over all other transmissions. On hearing a distress call, all stations must maintain radio silence on that frequency unless:

   • The distress is cancelled or the distress traffic is terminated;
   • The distress traffic has been transferred to another frequency;
   • The station controlling communications gives permission; or
   • The station itself has to render assistance.

25. **(Answer: D)** You have a transmitter failure. By asking you to turn, the controller is trying to establish whether you are able to still receive messages (the transponder ident feature may also be used for this purpose). If you did receive and comply with the instruction you would probably hear something like:

   "G-HH turn observed I will continue to pass instructions".

26. **(Answer: D)** In response to the transmission "take-off at your discretion" you are required to notify the FISO of your intentions; hence "Taking-off G-BH".

   As you can see, on departure we are REQUIRED to advise the FISO of our intentions. However, on landing CAP 413 details that the response to "land at your discretion" is simply "Roger" followed by your call sign. Practically it may add to the situational awareness of other pilots if you report your intentions, i.e. to land, continue or make a missed approach.

27. **(Answer: C)** Read back requirements were introduced in the interests of flight safety to ensure that the message has been received correctly as intended. The stringency of the requirement to readback is directly related to the possible seriousness of a misunderstanding. Reading back also ensures that the correct aircraft and that aircraft alone will act upon the instruction given. The ATC messages listed in the table below must be read back in full. If a pilot fails to read back any of these items the controller will ask him/her to do so.

   • **Level instructions**
   • **Heading instructions**
   • **Speed instructions**
   • **Airways or route clearances**
   • **Approach clearances**
   • **Runway in use**
   • **Clearances to enter, land on, take off from, backtrack, cross or hold short of an active runway**
   • **SSR (transponder) operating instructions**
   • **Altimeter settings**
   • **VDF information**
   • **Frequency changes**
   • **Type of radar service**
   • **Taxi instructions**
   • **Transition levels**

28. **(Answer: B)** Once satisfactory communication is established, and provided that no confusion is likely, the call sign may be abbreviated. The pilot of an aircraft may only abbreviate the call sign if the relevant aeronautical ground station has abbreviated it first.

29. **(Answer: C)** A Special VFR clearance enables a pilot to fly within a Control Zone in circumstances normally requiring an IFR clearance. Special VFR clearances are only permitted within Control ZONES, usually at the request of the pilot. Special VFR is a concession offered by ATC, which allows an aircraft to operate within a control zone which is Class A or in any other control zone in IMC or at night, without requiring compliance with the Instrument Flight Rules. Instead they will comply with instructions given by the Air Traffic Control Unit.

30. **(Answer: C)** Outside Controlled Airspace certain Air Traffic units are able to provide a Lower Airspace Radar Service to pilots flying in UK uncontrolled airspace up to and including FL 95, within approximately 30nm of each participating unit. Participating ATCUs are able to provide either a Traffic Service or a Deconfliction Service; both are available at the request of the pilot. The controller will inform pilots when they are receiving either a Radar Control, Traffic or Deconfliction service; and also whenever the level of service changes, this information should be read back by the pilot.

END OF EXPLANATIONS PAPER 3

The Human Performance & Limitations examination consists of 20 questions; the time allowed is 30 minutes.

The pass mark is 75%.

Each question is multiple choice with four possible answers A, B, C and D.

You should indicate your chosen answer by placing a cross in the appropriate box on the answer sheet.

Blank answer sheets are to be found at the end of this publication, these may be photocopied.

INTENTIONALLY BLANK

HUMAN PERFORMANCE & LIMITATIONS
PAPER 1

1. The Peripheral, Central and Autonomic are what type of system in the body?

   a. Circulatory
   b. Nervous
   c. Cardiac
   d. Digestive

2. The system that moves blood around the body is called the:

   a. Nervous system
   b. Digestive system
   c. Cardiac system
   d. Circulatory system

3. Within the atmosphere the proportion of oxygen:

   a. Increases as altitude increases
   b. Decreases as altitude increases
   c. Remains constant
   d. Initially increases then decreases

4. The body not having sufficient oxygen to meet its requirements is a condition known as:

   a. Hypoxia
   b. Hypoglycemia
   c. Hypochondria
   d. Hyperventilation

5. The initial signs of the onset of hypoxia include:

   a. Dizziness and tingling sensation in the fingers
   b. Euphoria, clumsiness and impaired judgement
   c. Anxiety and tingling sensation in the fingers
   d. Clumsiness and hot flushes

6. Chemical receptors in the brain govern the respiratory process. They are most sensitive to changes in the level of:

   a. Nitrogen
   b. Oxygen
   c. Carbon dioxide
   d. Calcium

7. The "time of useful consciousness" might be defined as:

   a. The time from the onset of hypoxia to unconsciousness
   b. The time from when the air supply is reduced to unconsciousness
   c. The time available to perform useful tasks before hypoxia sets in
   d. The time available before feeling euphoric

8. Although individuals vary, pilots should not suffer the effects of hypoxia when operating up to and including an altitude of:

   a. 8,000 ft
   b. 9,000 ft
   c. 10,000 ft
   d. 12,000 ft

9. The high pressure experienced when scuba diving increases the solubility of nitrogen into the body tissues. Decompression sickness is when:

    a.   The muscles start to cramp

    b.   The nitrogen forms bubbles when pressure is reduced

    c.   The nitrogen forms bubbles when pressure is increased

    d.   Dizziness and nausea begin

10. The human auditory range is:

    a.   20 to 20,000 Hz

    b.   20 to 200,000 Hz

    c.   200 to 20,000 Hz

    d.   200 to 200,000 Hz

11. A pilot suffering from gastro-enteritis is:

    a.   Probably fit to fly

    b.   Fit to fly with medication

    c.   Unfit to fly for more than one hour

    d.   Unfit to fly

12. With a flight visibility of 3nm a light aircraft and a military jet have a closing speed of 400kts. Approximately how much time do the pilots have to avoid a collision if visual contact was made at maximum range?

    a.   Approximately 27 seconds

    b.   Approximately 33 seconds

    c.   Approximately 38 seconds

    d.   Approximately 20 seconds

13. A light aircraft and a military jet are on a head on collision course with a closing speed of around 600 knots. In this situation how would the image of the military jet appear to grow as range decreased?

    a.   The image would grow very quickly at a constant rate

    b.   Initially the image would show only a small rate of growth until close to impact when it would grow rapidly

    c.   Initially it the image would grow rapidly until close to impact when the rate would slow

    d.   The image would grow slowly at a constant rate

14. Having allowed sufficient time for night vision to develop, when looking at an object beyond the aircraft, the maximum visual acuity is achieved by looking:

    a.   Slightly below the object

    b.   45° to the side of the object

    c.   Directly at the object

    d.   Slightly off centre by about 10°

15. If a runway is narrower than expected a pilot will tend to:

    a.   Fly a lower approach than normal and possibly land short

    b.   Fly a lower approach than normal and possibly overshoot

    c.   Fly a higher approach than normal and possibly land short

    d.   Fly a higher approach than normal and possibly overshoot

16. The way to maintain situational awareness is to:

    a.   Fly by reference to the aircraft's instruments

    b.   Interpret any new data to confirm where you should be

    c.   Maintain heading and obtain continual position fixes

    d.   Plan ahead and gather and consider all available data whilst updating you situation.

17. The diagram below represents runways with varying slopes. Which represents a runway with an up slope?

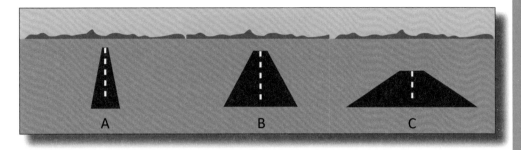

A   B   C

   a.   C
   b.   B
   c.   A
   d.   Between A and B

18. Ideally within a cockpit controls that operate different systems should be designed to:

   a.   Look and feel the same
   b.   Look and feel different
   c.   Look similar and be easy to use
   d.   Look the same but feel different

19. When operating at altitude or above cloud with an empty visual field a pilot should be aware that the eyes will tend to:

   a.   Focus at a point 1 to 2 metres away
   b.   Focus at infinity
   c.   Focus at the horizon
   d.   Focus at a point 10 to 12 metres away

20. The three needle altimeter is considered to be:

   a.   Accurate, reliable and rarely misread
   b.   Accurate, reliable and easily misread
   c.   Reasonably accurate, unreliable but easy to read
   d.   Easily misread by novice pilots

END OF HUMAN PERFORMANCE & LIMITATIONS PAPER 1

	A	B	C	D
1.		X		
2.				X
3.			X	
4.	X			
5.		X		
6.			X	
7.			X	
8.			X	
9.		X		
10.	X			
11.				X
12.	X			
13.		X		
14.				X
15	X			
16.				X
17.			X	
18.		X		
19.	X			
20.		X		

CORRECT ANSWERS: PERCENTAGES					
15	16	17	18	19	20
87%	90%	92%	95%	97%	100%

HUMAN PERFORMANCE & LIMITATIONS
PAPER 1: EXPLANATIONS

1.   **(Answer: B)** The nervous system is composed of the Peripheral, Central and Autonomic systems. The central nervous system is composed of the brain and spinal chord, and is the master controller. The peripheral nervous system, which includes the autonomic system, unconsciously controls body functions such as intestinal movements, heart beat regulation and sweating.

2.   **(Answer: D)** The circulatory, or cardiovascular, system moves blood around the body. It takes oxygen and nutrients to the body tissues and removes waste products and carbon dioxide.

3.   **(Answer: C)** The proportion of the gases which make up the atmosphere remains constant, although the actual mass and number of molecules of each gas is far less at high level. The make up is: Nitrogen 78%, oxygen 21% and small amounts of other gases and water vapour.

4.   **(Answer: A)** A lack of sufficient oxygen to the brain and body is called hypoxia.

5.   **(Answer: B)** Some of the initial symptoms of hypoxia include a sense of euphoria or well-being, impaired judgement, a difficulty completing mental tasks and a loss of muscle control.

SYMPTOMS OF HYPOXIA – initial signs first
Personality changes (euphoria) and impaired judgement
Confusion and difficulty concentrating
Loss of co-ordination (clumsiness)
Drowsiness
Headache, dizziness and nausea
Blue tinge to skin
Hyperventilation
Loss of basic senses – vision is likely to be first
Unconsciousness

6.   **(Answer: C)** Receptors in the brain are most sensitive to any changes in the level carbon dioxide; such changes in the level of carbon dioxide will trigger either an increase or decrease in breathing rate.

7.   **(Answer: C)** The time of useful consciousness may be described as the time available to pilots to perform useful tasks, without using supplemental oxygen, before hypoxia sets in and compromises their ability to deal with the situation. The symptoms of hypoxia are likely to begin above 10,000 feet (lower in some individuals, especially smokers); its effects are accelerated at higher altitudes where lower partial pressures of oxygen exist.

ALTITUDE TIME OF USEFUL CONSCIOUSNESS	
20,000 ft AMSL	5 to 10 minutes
30,0000 ft AMSL	45 to 75 seconds
40,000 ft AMSL	18 to 30 seconds
45,000 ft AMSL	12 seconds

8.   **(Answer: C)** Above 8,000 ft the effects of oxygen deprivation may start to be evident, especially in pilots under stress. At a cabin altitude of 10,000 ft most people can still deal with the reduced oxygen supply for short periods. Flight above 10,000 ft should not be prolonged without the use of supplemental oxygen.

9.   **(Answer: B)** The use of compressed air when scuba diving has been known to lead to decompression sickness (the bends) during flight as low as 6,000 feet. At high pressures nitrogen is absorbed into the blood. When pressure is reduced bubbles of nitrogen form in the bloodstream causing pain and immobility in the joints.

10.   **(Answer: A)** Human hearing is in the range of 20 Hz to 20,000 Hz. Voices are between 500 Hz and 3,000 Hz.

11.   **(Answer: D)** Gastro-enteritis can be extremely debilitating even with medication. It is an inflammation of the stomach and intestines often causing sudden and violent bouts of diarrhoea and vomiting. A pilot with gastro-enteritis will be unfit to fly.

12.   **(Answer: A)** Visibility 3 nm and closing speed 400 knots.

Time =   Distance
                Speed
Time =   3/400   =   0.0075 hours

This is the answer in hours to obtain the seconds we must multiply by 60 twice (once to get an answer in minutes and again to get seconds).

0.0075 x 60 =   0.45 minutes
0.45 x 60   =   27 seconds.
Nearest answer   27 seconds

13.   **(Answer: B)** The image of an aircraft approaching head-on at high speed would remain small, growing only slowly until it is very close. It will then appear to grow very quickly.

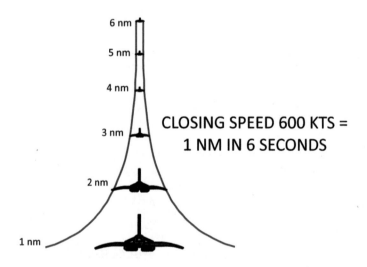

14.   **(Answer: D)** An object at night will be more readily visible when looking to the side of it by 10 to 20°, rather than directly at it. It is more effective at night to scan more slowly to permit such "off-centre" viewing of objects in your peripheral vision.

15. **(Answer: A)** A narrow runway will create the illusion of being too high, meaning you fly lower than "normal" with the possibility of undershooting the runway threshold or landing earlier (and probably more heavily) than expected.

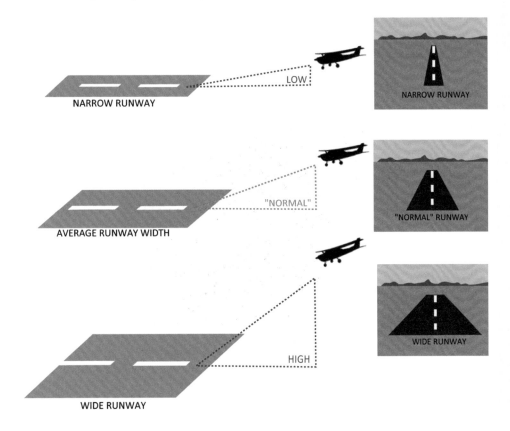

16. **(Answer: D)** In a pilot situational awareness means maintaining an accurate mental model of the environment. This requires that all available data is gathered, considered and interpreted. The situation should be regularly updated and good forward planning employed. It is an on-going process of observation and analysis of the information available to maintain an accurate mental model.

17. **(Answer: C)** An up sloping runway will look longer than it really is. "C" is the perspective for a down sloping runway, "B" for a level runway and "A" represents an up slope.

18. **(Answer: B)** As an aid to preventing incorrect selection, differentiation should be built into the design of controls enabling the pilot to easily identify the control by its shape, colour and feel. In particular colocated controls should be made to look and feel different.

19. **(Answer: A)** It may be difficult to detect other aircraft when there is an empty field of vision as the eyes have a natural resting tendency to focus at 1 to 2 metres. This is called "empty field myopia" and can be avoided by focusing on any available distant object to lengthen the focus, (e.g. a landmark or cloud), or if none are available a relatively distant part of the aircraft.

20. **(Answer: B)** A three point altimeter takes longer to read. Although it is very accurate it can be easily misinterpreted.

END OF EXPLANATIONS PAPER 1

HUMAN PERFORMANCE & LIMITATION
PAPER 2

1. The function of the circulatory system is to:

   a. Supply energy to the cells

   b. Remove the products of digestion

   c. Supply oxygen and nutrients to the body cells and remove waste products

   d. Supply carbon dioxide and nutrients to the body cells and remove waste

2. There are three nervous systems within the body. These are:

   a. Peripheral, Core and Automatic

   b. Peripheral, Core and Autonomic

   c. Peripheral, Central and Autonomic

   d. Peripheral, Central and Automatic

3. Respiration takes place as an involuntary action. It is regulated by:

   a. The amount of oxygen in the blood

   b. Any changes in air pressure

   c. Any changes in altitude

   d. The amount of carbon dioxide in the blood

4. Compared with a non-smoker, a tobacco smoker is likely to experience the symptoms of hypoxia at:

   a. A lower cabin altitude

   b. A higher cabin altitude

   c. The same cabin altitude

   d. Any altitude

5. Hyperventilation may be brought on by lack of oxygen, other possible causes are:

   a. Dehydration

   b. Concentrating too hard on a complex task

   c. Exhaustion

   d. Anxiety, heat, motion sickness or vibration

6. After scuba diving pilots are advised not to fly within ...(i)... hours, or ...(ii)... hours if a depth of 30 feet has been exceeded:

   a. i) 8   ii) 16

   b. i) 12   ii) 24

   c. i) 16   ii) 32

   d. i) 24   ii) 48

7. Decompression sickness is caused when which gas comes out of solution to form bubbles in the body tissues?

   a. Hydrogen

   b. Oxygen

   c. Nitrogen

   d. Carbon dioxide

8. Sensations of dizziness, tingling fingers and lips and anxiety experienced whilst operating below 10,000 ft AMSL, would indicate:

   a. Hypoxia

   b. Hyperglycemia

   c. Hyperactivity

   d. Hyperventilation

9. A remedy for hyperventilation is:

    a.   Consciously slowing down the rate of breathing

    b.   Giving oxygen

    c.   A good slap

    d.   Consciously speeding up the rate of breathing

10. How might carbon monoxide enter the cockpit?

    a.   A leak in the oxygen system

    b.   A leak in the cockpit heater or cigarette smoke

    c.   Passenger's breath

    d.   A cracked windscreen

11. Assume one unit is half a pint of beer, a standard glass of wine or a single measure of spirit. Approximately how long will it take to eliminate one unit of alcohol from the blood?

    a.   1 hour

    b.   30 minutes

    c.   2 hours

    d.   3 hours

12. Full adaptation to night vision in normal conditions takes:

    a.   15 to 20 minutes

    b.   10 to 15 minutes

    c.   30 to 40 minutes

    d.   40 to 45 minutes

13. The Eustachian tube serves what purpose?

    a.   It allows the middle ear to drain

    b.   It allows pressure in the middle ear to equalise with ambient pressure

    c.   It allows pressure in the outer ear to equalise with ambient pressure

    d.   It allows pressure in the sinus to equalise with middle ear pressure

14. With a flight visibility of 3nm a light aircraft and a military jet have a closing speed of 360kts. Approximately how much time do the pilots have to avoid a collision if visual contact was made at maximum range?

    a.   Approximately 20 seconds

    b.   Approximately 25 seconds

    c.   Approximately 30 seconds

    d.   Approximately 40 seconds

15. The visibility is 5 km, a military aircraft is operating at a speed of 420 knots; a light aircraft is approaching head on at a speed of 120 knots. The pilots will have a maximum time of .... in which to see the other aircraft and take avoiding action. Complete the statement.

    a.   Approximately 40 seconds

    b.   Approximately 35 seconds

    c.   Approximately 30 seconds

    d.   Approximately 20 seconds

16. The most effective method of visual scanning is:

    a.   A series of short regularly spaced eye movements to search 10° sector of sky

    b.   Slowly sweep the entire field of view from left to right

    c.   Concentrate on the most likely areas for traffic

    d.   Quickly sweep the entire field of view from left to right

17. A pilot in straight and level flight but decelerating may experience the illusory perception of:

    a.   Rolling left

    b.   Yawing right

    c.   Pitching down

    d.   Pitching up

18. Flying a visual approach to a down sloping runway which lacks any visual glide slope aids, is likely to result in a:

    a.   Shallower approach than intended

    b.   Close to the intended flight path

    c.   Steeper approach than intended

    d.   Very erratic approach

19. The best method of maintaining situational awareness is to:

    a.   Consider all available data whilst updating your situation and planning ahead

    b.   Ignore information that does not agree with your mental model

    c.   Rely on experience

    d.   Concentrate on where you are going

20. A pilot intending to self-medicate using a preparation that does not require a doctor's prescription should:

    a.   Check that the side effects have been evaluated and are minor

    b.   See if the drugs have any side effects before flying

    c.   Seek professional advice from a CAA AME

    d.   Be aware of any likely performance reducing side effects

---

END OF HUMAN PERFORMANCE & LIMITATIONS PAPER 2

	A	B	C	D
1.			X	
2.			X	
3.				X
4.	X			
5.				X
6.		X		
7.			X	
8.				X
9.	X			
10.		X		
11.	X			
12.			X	
13.		X		
14.			X	
15				X
16.	X			
17.			X	
18.			X	
19.	X			
20.			X	

CORRECT ANSWERS: PERCENTAGES					
15	16	17	18	19	20
87%	90%	92%	95%	97%	100%

HUMAN PERFORMANCE & LIMITATIONS
PAPER 2: EXPLANATIONS

1. **(Answer: C)** The circulatory, or cardiovascular, system moves blood around the body. It takes oxygen and nutrients to the body tissues and removes waste products and carbon dioxide.

2. **(Answer: C)** The nervous system is composed of the Peripheral, Central and Autonomic systems. The central nervous system is composed of the brain and spinal chord and is the master controller. The peripheral nervous system, which includes the autonomic system, unconsciously controls body functions such as intestinal movements, heart beat regulation and sweating.

3. **(Answer: D)** Receptors in the brain are very sensitive to any changes in carbon dioxide; changes in the level of carbon dioxide will trigger either an increase or decrease in breathing rate.

4. **(Answer: A)** Haemoglobin is a blood protein in red blood cells which combines with oxygen to transport it around the body. Haemoglobin has a higher affinity for carbon monoxide than it does for oxygen. The excess carbon monoxide in tobacco smoke will reduce the amount of oxygen in the blood stream, meaning that the symptoms of hypoxia could manifest at lower altitude.

5. **(Answer: D)** Hyperventilation is a condition where breathing is more rapid and deeper than is necessary; resulting in too much carbon dioxide being flushed from the body upsetting its chemical balance. Hyperventilation is most often associated with anxiety or intense stress; but may also be caused by vibration, turbulence, motion sickness and is itself a symptom of hypoxia.

6. **(Answer: B)** The use of compressed air when scuba diving has been known to lead to decompression sickness (the bends) during flight as low as 6,000 feet. At high pressures nitrogen is absorbed into the blood, when pressure is reduced bubbles of nitrogen form in the body tissues; causing pain and immobility in the joints. You should not fly within 12 hours of any scuba dive using compressed air and within 24 hours if a depth of 30 feet has been exceeded.

7. **(Answer: C)** The use of compressed air when scuba diving has been known to lead to decompression sickness (the bends) during flight as low as 6,000 feet. At high pressures nitrogen is absorbed into the blood, when pressure is reduced bubbles of nitrogen form in the bloodstream causing pain and immobility in the joints.

8. **(Answer: D)** Below 10,000 ft these symptoms would indicate hyperventilation. Hyperventilation is a condition where breathing is more rapid and deeper than is necessary; resulting in too much carbon dioxide being flushed from the body upsetting its chemical balance. Hyperventilation is most often associated with anxiety or intense stress; but may also be caused by vibration, turbulence, motion sickness and is itself a symptom of hypoxia.

SYMPTOMS OF HYPERVENTILATION
Dizziness, light headedness
Tingling sensations – especially in fingers, hands, lips and feet
Visual impairment – blurring, clouded or tunnel vision
Hot and cold feelings
Unconsciousness

9. **(Answer: A)** Remedies for hyperventilation: Consciously slowing down the breathing rate (talking helps) Breathing in and out of a paper bag (increases carbon dioxide level in the blood) If no recovery is evident, suspect hypoxia instead.

10. **(Answer: B)** Carbon monoxide is present in cigarette smoke. Light aircraft cabin heaters are often heat exchangers from a shroud around the engine exhaust system; alternatively a combustion heater may be fitted. As carbon monoxide is present in exhaust fumes a leak in either type of heat exchanger could lead to carbon monoxide mixing with the fresh heated air and being channelled into the cockpit.

11. **(Answer: A)** It takes the liver approximately one hour to remove one unit of alcohol from the blood stream.

12. **(Answer: C)** The rods are most important for night vision and take around 30 minutes to adapt to darkness. Bright lights will immediately impair your night vision adaptation and should be avoided in the 30 minutes prior to night flight.

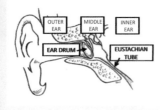

13. **(Answer: B)** The Eustachian tube enables pressure in the middle ear to be maintained at the same value as ambient pressure. It connects the interior of the middle ear with the nasal passages.

14. **(Answer: C)** Visibility 3 nm and closing speed 360 knots.

Time   = $\dfrac{\text{Distance}}{\text{Speed}}$

Time   =   3/360   =   0.00834 hours

This is the answer in hours, to obtain the seconds we must multiply by 60 twice (once to get an answer in minutes and again to get seconds).

0.00834 x 60   =   0.5004 minutes
0.5004 x 60   =   30.024 seconds.
Nearest answer 30 seconds

15. **(Answer: D)** Visibility 5 km and closing speed 540 knots.

5 km   =   roughly 2.7 nm
Time   = $\dfrac{\text{Distance}}{\text{Speed}}$
Time   =   2.7/540   =   0.005 hours

This is the answer in hours, to obtain the seconds we must multiply by 60 twice (once to get an answer in minutes and again to get seconds).

0.005 x 60   =   0.3 minutes
0.3 x 60   =   18 seconds.
Nearest answer 20 seconds

16. **(Answer: A)** The most effective method of scanning for other aircraft during the day is to use a series of short, regularly spaced eye movements to search each 10° sector of the sky.

17. **(Answer: C)** In an aircraft flying straight and level at constant speed gravity acts straight down. If the aircraft decelerates an extra force - inertia – is added and sensed by the otoliths in the inner ear. During deceleration the resultant force between "real up" and inertia due to the speed change is perceived as "up" leading to the sensation that the aircraft has pitched down. Therefore deceleration is sensed as a false pitch down; the danger being that the pilot will react by pitching up to correct leading to the speed decaying and a further temptation to pitch up.

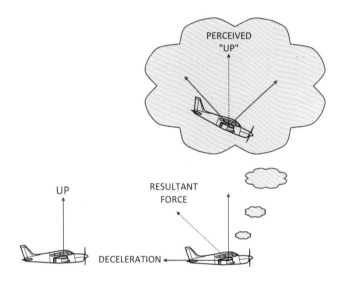

During a rapid deceleration the body senses the rearward angled resultant force as "up" causing the pilot to feel as if the aircraft has pitched down.

18. **(Answer: C)** A down sloping runway will look shorter than it really is, hence the pilot will feel low on the approach. The tendency will be to fly higher and make a steeper approach.

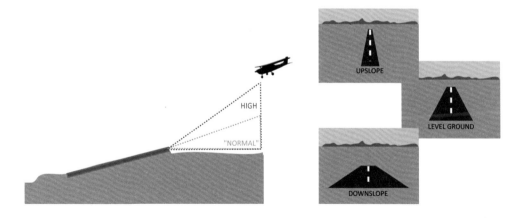

19. **(Answer: A)** In a pilot situational awareness means maintaining an accurate mental model of the environment. This requires that all available data is gathered, considered and interpreted. The situation should be regularly updated and good forward planning employed. It is an on-going process of observation and analysis of the information available to maintain an accurate mental model.

20. **(Answer: C)** It is advisable not to take any medicines before or during flight. If any doubt exists as to a non-prescription drug's effect an aviation doctor should be consulted.

INTENTIONALLY BLANK

HUMAN PERFORMANCE & LIMITATIONS
PAPER 3

1. As altitude increases the oxygen available to the body reduces because of a:

   a. Decrease in temperature
   b. Decrease in pressure
   c. Decrease in the proportion of oxygen
   d. Decrease in the proportion of carbon dioxide

2. Haemoglobin, a protein in red blood cells, transports oxygen but will more readily combine with:

   a. Nitrogen
   b. Carbon dioxide
   c. Hydrogen
   d. Carbon monoxide

3. Hyperventilation may be remedied by:

   a. Increasing the breathing rate
   b. Applying a cold compress
   c. Breathing in and out of a paper bag
   d. Shocking the subject

4. After scuba diving to depths in excess of 30 feet, you should allow:

   a. 6 hours before flying
   b. 12 hours before flying
   c. 24 hours before flying
   d. 48 hours before flying

5. The part of the eye that is sensitive to light is called the:

   a. Iris
   b. Lens
   c. Fovea
   d. Retina

6. Why should you not fly when suffering from a cold?

   a. The pressure between the inner ear and the middle ear may not be equalised
   b. The pressure between the inner ear and atmospheric air may not be equalised
   c. The pressure between the middle ear and atmospheric may not be equalised
   d. The pressure between the middle ear and the outer ear may not be equalised

7. With a flight visibility of 5 nm a light aircraft and a military jet have a closing speed of 500 knots. Approximately how much time do the pilots have to avoid a collision if visual contact was made at maximum range?

   a. 50 to 60 seconds
   b. 40 to 50 seconds
   c. 30 to 40 seconds
   d. 20 to 30 seconds

8. A light aircraft and a military jet have a closing speed of 500 knots. The visibility is 5 nm; however the pilots do not see each other's aircraft until there is 3 nm between them. How much time would the pilots have to avoid a collision?

   a. Approximately 30 seconds
   b. Approximately 20 seconds
   c. Approximately 40 seconds
   d. Approximately 50 seconds

9. In an aircraft with a design eye position indication seating should be:

   a. Adjusted during the cruise to allow the pilot optimum scan position

   b. Adjusted for take-off and landing

   c. Left as it was found, the previous pilot will have adjusted it

   d. Adjusted prior to departure and used for all phases of flight

10. A pilot can be said to be .....(?)..... when his/her perception of where he/she thinks the aircraft is matches where the aircraft actually is.

   a. Lucky

   b. Situationally aware

   c. On track

   d. On flight plan

11. Flying a visual approach to an up sloping runway which lacks any visual glide slope aids, is likely to result in:

   a. A shallower approach than intended

   b. An approach close to the intended flight path

   c. A steeper approach than intended

   d. A very erratic approach

12. If a runway is wider than expected a pilot will tend to:

   a. Fly a lower approach than normal and possibly land short

   b. Fly a lower approach than normal and possibly overshoot

   c. Fly a higher approach than normal and possibly land short

   d. Fly a higher approach than normal and possibly overshoot

13. A pilot in straight and level flight but accelerating may experience the illusory perception of:

   a. Pitching up

   b. Pitching down

   c. Rolling right

   d. Yawing left

14. Flying in hazy conditions may lead a pilot to believe that objects outside the aircraft are:

   a. Closer than in reality

   b. Further away than they are

   c. Larger than they actually are

   d. Closer and smaller than in reality

15. During a flight a pilot experienced prolonged exposure to exhaust gases, when could he/she be considered fit to fly again?

   a. After one or two hours

   b. After 4 or 5 hours

   c. After several days

   d. After 24 hours

16. One cause of motion sickness is:

   a. The movement of fluid in the inner ear

   b. Too many visual clues

   c. Eating shortly before flight

   d. A mismatch between signals from the eyes and the inner ear

17. Pilots aware they are experiencing spatial disorientation should:

    a.   Briefly close their eyes

    b.   Concentrate on and trust the aircraft instruments

    c.   Rely on external visual clues

    d.   Rely on somatosensory (seat of the pants) information

18. A prominent sloping cloud layer across your flight path may lead you to:

    a.   Pitch up

    b.   Bank the aircraft

    c.   Apply more rudder

    d.   Descend

19. Imagine you are flying with a more experienced pilot; he has chosen a course of action which you believe may endanger the flight. What should you do?

    a.   Accept the course of action so as not to compromise your relationship

    b.   Question his judgement only if you think he will react positively

    c.   Always express any doubts

    d.   Accept the course of action but be prepared to take control

20. When operating at low level a person breathing abnormally and displaying the symptoms of hypoxia is probably suffering from:

    a.   Hypoxia

    b.   Motion sickness

    c.   Fear of flying

    d.   Hyperventilation

END OF HUMAN PERFORMANCE & LIMITATIONS PAPER 3

	A	B	C	D
1.		X		
2.				X
3.			X	
4.			X	
5.				X
6.			X	
7.			X	
8.		X		
9.				X
10.		X		
11.	X			
12.				X
13.	X			
14.		X		
15			X	
16.				X
17.		X		
18.		X		
19.			X	
20.				X

CORRECT ANSWERS: PERCENTAGES					
15	16	17	18	19	20
87%	90%	92%	95%	97%	100%

1. **(Answer: B)** Air pressure reduces with altitude, as does the partial pressure of each constituent gas. The total air pressure being the sum of all the partial pressures. When air pressure falls so does the partial pressure of oxygen, meaning less oxygen is transferred into the bloodstream from the lungs.

2. **(Answer: D)** Haemoglobin is a blood protein in red blood cells which combines with oxygen to transport it around the body. Haemoglobin has a higher affinity for carbon monoxide than it does for oxygen.

3. **(Answer: C)** Remedies for hyperventilation: Consciously slowing down the breathing rate (talking helps) Breathing in and out of a paper bag (increases carbon dioxide level in the blood) If no recovery is evident, suspect hypoxia instead.

4. **(Answer: C)** The use of compressed air when scuba diving has been known to lead to decompression sickness (the bends) during flight as low as 6,000 feet. At high pressures nitrogen is absorbed into the blood. When pressure is reduced bubbles of nitrogen form in the body tissues; causing pain and immobility in the joints. You should not fly within 12 hours of any scuba dive using compressed air, and within 24 hours if a depth of 30 feet has been exceeded.

5. **(Answer: D)** The retina is the light sensitive layer at the back of the eye. It contains two types of light sensitive cells: rods (black and white) and cones (colour and fine detail).

6. **(Answer: C)** The Eustachian tube enables pressure in the middle ear to be maintained at the same value as ambient pressure. It connects the interior of the middle ear with the nasal passages. When a person has a cold the Eustachian tubes become swollen and inflamed hindering passage of air. The subsequent pressure equalisation problems, especially during descent, not only lead to pain, but also there is a danger of the eardrum collapsing inward meaning possible permanent hearing loss.

7. **(Answer: C)** Visibility 5 nm and closing speed 500 knots.

    Time = $\dfrac{\text{Distance}}{\text{Speed}}$

    Time = 5/500 = 0.1 hours

    This is the answer in hours to obtain the seconds we must multiply by 60 twice (once to get an answer in minutes and again to get seconds).

    0.1 x 60 = 0.6 minutes
    0.45 x 60 = 36 seconds.
    Nearest answer 30 to 40 seconds

8.   **(Answer: B)** Visibility 3 nm and closing speed 500 knots.

Time   = $\frac{\text{Distance}}{\text{Speed}}$

Time   =   3/500   =   0.006 hours

This is the answer in hours to obtain the seconds we must multiply by 60 twice (once to get an answer in minutes and again to get seconds).

0.006 x 60   =   0.36 minutes
60   =   21.6 seconds.
Nearest answer 20 seconds

9.   **(Answer: D)** The desired seating position should be adjusted before departure and used for all phases of flight. The seat should be comfortable and in a position that allows full control movement as well as permitting a balance between a full instrument scan and good outside visibility to be achieved.

10. **(Answer: B)** In a pilot situational awareness means maintaining an accurate mental model of the environment. This requires that all available data is gathered, considered and interpreted. The situation should be regularly updated and good forward planning employed. It is an ongoing process of observation and analysis of the information available to maintain an accurate mental model.

11. **(Answer: A)** An up sloping runway will look longer than it really is, hence the pilot will feel high on the approach. The tendency will be to fly lower and make a shallower approach.

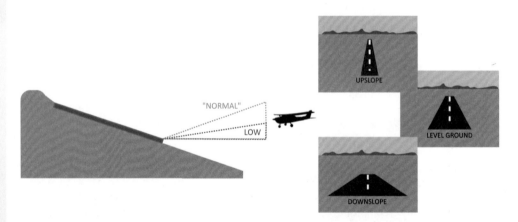

12. **(Answer: D)** A wide runway will create the illusion of being too low. This can lead to flying the approach higher than "normal" and overshooting the threshold. In the latter stages you may also flare and hold off too high.

13.   **(Answer: A)** In an aircraft flying straight and level at constant speed gravity acts straight down. If the aircraft decelerates an extra force - inertia – is added and sensed by the otoliths in the inner ear. Acceleration is sensed as a false pitch up; the tendency being that the pilot will want to pitch the aircraft's nose down.

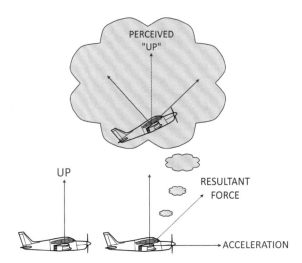

14.   **(Answer: B)** In hazy conditions depth perception can be difficult; the light rays are refracted, reducing their resolution and colours are muted. This leads to the illusion that objects are further away than they actually are, i.e. you are closer to them than you think.

15.   **(Answer: C)** Haemoglobin is a blood protein in red blood cells which combines with oxygen to transport it around the body. Haemoglobin has a higher affinity for carbon monoxide than it does for oxygen. Carbon monoxide is especially dangerous as it is colourless, odourless and has no taste. Recovery from prolonged exposure may take several days, even on pure oxygen.

16.   **(Answer: D)** Motion sickness can be caused by a mismatch of signals from the balance mechanism in the inner ears and visual signals from the eyes.

17.   **(Answer: B)** Orientation is our ability to determine our position in space. It is normally achieved using a combination of vision, balance and somatosensory (bodily feel or "seat of the pants") information. In most situations theses three inputs reinforce each other; this is not always so in flight. Sometimes the brain can misinterpret some of the information leading to spatial disorientation (not knowing which way is up). We should concentrate on and trust the aircraft instruments.

18.   **(Answer: B)** A very prominent sloping cloud layer may obscure the natural horizon, either partially or totally, creating the illusion that the aircraft is in a banked attitude. If this is believed the reaction would be to fly the aircraft in a banked attitude with cross controls to maintain heading.

19.   **(Answer: C)** Any pilot irrespective of experience or status should express any doubts relating to the actions of a more experienced pilot if such actions are perceived as dangerous or inappropriate. Do not be intimidated – experience does not stop a person being fallible!

20.   **(Answer: D)** Abnormal breathing is a sign of both hypoxia and hyperventilation. Hypoxia is rare below 10,000 feet. At low level a person breathing abnormally is probably hyperventilating.

SYMPTOMS OF HYPOXIA – initial signs first
Personality changes (euphoria) and impaired judgement
Confusion and difficulty concentrating
Loss of co-ordination (clumsiness)
Drowsiness
Headache, dizziness and nausea
Blue tinge to skin
Hyperventilation
Loss of basic senses – vision is likely to be first
Unconsciousness

SYMPTOMS OF HYPERVENTILATION
Dizziness, light headedness
Tingling sensations – especially in fingers, hands, lips and feet
Visual impairment – blurring, clouded or tunnel vision
Hot and cold feelings
Unconsciousness

END OF EXPLANATIONS PAPER 3

PART 5: AIRCRAFT GENERAL

The actual aircraft general examination consists of 50 questions; the time allowed is 1 hour 30 minutes. It will consist of questions from each of the different subject areas.

Please note that for convenience the practice examinations have questions mostly grouped by subject. Additionally, two of the practice papers have 50 questions, two have 30 questions. For the two papers with 30 questions allow yourself 1 hour.

The pass mark is 75%.

Each question is multiple choice with four possible answers A, B, C and D. You should indicate your chosen answer by placing a cross in the appropriate box on the answer sheet.

PART - 5

INTENTIONALLY BLANK

50 Questions; time allowed 1 Hour 30 Minutes

POWERPLANT

---

1. In a four-stroke piston engine a normal "Otto" cycle each valve will open:

    a. Twice

    b. Three times

    c. Once

    d. Four times

2. The compression ratio is:

    a. Cylinder volume when piston is TDC : Cylinder volume when piston is BDC

    b. Total cylinder volume : Volume when piston is BDC

    c. Cylinder volume when piston is BDC : Cylinder volume when piston is TDC

    d. Total cylinder volume : swept volume

3. During one complete "Otto" cycle each piston will move:

    a. Up once and down once

    b. Up twice and down once

    c. Up once and down twice

    d. Up twice and down twice

4. The cylinders of a piston engine are finned in order to:

    a. Decrease weight

    b. Improve cooling by increasing their surface area

    c. Increase the strength of the cylinder

    d. Streamline airflow around the cylinder

5. The cockpit oil temperature gauge is connected to a temperature probe. The probe senses the temperature of the oil:

    a. In the hottest part of the engine

    b. After it has passed the oil cooler, but before it is used within the hot sections of the engine

    c. Before the oil cooler

    d. In the oil sump

6. A "wet sump" lubrication system is one where:

    a. A scavenger pump collects oil from the sump and returns it to an oil tank

    b. Oil is not required for cooling and lubrication

    c. Oil is contained in a sump at the bottom of the engine and there is no oil tank

    d. An oil tank is used to re-fill the sump as necessary

7. Excessive oil pressure is prevented by:

    a. A pressure relief valve

    b. A non return valve

    c. A high capacity pressure pump

    d. A filter by-pass valve

8. In the event of an oil cooler blockage in flight, a by-pass valve will operate to circumvent the cooler. The by-pass valve is:

    a. Manually selected

    b. Temperature activated

    c. Density dependant

    d. Pressure dependant

9. The oil pressure gauge indicates the oil pressure at the:

    a.   Outlet side of the pressure pump

    b.   Inlet side of the pressure pump

    c.   Difference between the inlet side of the pressure pump and the outlet side

    d.   Difference between pressure at the pressure pump and pressure at the scavenger pump

10. A "dry sump" lubrication system is one where:

    a.   Oil is not required for cooling and lubrication

    b.   Oil is contained in a sump at the bottom of the engine and there is no oil tank

    c.   A scavenge pump collects oil from the sump and returns it to an oil tank

    d.   An oil tank is used to re-fill the sump as necessary

11. Some of the main uses of oil within an engine are:

    a.   Lubrication, heating and sealing

    b.   Lubrication, cleaning and heating

    c.   Lubrication, cooling and cleaning

    d.   Cooling, shock absorption and lubrication

12. When starting a cold engine, if the oil pressure gauge does not register a rise within around 30 seconds you should:

    a.   Leave the RPM at idle to allow the engine to warm up and the oil pressure to rise

    b.   Stop the engine immediately to avoid damage

    c.   Increase the RPM to try to increase the oil pressure

    d.   Ignore it, the low oil temperature is probably the cause, sufficient oil was observed during the visual inspection

13. During flight you notice that the oil pressure is fluctuating and indicating lower than normal together with a rise in the oil temperature. You should:

    a.   Monitor the readings, but continue as planned. Gauges are notoriously unreliable

    b.   Reduce power to improve cooling

    c.   Enrichen the mixture and apply power to increase the pressure

    d.   Land as soon as possible

14. A cowling fitted to an air-cooled aircraft engine is to:

    a.   Form an protective envelope around the engine and to retain heat

    b.   Duct air around the cylinders to heat them evenly and to reduce drag

    c.   Duct air around the cylinders to cool them evenly and to increase drag

    d.   Duct air around the cylinders to cool them evenly and to reduce drag

15. Prior to start, when priming the engine the fuel is usually delivered into:

    a.   The carburettor

    b.   The cylinder combustion chamber

    c.   The inlet valve port or the induction manifold

    d.   The fuel booster pump

16. It is essential that the correct grade of fuel is used. Avgas or 100LL is coloured ...(i)... all labels relating to this fuel are coloured ...(ii)...

    a.   i) blue   ii) red

    b.   i) red   ii) blue

    c.   i) blue   ii) black

    d.   i) yellow   ii) red

17. If water is present in the fuel system it will cause:

    a.   Icing

    b.   Contamination and loss of engine power

    c.   The fuel to freeze

    d.   Carburettor icing

18. By weight the ideal fuel: air ratio is roughly:

    a.   1:1

    b.   1:8

    c.   1:12

    d.   1:21

19. Detonation may result from using:

    a.   Too weak a mixture

    b.   Too rich a mixture

    c.   A higher fuel grade than usual

    d.   Too high a power setting

20. With increase in altitude, air density will ...(i)... if not adjusted the fuel: air mixture will become ...(ii)...:

    a.   i) increase   ii) weaker

    b.   i) increase   ii) richer

    c.   i) decrease   ii) weaker

    d.   i) decrease   ii) richer

21. In a piston engine the idle cut-off valve:

    a.   Increases fuel flow to the engine at idle power

    b.   Cannot be operated when the engine is above idle power

    c.   Stops fuel flow from the discharge nozzle

    d.   Helps the engine to run at idle power settings

22. To achieve the best fuel: air mix when operating at altitude the mixture control is moved towards the lean position until engine RPM:

    a.   Decreases, then the mixture control is moved slightly to the rich side of peak RPM

    b.   Decreases, then the mixture control is moved slightly to the lean side of peak RPM

    c.   Increases, then the control is moved slightly to the rich side of peak RPM

    d.   Increases, then the control is moved slightly to the lean side of peak RPM

23. When operating at high power, over 75%, a richer mixture is desirable because:

    a.   High power will lead to high pressure in the cylinders

    b.   The air in the cylinders will be more dense

    c.   Any excess fuel will be used to heat the engine

    d.   Any excess fuel will be used to cool the engine

24. Aircraft types that are permitted to use MOGAS are promulgated in:

    a.   Aeronautical Information Circulars

    b.   CAA Airworthiness Notices

    c.   NOTAMs

    d.   ICAO document 1224

25. Baffles are fitted within the engine cowling to:

    a.   Increase the strength of the cowling

    b.   Direct the flow of air evenly around all cylinders to aid cooling

    c.   Decrease the area for air leaving the engine compartment

    d.   Control the volume of air entering the engine compartment

26. In a four-stoke piston engine the purpose of the crankshaft is to:

    a. Convert rotary motion into linear motion

    b. Convert reciprocating motion into rotary motion

    c. Control the inlet and exhaust valve recoil

    d. Convert rotary motion into reciprocating

27. In a four-stroke piston engine for every revolution of the crankshaft the camshaft will rotate:

    a. Once, it operates at engine speed

    b. Twice, the camshaft operates at twice engine speed

    c. Half a revolution, the camshaft operates at half engine speed

    d. Four times, it operates at twice engine speed

28. Air flow through the carburettor venturi creates a:

    a. Rise in pressure and an increase in velocity at the carburettor throat

    b. Rise in pressure and a decrease in velocity at the carburettor throat

    c. Drop in pressure and a decrease in velocity at the carburettor throat

    d. Drop in pressure and an increase in velocity at the carburettor throat

29. In a carburettor the purpose of an accelerator pump is to:

    a. Avoid a weak-cut when the throttle is rapidly advanced

    b. Increase fuel delivery pressure

    c. Ensure sufficient fuel is available at altitude

    d. Ensure the correct volume of fuel is delivered to the cylinders

30. In a simple carburettor the pressure in the float chamber compared to the pressure at the venturi is:

    a. The same

    b. Lower

    c. Higher

    d. Variable and dependent upon the RPM selected

31. The purpose of the idling jet is to:

    a. Prevent a weak cut when the throttle is opened quickly

    b. Keep the engine running at low RPM by providing fuel near the butterfly

    c. Prevent the main jet giving too much fuel at low RPM

    d. Keep the engine running at low RPM by providing fuel directly into the cylinders

32. You are flying over the UK, clear of precipitation with an air temperature of + 14°C and a relative humidity of 40%. Serious carburettor icing would be likely to occur when:

    a. Operating at full power

    b. Operating at cruise power

    c. Operating at any power setting

    d. Operating at descent power

33. On engine start, after releasing the starter button if the starter warning light stays on you should:

    a. Increase the engine RPM until the light goes out

    b. Monitor the light for exactly one minute, if it remains on at the end of that time stop the engine

    c. Check the alternator output level

    d. Stop the engine immediately to avoid damage to the engine and/or starter motor

34. In a piston engine the high tension supply to the spark plugs is derived from:

    a. The battery during start and the magneto once the engine is running

    b. The magneto's self contained generation and distribution system

    c. The battery

    d. The magneto during start and the battery once the engine is running

35. When a magneto is switched off, the switch in the primary circuit:

    a. Closed and the primary circuit is earthed

    b. Closed and the primary circuit is not earthed

    c. Open and the primary circuit is not earthed

    d. Open and the primary circuit is earthed

36. When a magneto becomes detached from its ignition switch:

    a. The engine will fail to stop when both magnetos are selected to "Off"

    b. There is an instant drop in RPM

    c. The engine will fail if the other magneto is switched off

    d. The engine will run roughly

37. Under normal running conditions a magneto draws its primary circuit current from:

    a. The battery

    b. The generator

    c. A ground power unit

    d. Its self-contained electro-magnetic induction system

38. Impulse coupling:

    a. Is the means by which the ignition timing is advanced

    b. Is the slow release of stored energy causing the magnet to rotate slowly to generate a high voltage at the spark plug

    c. Is the means by which the rotating magnet is momentarily accelerated to generate a high voltage at the spark plug

    d. Is the rapid release of stored energy causing the magnet to rotate slowly to generate a low voltage at the spark plug

39. To prevent spark plug fouling you should:

    a. Avoid operating the engine at high RPM for long periods of time

    b. Avoid operating the engine at low RPM for long periods of time

    c. Apply power in short bursts when taxiing

    d. Position into wind for pre departure power checks

40. Your aircraft is fitted with a fixed pitch propeller. When accelerating using a constant throttle setting engine speed will:

    a. Decrease

    b. Remain constant

    c. Increase

    d. Remain constant and then slowly decrease

41. To provide an efficient angle of attack throughout the full length of the blade, the blade angle is:

    a. Progressively reduced from hub to tip

    b. Progressively increased from hub to tip

    c. Constant along the length of the blade

    d. Constant to 60% of the blade then reduces to the tip

42. An aeroplane is fitted with a clockwise rotating propeller (when viewed from the pilot's seat); on take-off torque reaction will tend to:

    a.   Cause the nose to rise

    b.   Cause roll – right wing down

    c.   Cause roll – left wing down

    d.   Cause the tail to rise

43. What is pre-ignition?

    a.   A slow but uncontrolled burning of the fuel/air mixture in a hot engine

    b.   A progressive burning of the fuel/air mixture ahead of the spark from the plug, caused by a hot-spot in the cylinder.

    c.   An explosive burning of the fuel/air mixture ahead of the spark from the plug, caused by an overly hot engine.

    d.   An uncontrolled explosion of the fuel/air mixture

44. In a carburettor an accelerator pump:

    a.   Adds extra fuel to the main jet

    b.   Prevents excessive fuel being delivered to the cylinders

    c.   Is a small plunger within the float chamber which is connected to the throttle linkage

    d.   Ensures the correct volume of fuel is delivered to the cylinders

---

AIRWORTHINESS

---

45. An aeroplane's Certificate of Airworthiness:

    a.   Is valid for the period specified on the certificate

    b.   Will not expire under any circumstances

    c.   Expires after ten years

    d.   Is valid indefinitely, providing the aircraft is maintained, repaired or modified in an approved manner.

46. A PPL may carry out certain minor repairs and services,. Any maintenance carried out by a private pilot:

    a.   Must be entered in the aircraft logbook if it relates to a primary control system

    b.   Must be entered in the aircraft logbook and certified by the pilot concerned

    c.   Must be entered in the aircraft logbook and certified by a licensed engineer

    d.   Need not be recorded

47. The Airworthiness Requirements (BCAR Section A Chapter 6-2) allow for minor adjustments to be made to a control system while away from base. The second part of the duplicate inspection may be carried out:

    a.   Only by the captain of the aircraft

    b.   By an engineer licensed on the aircraft type concerned

    c.   When the aircraft returns to base

    d.   By a pilot licensed for the aircraft type concerned

48. A PPL may carry out certain minor repairs and services, these are:

    a.   Listed in the Air Navigation (General) Regulations. The aeroplane concerned must be less than 5,700 kg

    b.   Listed in the Pilot's Operating Handbook. The aeroplane concerned must be less than 2,730kg

    c.   Listed in the Air Navigation (General) Regulations. The aeroplane concerned must be less than 2,730 kg and not used for public transport

    d.   Listed in the Certificate of Maintenance Review. The aeroplane concerned must be less than 5,700 kg and not used for public transport

49. Any defects requiring maintenance which are encountered during a flight should be recorded by the pilot:

    a.   On the Certificate of Maintenance Review

    b.   In the Aircraft Technical Log

    c.   On the Certificate of Release to Service

    d.   On any handy scrap of paper which should be left in the aircraft

50. Before a flight, the legal responsibility to ensure that all of an aircraft's maintenance documentation is current rests with the:

    a.   Pilot

    b.   Aircraft Owner

    c.   Aircraft Operator

    d.   Chief Engineer

END OF AIRCRAFT GENERAL PAPER 1

	A	B	C	D			A	B	C	D
1			X			26		X		
2			X			27			X	
3				X		28				X
4		X				29	X			
5		X				30			X	
6			X			31		X		
7	X					32				X
8				X		33				X
9	X					34		X		
10			X			35	X			
11			X			36	X			
12		X				37				X
13				X		38			X	
14				X		39		X		
15			X			40			X	
16	X					41	X			
17		X				42			X	
18			X			43		X		
19	X					44			X	
20				X		45				X
21			X			46		X		
22	X					47				X
23				X		48			X	
24		X				49		X		
25		X				50	X			

CORRECT ANSWERS: PERCENTAGES													
38	39	40	41	42	43	44	45	46	47	48	49	50	
76%	78%	80%	82%	84%	86%	88%	90%	92%	94%	96%	98%	100%	

1. **(Answer: C)** During an Otto cycle each valve will open once.

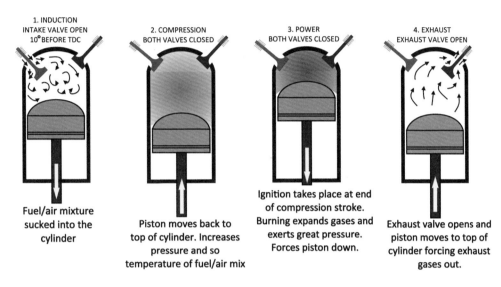

1. INDUCTION
INTAKE VALVE OPEN
10° BEFORE TDC

2. COMPRESSION
BOTH VALVES CLOSED

3. POWER
BOTH VALVES CLOSED

4. EXHAUST
EXHAUST VALVE OPEN

Fuel/air mixture sucked into the cylinder

Piston moves back to top of cylinder. Increases pressure and so temperature of fuel/air mix

Ignition takes place at end of compression stroke. Burning expands gases and exerts great pressure. Forces piston down.

Exhaust valve opens and piston moves to top of cylinder forcing exhaust gases out.

2. **(Answer: C)** Compression ratio is the ratio between the total cylinder volume (piston bottom dead centre) compared to the clearance volume (piston top dead centre).

Compression ratio = Total volume: Clearance volume

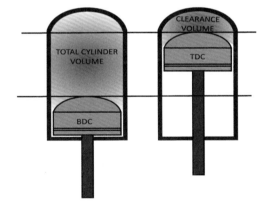

CLEARANCE VOLUME

TOTAL CYLINDER VOLUME

TDC

BDC

3. **(Answer: D)** During one Otto cycle the piston will move up twice and down twice.

4. **(Answer: B)** Cylinders are finned to improve cooling

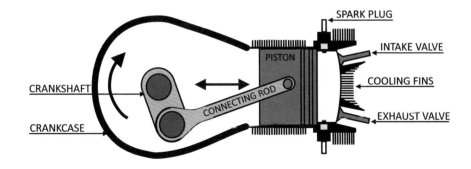

SPARK PLUG

INTAKE VALVE

PISTON

COOLING FINS

CRANKSHAFT

CONNECTING ROD

EXHAUST VALVE

CRANKCASE

WET SUMP

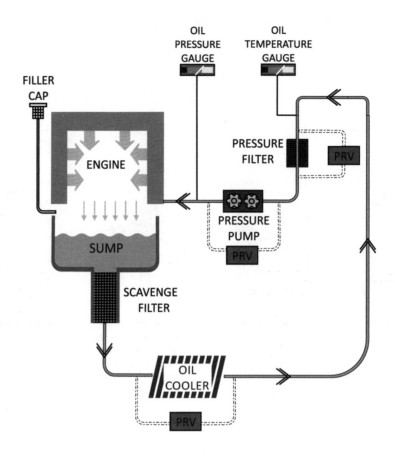

DRY SUMP

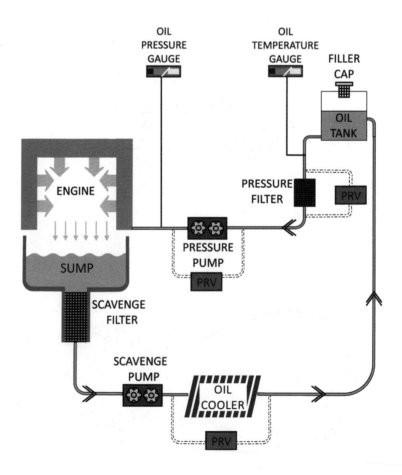

5.   **(Answer: B)** The probe senses the temperature of the oil after it has passed the oil cooler, but before it is used within the hot sections of the engine.

6.   **(Answer: C)** A wet sump system does not have a storage tank, instead oil is collected at the bottom of the engine. A pressure pump will draw oil directly from the sump via a scavenger filter and a pressure filter from where it continues into the main oil gallery.

7.   **(Answer: A)** Excessive oil pressure is relieved by a pressure relief valve. This will be situated downstream of the pump, and when open the PRV will allow some oil to route back to the inlet side of the pressure pump.

8.   **(Answer: D)** A blockage in the oil cooler could be extremely serious leading to starvation of oil to the main gallery and failure of the engine. Should this occur a pressure relief valve will activate allowing oil to by-pass the cooler.

9.   **(Answer: A)** The reading on the oil pressure gauge is taken from the outlet side of the pressure pump.

10. **(Answer: C)** A dry sump system scavenges oil from the bottom of the engine and returns it to an oil storage tank. The scavenge pump will have a larger capacity than the pressure pump to ensure the supply to the oil tank.

11. **(Answer: C)** Some of the main uses for oil in an engine are:
     - *Lubrication, allowing two metal surfaces to move past one another without actually touching.*
     - *Cooling, to help dissipate any heat generated by friction and from combustion. The oil itself is cooled by having an oil cooler incorporated in the system.*
     - *Cleaning, oil circulation around the engine will carry away dirt and any foreign particles. Any contaminants are removed by the oil filter.*

12. **(Answer: B)** When starting a cold engine, if the oil pressure gauge does not register a rise within around 30 seconds you should stop the engine immediately to avoid damaging the engine. After an aircraft has been standing oil will drain from the oil galleries and collect in the sump, or at the bottom of the crankcase. One other factor to consider is that in cold weather the oil will become thicker and more viscous which will hinder its flow around the engine. On start 30 seconds will allow time for the oil to begin to circulate and, if the system is operating normally, for pressure to register.

13. **(Answer: D)** Fluctuating oil pressure together with increasing oil temperature is associated with low oil quantity. Insufficient oil will cause a rise in oil temperature, as the lack of oil will not transport heat from the engine's hot areas nor lubricate effectively. Low quantity may also cause the pump to cavitate leading to pressure fluctuations. Cavitation is where vapour bubbles form in a flowing liquid due to low pressure. No oil = engine seizure = land as soon as possible.

14. **(Answer: D)** Engine cowlings are installed to ensure correct operating temperatures are maintained by promoting even cooling. This is achieved by ducting air inside the cowling around the engine. The cowling also streamlines the airflow around the engine, reducing drag.

15. **(Answer: C)** To aid starting a cold engine a hand operated primer pump is used to inject fuel directly into the induction manifold near the combustion chamber or to the inlet valve port.

Cold air is also very dense meaning that fuel entering the chamber is reluctant to evaporate, priming adds extra fuel so that some will evaporate and sustain combustion. It is essential that the primer is locked after use and during flight. Leaving it open may lead to excessive fuel entering the cylinders meaning the fuel/air mixture will become too rich, which could stop the engine (a "rich cut").

16. **(Answer: A)** Grade 100LL fuel is dyed blue. All labels relating to the delivery and storage of 100LL are red.

17. **(Answer: B)** Water entering the engine will cause a loss of power, or worse, cause the engine to stop. This is why the contents of the fuel tanks are checked before each flight. Water has a higher specific gravity than Avgas and will therefore settle to the bottom of the fuel tanks and appear as a "bubble" at the bottom of the fuel tester tube.

18. **(Answer: C)** By weight the fuel: air ratio should be approximately 1 part fuel to 12 parts air. At altitude the weight of air is less, therefore the mixture should be leaned to maintain the ratio. If the mixture is too lean detonation could occur. If the mixture is too rich the engine will not run efficiently and less power will be generated.

19. **(Answer: A)** Detonation will occur if too weak a mixture is used. Combine this with high cylinder head temperatures (fuel is also a cooling agent in the engine) and the fuel: air mix can spontaneously ignite and burn in a violent and uncontrolled manner. The explosive increase in pressure that is created can cause severe damage to the engine, possibly even leading to failure of the engine.

    You would detect detonation by the engine running roughly and an increase in cylinder head temperatures. Corrective action is to:
    * *Enrichen the mixture*
    * *Throttle back (reduce pressure in the cylinders)*
    * *Increase airspeed to aid cooling*

    Apart from an overly lean mixture, other factors that can lead to detonation are:
    * *Using a lower grade of fuel than recommended*
    * *Using time-expired fuel*
    * *An over-heated engine*
    * *Excessive manifold pressure*

20. **(Answer: D)** With increase in altitude, air density reduces and if not adjusted the fuel: air mixture will become richer. An overly rich mixture will lead to the engine running roughly and if not corrected possibly a rich cut.

21. **(Answer: C)** The idle cut-off is the usual way of shutting down the engine in a light aircraft. When the mixture control is moved to the idle cut-off position, the ICO valve stops fuel flow from the discharge nozzle. Normally the engine will continue to run for a few seconds whilst all remaining fuel in the cylinders and inlet manifold is burned.

22. **(Answer: A)** To lean the mixture the mixture control should be moved slowly towards the lean position. As the correct fuel: air ratio is achieved the RPM will increase, but with further leaning the RPM will decrease and will be combined with a slight roughness in the running of the engine.

    From this point the mixture control should then be moved towards the rich position until the best RPM is achieved and the engine runs smoothly. The chemically correct mixture is now feeding the engine.

Finally the mixture should be enriched a little more, to ensure that the engine is running just on the rich side of the chemically correct mixture. Remember fuel also serves a cooling function.

23. **(Answer: D)** Fuel is also a cooling agent, if a rich mixture is selected excess fuel entering the combustion chamber will evaporate and absorb heat from the cylinder head. This will help to maintain an optimum operating temperature.

    Situations where this may be useful include climbing where low airspeed (and therefore less air cooling) combined with high power may lead to an increase in cylinder head temperature.

    Any power setting above 75% is deemed to be "high", in the cruise aircraft piston engines aregenerally operated between 60 to 65%.

24. **(Answer: B)** Aircraft types that are approved to use MOGAS are detailed in CAA Airworthiness Notices, specifically number 98. Generally the use of MOGAS is not permitted as the quality control systems that are in place for AVGAS are not present; also motor fuel is more volatile and evaporates more readily which could lead to vapour locks in an aircraft's fuel system and possibly fuel starvation. Other problems are that using MOGAS in light aircraft can lead to low power output, fowling of the spark plugs and detonation.

25. **(Answer: B)** Baffles are fitted to direct cooling air as evenly as possible around the cylinders.

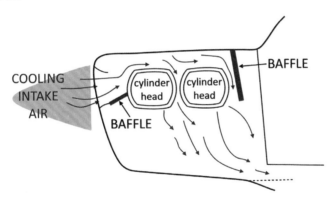

26. **(Answer: B)** The back and forth movement of the pistons is reciprocating motion – hence the name reciprocating engine. To convert this reciprocating motion to rotary, the pistons are attached to the crankshaft via connecting rods or conrods. As the piston is forced back down the cylinder during the power stroke the conrod also moves in such a way as to turn the crankshaft.

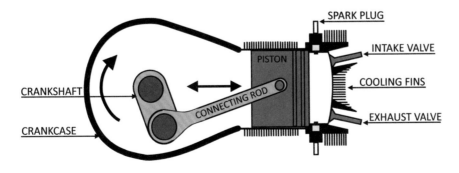

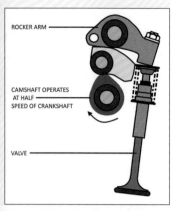

27. ANSWER C

27. **(Answer: C)** The camshaft is attached to the crankshaft via a gearing system. It is a reduction gearing system with a 2:1 ratio causing the camshaft to turn once for every two revolutions of the crankshaft, in other words half engine speed.

The camshaft operates the inlet and exhaust valves to the cylinder via push rods and rocker arms. As each valve only needs to open once in every two revolutions of the crankshaft (once in every four strokes of the piston) the camshaft needs to operate at half the speed.

28. **(Answer: D)** In a carburettor the venturi causes the airflow to increase in speed resulting in a drop in pressure (Bernoulli's theorem) in the carburettor throat.

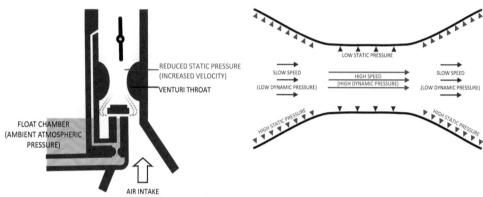

FLOAT TYPE CARBURETTOR

28. ANSWER D

Float Type Carburettor

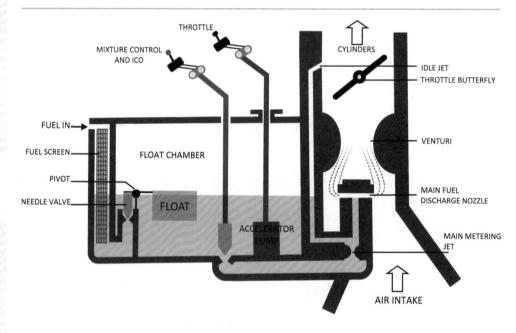

FLOAT CHAMBER: Fuel level is maintained by a float-type device

MIXTURE NEEDLE: Controls fuel to the discharge nozzle. Its position is adjusted using the mixture control.

DISCHARGE NOZZLE: Fuel is forced into the venturi by the greater ambient atmospheric pressure in the float chamber.

VENTURI: Its shape creates an area of low pressure

THROTTLE VALVE: Controls the flow of the fuel/air mixture. It is adjusted via the throttle control in the cockpit

29. **(Answer: A)** When the throttle is opened quickly airflow through the carburettor venturiincreases at a greater rate than fuel flow, which would lead to an overly weak mixture. The accelerator pump prevents any lag in the power increase by providing an extra spurt of fuel as the throttle is opened.

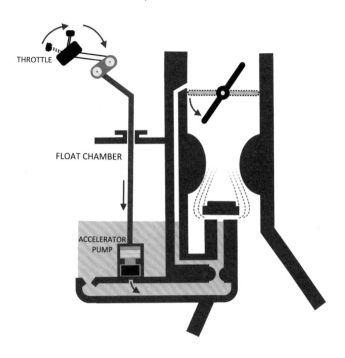

30. **(Answer: C)** The pressure in the float chamber is the same as the ambient atmosphericpressure. The acceleration of airflow through the venturi causes a decrease in static pressure. The higher pressure in the float chamber forces fuel through the main jet to join the venturi airflow. *(See diagram with question 28).*

31. **(Answer: B)** With the engine at idle the butterfly valve is practically closed; in this situation the pressure differential between the venturi and the float chamber will not be sufficient to force fuel through the main jet. To provide sufficient fuel at low rpm an idle jet is located close to the butterfly valve where there is a small venturi effect.

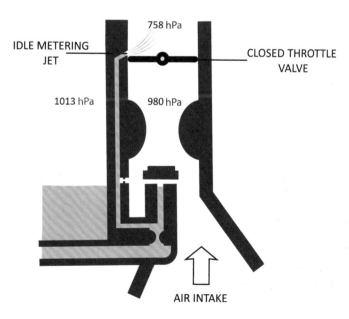

32.   (Answer: D) Causes of engine icing:

EXPANSION: AS air accelerates in the venturi the pressure drops and so does the temperature. Warm air can cool rapidly to below zero and if the air is moist enough ice will form.

IMPACT ICE: Where super-cooled water droplets in the intake air impact and immediately freeze on the inlet air scoop and the induction to the carburettor. (Note: this type of icing can also affect fuel injected aircraft)

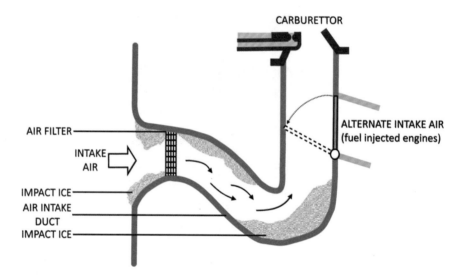

FUEL ICING: Downstream of the jet fuel vaporises absorbing latent heat and leading to a significant drop in temperature. Ice may form on any surface including the inlet walls and the throttle butterfly seriously restricting the airflow to the engine. Fuel icing can occur at temperatures well above freezing, even up to +30°C when the relative humidity is over 50%.

THROTTLE ICING: Occurs when the fuel: air mix accelerates past the throttle butterfly valve resulting in a temperature drop and leading to the possibility of ice forming on the throttle valve. At small throttle openings the acceleration and temperature drop are at their greatest, a situation exacerbated by the fact that at small throttle openings not a great deal of ice is necessary to form a blockage. For this reason there is a greater likelihood of carburettor icing at reduced power settings.

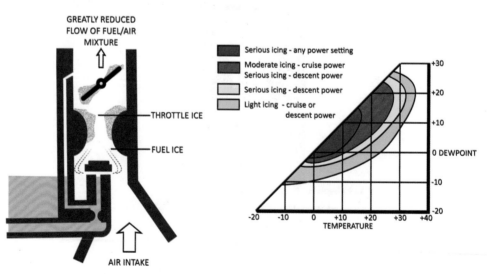

33. **(Answer: D)** Electric starters have a starter warning light which shows that the starter solenoid is energised and engaged with the engine. If, for some reason, the relay sticks the warning light will remain on, meaning that the starter motor is still engaged with, and is now being driven by, the engine. This could result in very serious damage to both the starter and the engine.

    The engine must be shut down immediately if the starter warning light does not go out after the starter is released.

34. **(Answer: B)** The high tension supply to the spark plugs is derived from the magneto's self contained generation and distribution system.

HOW A MAGNETO WORKS

"Electromagnetism" describes a force that has both an electrical field and a magnetic one; both are therefore intrinsically linked to each other. A changing electrical field generates a magnetic field; conversely a changing magnetic field generates an electrical field. This effect is called electromagnetic induction, and is the basis of operation for a magneto. Because it requires no battery or other source of energy, the magneto is a compact and reliable self-contained ignition system, which is why it is used in many general aviation aircraft.

A magneto consists of a permanent magnet which is rotated close to a conductor; the magnet is turned using ancillary gears from the engine. A coil of wire is wound around the conductor – this is called the primary coil and the rotation of the magnet induces an alternating electrical current to flow within it.

The primary coil consists of around 200 turns of copper wire; one end is permanently grounded to the magneto case, the other is connected to a set of cam-operated breaker points. Usually the breaker points are closed grounding both ends of the primary coil allowing the induced current to flow continuously around the coil.

At the moment of ignition the magneto's cam opens the breaker points, interrupting the current flow in the primary coil and collapsing the magnetic field that has built up around it. This induces a large voltage spike in the primary coil in the region of 200 to 300 volts.

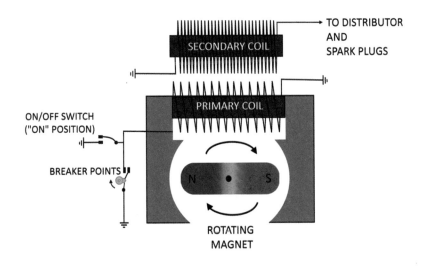

201

Around the primary coil a second coil of wire is wound (they are depicted as separate in the diagram above for clarity, but are actually wound around the same armature). The second coil is made of thinner wire and has many more turns than the primary (approximately 20,000) making it a kind of step-up transformer. The collapse of the magnetic field around the primary coil induces a high voltage current in the secondary winding. In this way the fairly low primary voltage is converted into a much higher voltage in the secondary circuit, in the order of 20,000 to 30,000 volts, it is this high tension current that is then directed to each spark plug at the appropriate moment.

Every cylinder has two spark plugs and a high voltage spark is timed to occur just before the piston reaches TDC. For increased safety most light aircraft have two magnetos supplying two independent ignition systems. Each system sends high tension voltage to one of the two spark plugs in each cylinder. This arrangement also provides better engine performance as well as redundancy in the event of a failure of one of the magnetos. Under normal circumstances two sparks will provide two flame fronts within the cylinder. The two flame fronts decrease the time needed for the complete fuel charge to start burning, as a result the fuel burns at a lower temperature and pressure.

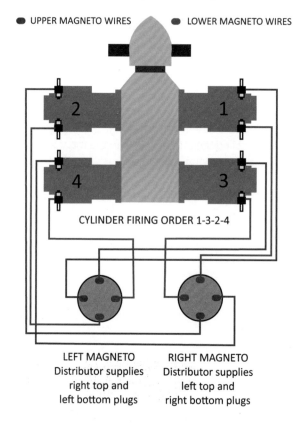

35. **(Answer: A)** When the magneto switches are "Off" the switch in the primary circuit is closed and the primary circuit is earthed. This ensures that even if the magnet rotates it cannot induce a voltage in the secondary coil.

36. **(Answer: A)** With the magnetos selected to "Off" the primary circuit is closed, and the lowvoltage current is sent to earth. This renders the breaker points ineffective and hence no high voltage current can be generated. Should a magneto become detached from the switch it will not earth and the engine will continue to run even when the ignition switch was selected to "Off".

37. **(Answer: D)** A magneto is a self-contained electro-magnetic unit driven by the engine camshaft; it is independent of the other aircraft electrical systems.

38. **(Answer: C)** Impulse coupling accelerates the rotating magnet momentarily to generate a high voltage; it also retards the ignition timing at low RPM until after top dead centre. After start the timing of the spark returns to just before top dead centre.

39. **(Answer: B)** Spark plug fouling can be prevented by not operating at low RPM for long periods of time. When operating at low engine RPM the combustion of the fuel: air mixture is not efficient as the engine is not at its optimum operating temperature. Unburned fuel can cause carbon deposits to build up, especially on the spark plug electrodes and exhaust valves. The build up on the spark plugs can lead to rough running and misfiring.

40. **(Answer: C)** On an aircraft with a fixed pitch propeller as the speed increases the engine RPM will also increase even though the throttle setting remains unchanged.

41. **(Answer: A)** Ideally a propeller should produce uniform thrust along the length of the blade. Therefore the blade is twisted so that the blade angle, and hence the angle of attack, reduces from hub to tip. The result is that the faster moving parts of the propeller have a smaller angle of attack and the slower segments have a larger angle of attack, hence overall the thrust is even along the length of the blade.

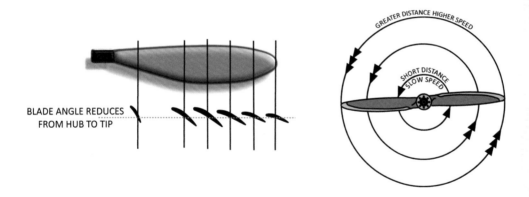

42. **(Answer: C)** If the propeller rotates clockwise (when viewed from behind) torque reaction will tend to rotate the aircraft anti-clockwise and roll it to the left.

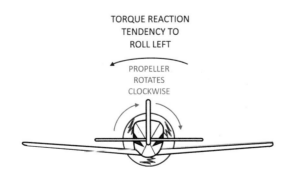

43.   **(Answer: B)** Pre-ignition is the progressive burning of the fuel: air mixture occurring in advance of the spark from the plug. It can be caused by a hot-spot, usually a carbon deposit in the cylinder becoming red hot and igniting the mixture. The effect would be rough running, perhaps back firing and a rise in cylinder head temperature. A possible cause is using high power with too lean a mixture meaning that there is no excess fuel to provide cooling.

44.   **(Answer: C)** The accelerator pump is a small plunger within the float chamber, it is attached to the throttle linkage. When the throttle is opened quickly airflow through the carburettor venturi increases at a greater rate than fuel flow, which would lead to an overly weak mixture. The accelerator pump prevents any lag in the power increase by providing an extra spurt of fuel as the throttle is opened. *(See diagram at question 29).*

AIRWORTHINESS

---

45.   **(Answer: D)** EASA Certificates of Airworthiness are non-expiring, provided that the aircraft is modified, repaired and maintained in an approved manner. Aircraft governed by EASA must be maintained in accordance with a Light Aircraft Maintenance Program (LAMP).

46.   **(Answer: B)** Owners or aircraft operators holding a PPL or higher are allowed to carry out minor repairs or servicing on their aircraft. The legislation is set out in the ANO Article 16(7). Pilots should record any minor work carried out in the appropriate logbook and certify it with their licence number and signature.

47.   **(Answer: D)** In order for an aircraft to be considered airworthy again following any adjustments made to either the flight controls and/or the engine controls an inspection must be made by two licensed personnel, either engineers or inspectors. However, the Airworthiness Requirements (BCAR Section A Chapter 6-2) allow for minor adjustments to be made to a control system while the aircraft is away from base and for the second part of the Duplicate Inspection to be carried out by a pilot licensed for the type of aircraft concerned.

48.   **(Answer: C)** Owners or aircraft operators holding a PPL or higher are allowed to carry out minor repairs or servicing on their aircraft. The minor repairs and replacements permitted are listed in the Air Navigation (General) Regulations Part 4. The aeroplane concerned must weigh less than 2,730 kg and must not used for public transport.

49.   **(Answer: B)** The Aircraft Technical Log is the place where a pilot may record any defect immediately following a flight. Subsequently an engineer will record the maintenance performed to correct the fault. Pilots should also review the Tech Log (as well as the Certificate of Maintenance Review and Certificate of Release to Service) prior to flight.

50.   **(Answer: A)** Prior to flight it is legally the pilot's responsibility to ensure that the aircraft's maintenance documentation is current and correct.

AIRCRAFT GENERAL PAPER 2

50 Questions; Time allowed 1 hour 30 minutes

PRINCIPLES OF FLIGHT

1. The International Standard Atmosphere sets out:

   a. Actual values for temperature, pressure and density at all altitudes

   b. Ambient values for temperature, pressure and density at all altitudes

   c. Theoretical values for temperature, pressure and density at all altitudes

   d. Ambient sea level values for temperature, pressure and density at all altitudes

2. The temperature at 14,000 feet is -9°C. How does this deviate from the ISA temperature?

   a. ISA +6°C

   b. ISA +4°C

   c. ISA -4°C

   d. ISA -6°C

3. The main constituents of the Earth's atmosphere are:

   a. Oxygen, hydrogen and carbon dioxide

   b. Oxygen, nitrogen and water vapour

   c. Carbon dioxide, nitrogen and water vapour

   d. Nitrogen, oxygen and carbon dioxide

4. By volume the ratio of oxygen to nitrogen in the atmosphere is roughly:

   a. 4:1

   b. 3:1

   c. 1:3

   d. 1:4

5. The troposphere is characterised by:

   a. A continuous rise in temperature with increasing height

   b. A continuous reduction in temperature with decreasing height

   c. A continuous reduction in temperature with increasing height

   d. A constant temperature up to the tropopause

6. Air density has a great effect on both airframe and engine performance, which of the following statements is correct?

   a. Density is proportional to pressure and inversely proportional to temperature

   b. Density is proportional to temperature and inversely proportional to pressure

   c. Density is proportional to both temperature and pressure

   d. Density is inversely proportional to both temperature and pressure

7. If the temperature of an airmass remains constant, increasing the pressure will:

   a. Cause the density to increase

   b. Cause the density to decrease

   c. Have no effect on air density

   d. Cause the volume to increase

8. The co-efficient of lift reaches its maximum value at:

   a. An angle of attack of between 5 and 8 degrees

   b. At V_{MD}

   c. At V_{SO}

   d. Just prior to the stalling angle of attack

9. Theoretically, if the angle of attack and other factors remain constant but speed is doubled, the lift created at this higher speed will be:

    a. Two times greater than at the lower speed

    b. The same as at the lower speed

    c. Four times greater than at the lower speed

    d. Half as much as at the lower speed

10. Angle of attack may be defined as the angle between:

    a. The chord line of an aerofoil and the horizon

    b. The chord line of an aerofoil and the relative airflow

    c. The chord line of an aerofoil and the aircraft's longitudinal axis

    d. The chord line of an aerofoil and the aircraft's lateral axis

11. Compared to the free stream airflow, in normal flight air over the top of a wing will:

    a. Decrease in speed

    b. Have the same speed

    c. Increase in speed

    d. Have higher pressure

12. Which of the following statements is correct regarding induced drag:

    a. Induced drag increases as airspeed increases

    b. Induced drag decreases as airspeed increases

    c. Induced drag is unaffected by changes in airspeed

    d. Induced drag decreases as airspeed decreases

13. Which of the following statements is correct regarding parasite drag:

    a. Parasite drag increases as airspeed increases

    b. Parasite drag decreases as airspeed increases

    c. Parasite drag is unaffected by changes in airspeed

    d. Parasite drag decreases as airspeed decreases

14. In relation to drag which of the following statements is correct?

    a. Speed has no effect on drag

    b. Parasite drag has more influence at low speeds; induced drag has more influence at high speed

    c. Both parasite and induced drag increase with increasing speed

    d. Induced drag has more influence at low speeds; parasite drag has more influence at high speed

15. Maintaining a constant angle of attack and increasing airspeed will cause:

    a. Lift and drag to decrease

    b. Lift to increase and drag to decrease

    c. Lift to decrease and drag to increase

    d. Lift and drag to increase

16. Compared to the free stream flow, in normal flight air pressure under a wing will be:

    a. Lower

    b. Higher

    c. The same

    d. Initially higher, then lower

17. In flight, an aircraft is said to be in equilibrium when:

    a. Lift is balanced by drag and weight is balanced by thrust

    b. Weight is balanced by lift and drag is balanced by thrust

    c. Weight is balanced by drag and lift is balanced by thrust

    d. Lift is balanced by thrust and weight is balanced by drag

18. Increasing airspeed will cause:

    a. Induced drag to increase and parasite drag to decrease

    b. Induced drag to increase and parasite drag to increase

    c. Parasite drag to decrease and induced drag to decrease

    d. Parasite drag to increase and induced drag to decrease

19. In straight and level flight, if the centre of pressure is behind the centre of gravity a ...(i)... couple is produced, requiring the tailplane to produce a ...(ii)... force

    a. i) nose down   ii) downward

    b. i) nose down   ii) upward

    c. i) nose up   ii) downward

    d. i) nose up   ii) upward

20. Movement of an aeroplane around its lateral axis is called:

    a. Rolling

    b. Pitching

    c. Yawing

    d. Spinning

21. Movement of an aeroplane around its normal axis is called:

    a. Rolling

    b. Pitching

    c. Yawing

    d. Spinning

22. The primary effect of aileron input is to create roll, the secondary effect is:

    a. Yaw followed by spiral dive

    b. Pitch, from the extra lift generated by the down going wing

    c. Turn followed by spiral dive

    d. Bank followed by spiral dive

23. Directional stability is achieved by:

    a. The tailplane

    b. The ailerons

    c. The fin

    d. The rudder

24. The up-going aileron is rigged to move further than the down-going aileron to counteract:

    a. Inertia

    b. Static stability

    c. Lateral stability

    d. Adverse aileron yaw

25. The secondary effect of aileron is ... (i)... and the secondary effect of rudder is ...(ii)...:

    a. i) yaw   ii) roll

    b. i) roll   ii) yaw

    c. i) bank   ii) yaw

    d. i) roll   ii) bank

26. Static stability is an indicator of an aircraft's readiness to:

    a. Continue to diverge from its original position

    b. Return to its original position

    c. Remain at its new position

    d. Oscillate about the original flight path and finally diverge from it

27. Washout on an aircraft's wing is employed to:

    a. Decrease aileron effectiveness

    b. Ensure that the wing tip stalls first

    c. Ensure that the inboard section of the wing stalls first

    d. Ensure the wing stalls evenly along its length

28. A fixed trim tab, or balance tab, on an aileron:

    a. Is adjusted on the ground after a test flight to ensure longitudinally level flight

    b. Is set at the time of manufacture and must not be altered

    c. Is adjusted by the pilot during flight to relieve unwanted control pressures

    d. Is adjusted on the ground after a test flight to ensure laterally level flight

29. On a control surface a "Mass Balance":

    a. Moves the surface's centre of gravity aft

    b. Prevents flutter at high speed

    c. Makes it easier for the pilot to move the control surface

    d. Provides resistance, making it more difficult for the pilot to move the control surface

30. Following a disturbance, an aircraft which returns to its original flight path without the pilot taking any corrective action is said to have:

    a. Stability

    b. Instability

    c. Neutral stability

    d. Neutral instability

31. A wing stalls at:

    a. A given speed

    b. A given angle of incidence

    c. A given angle of attack

    d. A given weight

32. At a given constant weight the stall speed of an aircraft is proportional to the:

    a. Square of the aircraft's weight

    b. Square root of the load factor

    c. Square of the load factor

    d. Square of the aircraft's weight

33. An anti-balance tab is fitted to a control surface to:

    a. Aid the pilot in moving the control surface at high speed

    b. Aid the movement of the control column

    c. Ensure that control column loads increase with increased deflection of the control surface

    d. Control the position of the centre of pressure on the control surface

34. Following a disturbance from a stable trimmed position, an aircraft with neutral stability will:

    a. Return to its original attitude

    b. Continue to diverge from its original attitude

    c. Remain in its new attitude

    d. Return to its original attitude, overshoot but eventually return to its original attitude

35. Using small flap settings during take-off:

    a. Gives a shorter take-off ground run

    b. Improves the initial rate of climb

    c. Gives a steeper climb angle

    d. Gives a longer take-off ground run

36. When compared to the chord line of a clean aerofoil, extending trailing edge flaps will give:

    a.   A lower stalling angle of attack

    b.   A higher stalling angle of attack

    c.   No change in the critical angle

    d.   A higher angle of incidence

37. Slots increase the stalling angle of attack by:

    a.   Providing extra lift from the leading edge

    b.   Increasing the effective wing area

    c.   Changing the camber of the wing

    d.   Delaying the breakup of laminar air flow over the upper surface

38. The illustration below depicts an aircraft in a balanced level turn to port. Lift is represented by vector:

    a.   D

    b.   C

    c.   B

    d.   A

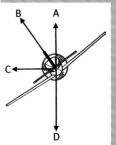

39. Some control surfaces have a tendency to "flutter" at high speed, this can be avoided:

    a.   With the use of a balance tab

    b.   With the use of a mass balance

    c.   With the use of an anti-balance tab

    d.   With the use of a spring tab

40. The basic stall speed of an aircraft is 80 knots. In a level turn with a 60° angle of bank, the same aircraft will have a stalling speed of:

    a.   195 knots

    b.   103 knots

    c.   121 knots

    d.   113 knots

41. Should the centre of gravity be at or close to its aft limit one effect will be:

    a.   An increase in longitudinal stability

    b.   The stalling speed will increase

    c.   A reduction in elevator force required during the flare

    d.   An increase in elevator force required during the flare

42. With a simple trim tab set during flight, any movement of the associated control surface will cause the tab to:

    a.   Move in the opposite direction to the control surface

    b.   Move in the same direction as the control surface and will need to be re-set

    c.   Remain in a constant position relative to the control surface

    d.   Remain in a constant position relative to the airflow

43. Should the centre of gravity be at or close to its forward limit one effect will be:

    a.   A decrease in longitudinal stability

    b.   A requirement for high elevator forces during the flare

    c.   A reduction in the stalling speed

    d.   A reduction in elevator force required during the flare

44. An aircraft wing will stall at a particular...(i)... The onset of a stall is characterised by a ...(ii)... attitude and ...(iii)...

    a.   i) airspeed   ii) pitch up   iii) the aircraft sinking

    b.   i) angle of incidence   ii) pitch down   iii) a wing drop

    c.   i) airspeed   ii) pitch down   iii) a wing drop

    d.   i) angle of attack   ii) pitch down   iii) the aircraft sinking

45. Leading edge slots increase the stalling, or critical angle, of a wing by:

    a.   Delaying the breakup of laminar air flow over the upper surface

    b.   Increasing the effective wing area

    c.   Changing the camber of the wing

    d.   Providing extra lift from the leading edge

46. The temperature at 11,000 feet is -2°C. How does this deviate from the ISA temperature?

    a.   ISA + 3°C

    b.   ISA - 7°C

    c.   ISA +7°C

    d.   ISA +5°C

47. A parcel of saturated air, when compared to a parcel of dry air at the same temperature and pressure will be:

    a.   Less dense

    b.   More dense

    c.   Of exactly the same density

    d.   Twice the volume

48. The basic stall speed of an aircraft is 60 knots. In a level turn with a 60° angle of bank, the same aircraft will have a stalling speed of:

    a.   101 knots

    b.   85 knots

    c.   146 knots

    d.   95 knots

49. Small flap settings used on take-off and initial climb will:

    a.   Reduce the take-off roll and the initial climb rate

    b.   Reduce the take-off roll and increase the initial rate of climb

    c.   Increase the take-off roll but reduce the initial rate of climb

    d.   Increase the take-off roll and the initial climb rate

50. With no change in weight the stall speed of an aircraft is proportional to:

    a.   Square of the aircraft's weight

    b.   Square of the load factor

    c.   Square of the aircraft's weight

    d.   Square root of the load factor

END OF AIRCRAFT GENERAL PAPER 2

INTENTIONALLY BLANK

AIRCRAFT GENERAL PAPER 2: ANSWERS

	A	B	C	D			A	B	C	D
1			X			26		X		
2		X				27			X	
3		X				28				X
4				X		29		X		
5			X			30	X			
6	X					31			X	
7	X					32		X		
8				X		33			X	
9			X			34			X	
10		X				35	X			
11			X			36	X			
12		X				37				X
13	X					38			X	
14				X		39		X		
15				X		40				X
16		X				41			X	
17		X				42			X	
18				X		43		X		
19	X					44				X
20		X				45	X			
21			X			46				X
22	X					47	X			
23			X			48		X		
24				X		49	X			
25	X					50				X

CORRECT ANSWERS: PERCENTAGES												
38	39	40	41	42	43	44	45	46	47	48	49	50
76%	78%	80%	82%	84%	86%	88%	90%	92%	94%	96%	98%	100%

PRINCIPLES OF FLIGHT

1. **(Answer: C)** The International Standard Atmosphere has been developed by ICAO to describe a theoretical set of atmospheric conditions throughout all levels. The ISA is used as a yardstick with which to compare actual conditions. This is useful to enable aircraft performance to be calculated and instruments calibrated.

    The ISA has mean sea level values of:
    - Pressure: 1013.2 hPa
    - Temperature: + 15°C
    - Density: 1225 g/m³
    - Lapse Rate: Temperature reducing at 1.98°C per 1000 feet to the tropopause (36,090 feet), above this temperature is assumed to be a constant -56.5°C

2. **(Answer: B)** For practical purposes the ISA lapse rate of 1.98°C/1000 feet can be rounded up to 2°C/1000 feet.

    The actual temperature given in the question of -9°C is four degrees warmer than the theoretical ISA temperature of -13°C. This is expressed as ISA +4°C.

    14,000 feet ISA TEMPERATURE

    $= +15 - (2°C \times 14)$
    $= +15 - 28 = -13°C$

    ISA LAPSE RATE
    2°C/1000 FEET

    ISA MSL +15°C

3. **(Answer: B)** The main constituent gases within a dry atmosphere are:

    Nitrogen 78%, Oxygen 21% and other gases 1%. In nature there is always some water vapour present up to a maximum of approximately 4%.

4. **(Answer: D)** The main constituent gases within a dry atmosphere are: Nitrogen 78%, Oxygen 21% and other gases 1%. This represents oxygen: nitrogen ratio of 1:4.

5. **(Answer: C)** The troposphere is characterised by a decrease in temperature with increasing height up to the tropopause. Above the tropopause temperature remains constant with further increase in altitude.

6. **(Answer: A)** Density is proportional to pressure, as pressure increases so does density. Conversely if pressure is reduced the air expands and becomes less dense. Density is inversely proportional to temperature, heating an air mass will cause it to expand and reduce its density; in other words as temperature increases, density decreases. Density affects both engine and aerodynamic performance, from the above we can glean that both will be degraded at high altitude (low pressure leading to reduced density) and on hot days (high temperature leading to reduced density).

7. **(Answer: A)** Density is proportional to pressure, as pressure increases so does density. If pressure is reduced the air expands and becomes less dense.

8. **(Answer: D)** The coefficient of lift is a measure of the amount of lift a wing produces, and is dependent on many factors, namely:

    - wing shape
    - air density
    - speed (squared)
    - wing surface area and
    - angle of attack

    The amount of lift generated by a wing can be calculated using the following formula:
    Lift = Coefficient of Lift X ½ density X velocity squared X wing surface area
    Lift = C$_L$ X ½ρ X V² X S

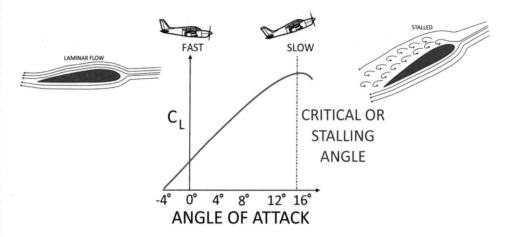

    Plotting angle of attack against coefficient of lift we can see that initially lift increases with increasing angle of attack. At the critical angle (around 16° in a typical training aircraft) there is a sharp drop in the coefficient of lift as the laminar airflow over the wing surface separates and breaks up into eddies, when this happens the wing is said to be stalled. The maximum coefficient of lift occurs just prior to the stall.

9. **(Answer: C)** From the lift equation we can see that lift is proportional to the square of the aircraft's velocity: **Lift = C$_L$ X ½ρ X V² X S**

    If the angle of attack and other factors remain constant, an aircraft flying at 200 knots will generate four times the lift that it would do if travelling at 100 knots.

10. **(Answer: B)** The angle of attack is the angle between the chord line of an aerofoil and the relative airflow.

    The mean camber line is a line drawn halfway between the upper and lower surfaces of an aerofoil. The chord line is a straight line joining the ends of the mean camber line.

11. **(Answer: C)** Compared to the free stream airflow, in normal flight air over the top of a wing will increase in speed. There are many theories as to exactly how an aerofoil produces lift. The only one we need to be concerned with for now is the "Equal Flow Theory". This theory states that because of an aerofoil's shape the distance air will have to travel is greater over the upper surface than the lower. Airflow over the upper surface will therefore have to accelerate to meet the air flowing below the wing.

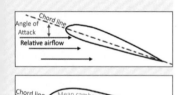

10. ANSWER B

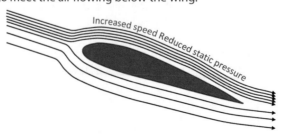

Bernoulli's principle: states that an increase in velocity will lead to a decrease in pressure.

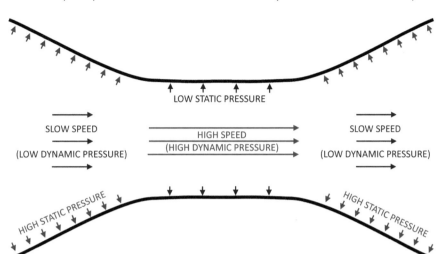

12. **(Answer: B)** Induced drag decreases as airspeed increases. Induced drag is related to angle of attack and is a by-product of lift.

Over most angles of attack there is lower static pressure above a wing than below it; at the wing tip some airflow spills over from the high pressure area under the wing to the low pressure area above creating wing tip vorticies. This creates a span-wise movement towards the tip below the wing and towards the fuselage on the upper surface.

The upward motion of the wing tip vortex is outside the span of the wing, however the downward flow is within the span of the wing behind the trailing edge. Additionally there are less powerful trailing edge vortices along the whole wing span. The overall effect is a downwash of air behind the trailing edge.

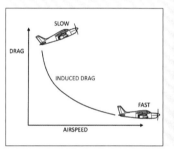

12. ANSWER B

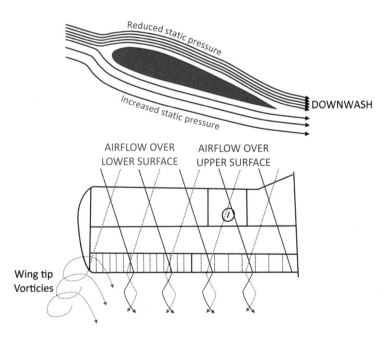

This displacement of air causes a resistance which we call induced drag. The actual amount of induced drag is proportional to the coefficient of lift; the higher the CL the greater the induced drag. The CL also increases with angle of attack and high angles of attack are used at slow speeds and also when manoeuvring.

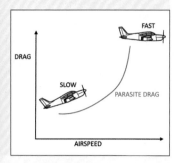

13. ANSWER A

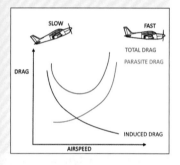

14. ANSWER D

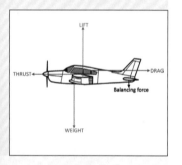

17. ANSWER B

13. **(Answer: A)** Parasite drag increases as airspeed increases.

Parasite drag is composed of:
Skin friction – the friction force between the aircraft and the air through which it is moving.

Form drag – the resistance caused by moving an object through the air. The larger the object the larger the "form" presented to the airflow. The key to minimising form drag is to streamline the object concerned.

Interference drag – due to airflow "interference" at the junctions between the various parts of the aircraft; for example between the wing and fuselage, tail and fuselage, etc...With zero airspeed there is no relative motion between the aircraft and the air flow, therefore there is no parasite drag. With an increase in airspeed skin friction, form drag and interference drag all increase. Doubling the airspeed will give four times the parasite drag.

Drag = C_D X ½ρ X V² X S

14. **(Answer: D)** Induced drag has more influence at low speeds (high angles of attack); parasite drag has more influence at high speed.

15. **(Answer: D)** Maintaining a constant angle of attack and increasing airspeed will cause an increase in both lift and drag. Lift and drag are both proportional to the square of speed, at high speed total drag is almost entirely due to parasite drag *(induced drag is virtually nil)*.

Lift = C_L X ½ρ X V² X S

Drag = C_D X ½ρ X V² X S

16. **(Answer: B)** Compared to the free stream flow, in normal flight air pressure under a wing will be higher. *See diagram with question 12.*

17. **(Answer: B)** For an aircraft in straight and level flight to be in equilibrium lift has to equal weight and thrust must equal drag. In this situation the two couples balance out and there is no resultant force acting on the aircraft.

Weight – acts vertically downwards and acts through the centre of gravity.

Lift – is a force which acts upwards at right angles to the relative airflow, it acts through the centre of pressure.

Thrust – is the forward reaction to air being accelerated backwards by a propeller, it acts through the propeller shaft.

Drag – acts to oppose the motion of the aircraft and acts parallel to the relative airflow in the opposite direction to the flight path. Any remaining pitching moment is balanced by the tailplane.

18. **(Answer: D)** Increasing airspeed will cause parasite drag to increase and induced drag to decrease.

Parasite drag – is composed of form drag, interference drag and skin friction, it is proportional to airspeed.

Induced drag – is a by-product of lift and is proportional to angle of attack. It has more influence at low speed when a high angle of attack is required. *See diagram at question 14.*

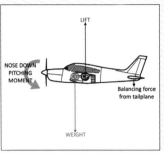

19. **(Answer: A)** In straight and level flight, if the centre of pressure is behind the centre of gravity a nose down couple is produced, requiring the tailplane to produce an aerodynamic downward force.

20. **(Answer: B)** The lateral axis runs from one side of the aeroplane to the other passing through the centre of gravity. Movement about the lateral axis is called pitching.

19. ANSWER A

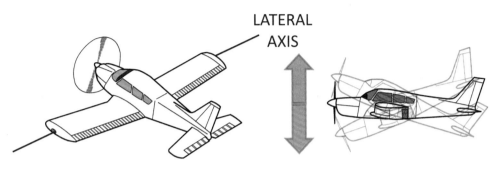

LATERAL AXIS

21. **(Answer: C)** Movement of an aeroplane around its normal axis is called yawing.

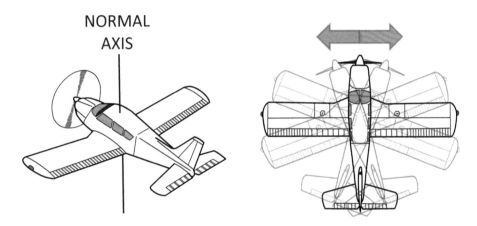

NORMAL AXIS

22. **(Answer: A)** The primary effect of aileron input is to create roll. The secondary effect is yaw, which if uncorrected will lead to a spiral dive. Following the initial roll a sideslip force is introduced which acts on the keel surfaces of the aircraft. This happens because the lift vector is tilted into the turn and now has a horizontal component that is not opposed by any other force, the aircraft will therefore slip in that direction. Since there is a larger keel surface behind the centre of gravity than ahead of it, the aircraft's nose will slew in the direction of the sideslip – this motion is yaw towards the lower wing.

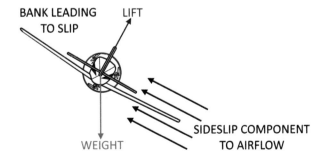

BANK LEADING TO SLIP   LIFT

WEIGHT

SIDESLIP COMPONENT TO AIRFLOW

217

The further effect of yaw is roll, because extra lift is generated from the faster moving outer wing. If not corrected by the pilot his cycle of roll leading to yaw leading to roll will continue and eventually develop into a spiral dive.

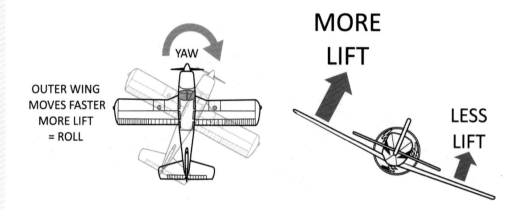

23. **(Answer: C)** The fin. Directional stability refers to an aircraft's natural ability to recover from a disturbance in the yawing plane, that is, movement about the normal axis. Should an aircraft be disturbed from its path a sideways motion is introduced. The fin which is a symmetrical aerofoil is now experiencing an angle of attack and will generate a force to restore the nose to its original position.

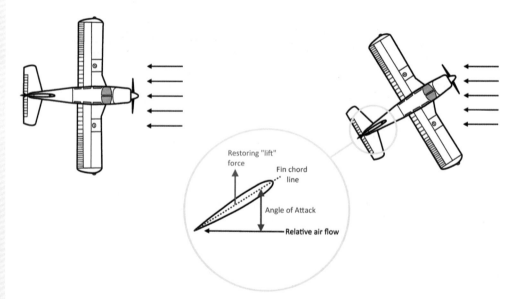

The fin exerts a powerful turning effect as it has a large area and a long moment arm between it and the aircraft's centre of gravity.

24. **(Answer: D)** Differential ailerons are designed to minimise adverse aileron yaw. When an aileron is deflected down the effective camber of that wing is increased, also increasing its angle of attack. The lift generated by this wing increases, sadly so does the induced drag. The reverse happens on the wing with the up-going aileron: the effective camber is decreased as is the effective angle of attack, lift decreases and so does drag.

Lift causes the aircraft to bank in one direction, however the differing drag forces create yaw in the opposite direction.

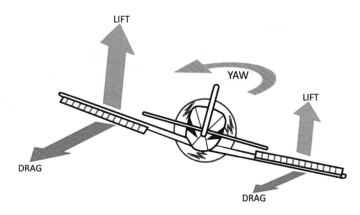

Differential ailerons increase the drag on the down-going wing, by deflecting the up aileron through a greater angle compared to the down aileron on the up-going wing.

**UP-GOING AILERON
HIGH PROFILE DRAG**

**DOWN-GOING AILERON
LOW PROFILE DRAG**

The up aileron generates an increase in profile drag which will tend to yaw the aircraft into the bank. Other methods of reducing adverse aileron yaw are Frise-type aileron (where profile drag is increased on the up-going aileron by projecting its leading edge into the airflow below the wing) or designs coupling the rudder to the ailerons.

FRISE-AILERON

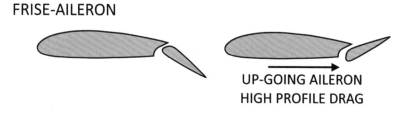

**UP-GOING AILERON
HIGH PROFILE DRAG**

25. **(Answer: A)** The secondary effect of aileron is yaw and the secondary effect of rudder is roll.

Aileron: When aileron is used to roll, the aircraft will adopt a banked attitude, the lift vector now has a horizontal component and the aircraft will tend to side slip towards the lower wing. The side slip causes a relative airflow against the keel surface of the aircraft; there is a larger surface area behind the Centre of Gravity hence the aircraft will turn about its normal axis – yaw. If left uncorrected a spiral dive will develop.

Rudder: As an aircraft yaws the outer wing will move faster and produce more lift than the inner wing giving a tendency to roll towards the inner wing. *See diagram at question 22.*

26. **(Answer: B)** Static stability is a measure of how readily an aircraft tends to return to its original condition when disturbed from a condition of steady flight.

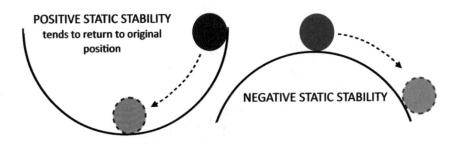

Static stability - refers to the aircraft's initial response to a disturbance.

Dynamic stability - refers to the aircraft's subsequent behaviour after the initial static stability response.

27. **(Answer: C)** Washout is a reduction in the angle of incidence (and consequently the angle of attack) from wing root to wing tip. The angle of incidence is set by the aircraft designer and describes the angle subtended by the wing chord and the aircraft's longitudinal axis.

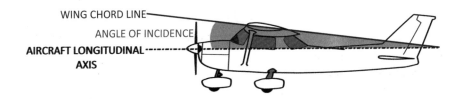

Since a wing will stall at a particular angle of attack washout ensures that any stall will begin at the root. It is undesirable for the wing tip to stall first as any use of aileron when approaching the critical angle could induce yaw and lead to an incipient spin; with the stall starting at the root, controllability, though reduced, can be maintained.

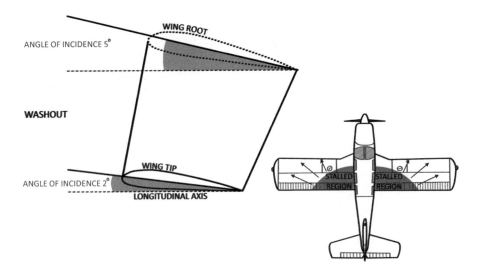

An additional benefit to washout is that there is a lesser pressure difference between the lower and upper surfaces at the tip meaning reduced wing tip vortices and lower induced drag.

28. **(Answer: D)** A fixed trim or balanced tab is a small flexible metal tab affixed to the rear of a control surface. If an aircraft exhibits a consistent fault when flying, for example flying with one wing low, the tab can be bent to alter forces on the control surface. Any adjustments can only be done on the ground and the efficacy of the alteration established by a test flight. Essentially corrections to a fixed tab will involve a series of trial and error adjustments and test flights.

29. **(Answer: B)** Some control surfaces have a tendency to "flutter" when operating in the higher speed range as a result of changes in pressure distribution over the surface with angle of attack changes. Flutter can cause serious oscillations to develop and to prevent it aircraft designers must alter the mass distribution of the surface. A mass balance will achieve this and is placed forward of the hinge line in order to move the centre of gravity of the surface forward.

29. ANSWER B

30. **(Answer: A)** Following a disturbance, an aircraft which returns to its original flight path without the pilot taking any corrective action is said to have positive stability.

Static stability - refers to the aircraft's initial response to a disturbance.

Dynamic stability - refers to the aircraft's subsequent behaviour after the initial static stability response. *Stability may be further classified as follows:*

Positive stability - the aircraft tends to return to original condition after a disturbance.

Negative stability - the aircraft tends to increase the disturbance.

Neutral stability - the aircraft remains at the new condition.

ALL THE AIRCRAFT BELOW POSSESS POSITIVE STATIC STABILITY:
The initial tendency is to return to the original position

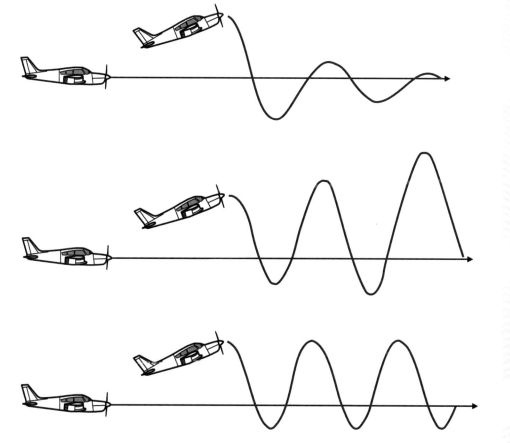

Positive Dynamic Stability

Negative Dynamic Stability

Neutral Dynamic Stability

31. **(Answer: C)** A wing always stalls at a given angle of attack, the critical angle.

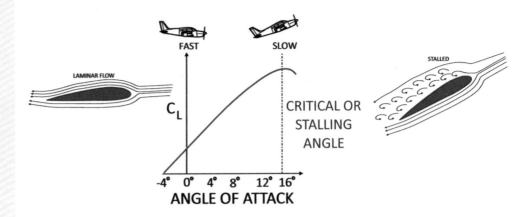

The speed at which the stall will occur varies according to the:
- **Lift produced by the aerofoil** – any manoeuvre that requires extra lift (e.g. turning) will increase the stalling speed.
- **Aircraft's weight** – stalling speed will increase with increase in weight.
- **Load factor** – stall speed increases with load factor
- **Power** – approaching the stall a vertical component of thrust can support some weight, leading to a lower stall speed
- **Bank angle** – increases load factor. In a 60° bank you will experience 2g. The stall speed will increase by $\sqrt{2}$ (which equates to around a 41% increase)
- **Flap selection** – use of flap lowers the stall speed, as the aerofoil will have a higher C_L max

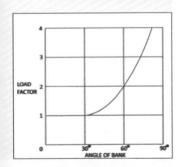

32. ANSWER B

32. **(Answer: B)** At a given constant weight the stall speed of an aircraft is proportional to the square root of the load factor. Any situation that requires more lift to be generated by the wings will increase the load factor and consequently the stalling speed.

Load factor is traditionally referred to as g, because of the relation between load factor and apparent acceleration of gravity felt on board the aircraft. A load factor of one, or 1 g, represents conditions in straight and level flight, where the lift is equal to the weight. Load factors greater or less than one are the result of manoeuvres, turbulence or wind gusts. At 2g the stall speed increases by $\sqrt{2} = 1.41$. Equating to 41% increase in stall speed. At 3g the stall speed increases by $\sqrt{3} = 1.73$. Equating to 73% increase in stall speed.

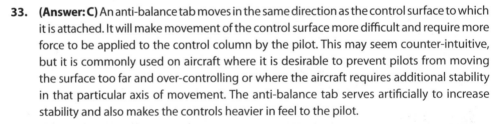

33. **(Answer: C)** An anti-balance tab moves in the same direction as the control surface to which it is attached. It will make movement of the control surface more difficult and require more force to be applied to the control column by the pilot. This may seem counter-intuitive, but it is commonly used on aircraft where it is desirable to prevent pilots from moving the surface too far and over-controlling or where the aircraft requires additional stability in that particular axis of movement. The anti-balance tab serves artificially to increase stability and also makes the controls heavier in feel to the pilot.

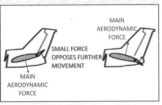

33. ANSWER C

Anti-balance tabs are often fitted to horizontal stabilators where, because of their large area, small control inputs can generate large aerodynamic forces.

34. **(Answer: C)** Following a disturbance from a stable trimmed position, an aircraft with neutral stability will remain in its new attitude.

35. **(Answer: A)** Using small flap settings (up to approximately 20°) during take-off decreases the ground run required. If a large flap setting is used drag will greatly increase and no benefit will be gained; small settings, however, will lower the stalling speed enabling both the lift-off and take-off safety speeds to be reduced. Consequently the aircraft will reach its lift-off speed after a shorter ground roll, meaning that shorter runways can be used or runways with a poor surface can be left behind more quickly!

Though the ground run is reduced due to the increased lift generated by the use of flap, the initial rate and angle of climb will both be reduced due to the increase in drag. Although small flap settings do have a drag penalty, generally speaking it is relatively small. Large flap settings (the last stage) add little lift, but do add a large amount of drag. The use of this setting on take off would reduce acceleration and significantly degrade climb performance; hence their use is restricted to landing.

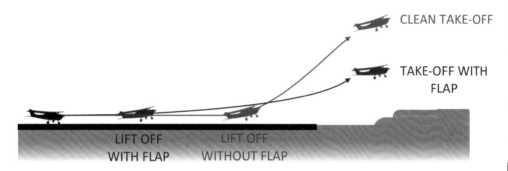

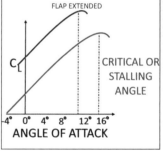

36. ANSWER A

36. **(Answer: A)** When compared to the chord line of a clean aerofoil, extending trailing edge flaps will give a lower stalling angle of attack. Extending flaps increases the camber of the wing aerofoil, thus raising the maximum lift coefficient. This increase in maximum lift coefficient allows the aircraft to generate a given amount of lift with a slower speed. Therefore, extending the flaps reduces the stalling speed of the aircraft, but will lower the critical angle.

37. **(Answer: D)** A leading edge slot is a fixed (non-closing) gap behind the wing's leading edge. Air from the high pressure area below the wing can accelerate through the slot towards the low pressure region above the wing. This high-speed flow mixes with and re-energises the boundary layer attached to the upper surface and delays boundary layer separation from the upper surface. Slots naturally exact a penalty on the aircraft in which they are used because they contribute extra drag compared to an unslotted wing. Hence more sophisticated aircraft will have moveable slats on the leading edge, which may be deployed to create a slot when required.

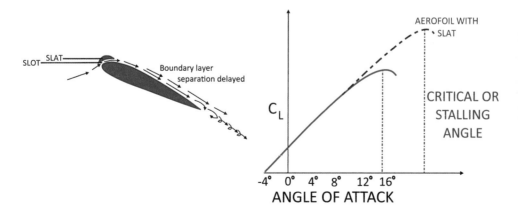

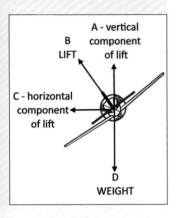

38. ANSWER C

41. ANSWER C

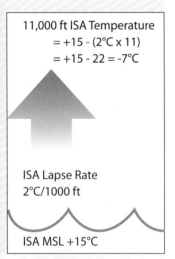

11,000 ft ISA Temperature
= +15 - (2°C x 11)
= +15 - 22 = -7°C

ISA Lapse Rate
2°C/1000 ft

ISA MSL +15°C

46. ANSWER D

38.   **(Answer: C)** Lift is represented by vector B. A represents the vertical component of lift and C the horizontal component of lift in the turn.

39.   **(Answer: B)** Some control surfaces have a tendency to "flutter" when operating in the higher speed range as a result of changes in pressure distribution over the surface with changes in angle of attack. Flutter can cause serious oscillations to develop and to prevent it aircraft designers must alter the mass distribution of the surface. A mass balance will achieve this, and is placed forward of the hinge line in order to move the centre of gravity of the surface forward. *See diagram at question 29.*

40.   **(Answer: D)** In a 60° bank the load factor is 2. At 2g the stall speed increases by √2 which is 1.41. Equating to 41% increase in stall speed.

   Basic stalling speed = 80 knots
   41% of 80 = 80 x $\frac{41}{100}$ = 32.8
   Stalling speed at 60° bank = 80 + 32.8 = 112.8 knots

41.   **(Answer: C)** If the centre of gravity is at or close to its aft limit the aircraft's longitudinal stability is reduced, i.e. it becomes less stable in pitch. With an aft C of G lift generated from the wing will give a nose-up pitching moment, even a slight increase in angle of attack will cause the lift to increase and a greater nose-up pitching moment to be experienced. With an aft C of G it is the aircraft's natural tendency to pitch up meaning that only very slight elevator forces will be required in the flare. The danger here would be to over pitch and stall onto the runway.

42.   **(Answer: C)** Once the trim tab has been set, any subsequent movement of the associatedcontrol surface by the pilot will not affect the trim tab. With respect to the control surface the tab will remain in the same position until the pilot decides to re-trim.

43.   **(Answer: B)** If the centre of gravity is at or close to its forward limit the aircraft's longitudinal stability is increased, i.e. it becomes more stable in pitch. The aircraft will feel extremely noseheavy and resistant to changes in pitch. It is probable that the pilot may not be able to prevent the nose pitching down at low speed, for instance when landing, even with the control column fully aft.

44.   **(Answer: D)** An aircraft wing will stall at a particular angle of attack. The onset of a stall is characterised by a pitch down attitude and the aircraft sinking.

45.   **(Answer: A)** A leading edge slot is a fixed (non-closing) gap behind the wing's leading edge. Air from the high pressure area below the wing can accelerate through the slot towards the low pressure region above the wing. This high-speed flow mixes with and re-energises the boundary layer attached to the upper surface and delays boundary layer separation from the upper surface.

   Slots naturally exact a penalty on the aircraft in which they are used because they contribute extra drag compared to an unslotted wing. Hence more sophisticated aircraft will have moveable slots on the leading edge, which may be deployed to create a slot when required. *See diagram with question 37.*

46.   **(Answer: D)** The temperature at 11,000 feet is -2°C, 5 degrees warmer than the theoretical ISA temperature of -7°C. The atmosphere is ISA +5°C.

47.   **(Answer: A)** Water vapour is lighter than other atmospheric gases, moist air is therefore less dense than dry air. (Molecular masses: N_2 = 28, O_2 = 30, H_2O =17)

48. **(Answer: B)** In a 60° bank the load factor is 2. At 2g the stall speed increases by √2 which is 1.41. Equating to 41% increase in stall speed.

    Basic stalling speed = 60 knots
    41% of 60 = 60 x 41 = 24.6
                     100
    Stalling speed at 60° bank = 60 + 24.6 = 84.6 knots

49. **(Answer: A)** Using small flap settings (up to approximately 20°) during take-off decreases the ground run required. If a large flap setting is used drag will greatly increase and no benefit will be gained; small settings, however, will lower the stalling speed enabling both the lift-off and take-off safety speeds to be reduced. Consequently the aircraft will reach its lift-off speed after a shorter ground roll, meaning that shorter runways can be used or runways with a poor surface can be left behind more quickly!

    Though the ground run is reduced due to the increased lift generated by the flaps, the initial rate and angle of climb will both be reduced due to the increase in drag from the flaps. *See diagram at question 35.*

50. **(Answer: D)** At a given constant weight the stall speed of an aircraft is proportional to the square root of the load factor. Any situation that requires more lift to be generated by the wings, will increase the load factor and consequently the stalling speed.

    Load factor is traditionally referred to as g, because of the relationship between load factor and apparent acceleration of gravity felt on board the aircraft. A load factor of one, or 1 g, represents conditions in straight and level flight, where the lift is equal to the weight. Load factors greater or less than one are the result of manoeuvres, turbulence or wind gusts.

    At 2g the stall speed increases by √2 = 1.41. Equating to 41% increase in stall speed.
    At 3g the stall speed increases by √3 = 1.73. Equating to 73% increase in stall speed.

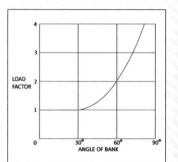

50. ANSWER D

    Factors that increase stall speed summary

    Increased Weight
    Increased Load Factor
    Increased Angle of Bank
    Reduced Power
    Reduced Flap Setting
    Forward Centre of Gravity

END OF EXPLANATIONS PAPER 2

INTENTIONALLY BLANK

AIRCRAFT GENERAL PAPER 3

30 Questions; Time allowed 1 hour

1. The green arc on the airspeed indicator shows the:
   a. Flap operating range
   b. Caution range
   c. V_{NE} range
   d. Normal operating range

2. The yellow arc on the airspeed indicator shows the:
   a. Caution range
   b. Normal operating range
   c. Flap operating range
   d. V_{NE} range

3. For an aircraft in flight the pressure entering the forward facing hole of a pitot tube is:
   a. Dynamic pressure plus pitot pressure
   b. Dynamic pressure
   c. Static pressure
   d. Dynamic pressure and static pressure

4. Dynamic pressure is found in the ASI by:
   a. Subtracting pitot tube pressure from static line pressure
   b. Adding static line pressure and pitot tube pressure
   c. Subtracting total pressure from static line pressure
   d. Subtracting static line pressure from pitot tube pressure

5. During flight you suspect that the static line may be blocked and elect to use the alternate static source. When compared to the main static source, alternate static pressure is:
   a. Higher
   b. Lower
   c. The same
   d. Either higher or lower depending on the ambient pressure

6. With in an altimeter:
   a. As the aircraft climbs the aneroid capsule inside contracts. The movement is transmitted to a pointer via appropriate linkages which moves around the scale of the instrument.
   b. Static line pressure is connected to the aneroid capsule; pitot pressure is connected to the capsule surrounding the capsule.
   c. As the aircraft descends the aneroid capsule inside contracts. The movement is transmitted to a pointer via appropriate linkages which moves around the scale of the instrument.
   d. Pitot pressure is connected to the aneroid capsule; static line pressure is connected to the capsule surrounding the capsule.

7. During descent the static supply to the altimeter and airspeed indicator becomes blocked. The result is that:
   a. Both the altimeter and ASI will over-read
   b. The altimeter will over-read and the ASI under-read
   c. Both the altimeter and ASI will under-read
   d. The altimeter will under-read and the ASI will over-read

8. A Vertical Speed Indicator indicates:

   a. Rate of change of altitude in feet per minute
   b. Rate of change of speed in feet per minute
   c. Rate of change of altitude in knots
   d. Rate of change of speed in knots

9. A Vertical Speed Indicator converts rate of change of ...(i)... to a rate of change of ...(ii)...

   a. i) pitot   ii) altitude
   b. i) pitot   ii) speed
   c. i) static   ii) altitude
   d. i) static   ii) speed

10. Gyroscopes are used in the:

   a. Attitude Indicator, Airspeed Indicator, Turn Coordinator and Direction Indicator
   b. Attitude Indicator, Turn Coordinator and Direction Indicator
   c. Altimeter, Turn Coordinator, and Attitude Indicator
   d. Altimeter, Turn Coordinator and Heading Indicator

11. A gyroscope possesses a property called "rigidity in space". Which of the following best describes the factors controlling the degree of rigidity displayed by a gyroscope?

   a. The speed of rotation and the position of its centre of gravity
   b. The speed of rotation, the rotor mass and the position of its centre of pressure
   c. The speed of rotation, the rotor mass and the position of its centre of gravity
   d. The speed of rotation and the rotor mass

12. The gyroscope in an Artificial Horizon is:

   a. A tied gyro rotating in the vertical plane around the horizontal axis
   b. A space gyro rotating in the vertical plane around the horizontal axis
   c. An earth gyro rotating in the horizontal plane around the vertical axis
   d. A space gyro rotating in the horizontal plane around the vertical axis

13. The Direction Indicator suffers from apparent drift due to:

   a. The spin axis of the gyroscope moving
   b. Errors within the instrument
   c. Changes in the rotor RPM
   d. The rotation of the earth

14. The Direction Indicator should be aligned with the magnetic compass every 10 to 15 minutes when:

   a. The aircraft is in unaccelerated straight and level flight
   b. The aircraft is in a level coordinated turn
   c. The aircraft is in a steady, coordinated descent
   d. The aircraft is in a balanced climb

15. A compass deviation card is necessary to show:

   a. The correction to be applied to the compass reading to obtain compass heading
   b. The correction to be applied to the compass reading to obtain magnetic heading
   c. The correction to be applied to the magnetic heading to obtain true heading
   d. The correction to be applied to the compass reading to obtain true heading

AIRFRAME

16. A monocoque structure is one where:

    a. There is an internal structure but stresses are mostly carried by the skin

    b. There is no internal structure and stresses are carried by the skin

    c. There is no internal structure and stresses are carried by formers

    d. There is an internal structure and stresses are carried by formers

17. A semi-monocoque structure is one where:

    a. There is a heavy duty framework covered with an aluminium skin

    b. There is a light framework covered by an aluminium skin

    c. There is a heavy duty framework covered with a doped fabric skin

    d. There is a light framework covered with a doped fabric skin

18. Identify the component parts of a wing structure indicated:

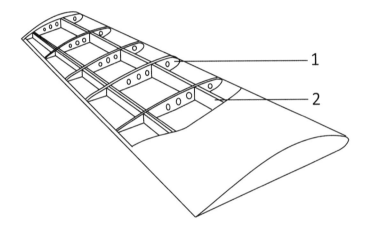

    a. 1. Former   2. Main Spar

    b. 1. Rib   2. Primary Spar

    c. 1. Rib   2. Main Spar

    d. 1. Former   2. Stringer

19. Flying control locks are used:

    a. On the ground to ensure that the control surfaces are not damaged in high winds

    b. In the air in the event of the failure of rigging to a control surface

    c. On the ground to ensure that the trim tabs are not damaged in high winds

    d. In the air to ease the pilot's workload

20. Wing spars carry the major loads experienced by the wing. Where lift is generated these are ...(i)... bending loads, where the fuselage and fuel tanks are supported they are ...(ii)... bending loads.

    a. i) downward   ii) downward

    b. i) downward   ii) upward

    c. i) upward   ii) downward

    d. i) upward   ii) upward

21. A pilot can identify tyre creep using:

    a. Two opposing arrows painted on the side wall of the tyre

    b. Two alignment marks, one painted on the tyre side wall and one on the wheel flange

    c. Two opposing arrows painted on the wheel flange

    d. A pressure check together with checking the condition of the inflation valve

22. During the pre-flight check of the landing gear some of the items a pilot should check are:

    a. Tyre creep, tyre inflation and matching tread patterns

    b. Tyre creep, tyre inflation and wheel balancing

    c. Tyre creep, tyre inflation, tyre colour and size

    d. Tyre creep, tyre inflation, flat spots caused by skidding and the condition of the side wall

23. On light aircraft nose wheel steering is usually achieved by:

    a. Using differential braking

    b. An electro-mechanical linkage

    c. Push-pull rods operated by cables attached to the rudder pedals

    d. Push-pull rods operated by cables attached to the control column

GENERAL FLIGHT SAFETY

24. A BCF fire extinguisher

    a. Is only suitable for brake fires

    b. Is suitable for fabric fires and not really suitable for use in an aircraft cockpit

    c. Gives off highly toxic fumes when discharged and must never be used in an enclosed cockpit

    d. Is safe to use in an enclosed cockpit provided that the cockpit is subsequently ventilated

25. The safest extinguisher to use on a wheel (brake) fire is:

    a. Dry powder

    b. Water

    c. Carbon dioxide

    d. Hydrogen

26. Unless the flight manual gives specific contrary instructions, generically speaking in the event of a fire in the engine bay during flight, the immediate actions to take would be to:

    a. Open the throttle and put the aircraft into a fast dive

    b. Close the throttle, switch off the ignition and open the cabin heat control

    c. Close the throttle, turn off the fuel and close the cabin heat and demister controls

    d. Use the hand held fire extinguisher to attempt to put out the fire

27. A defect in the aircraft exhaust system may allow carbon monoxide to enter the aircraft cabin. Carbon monoxide:

    a. Has a bluish colour and can be detected visually

    b. Is harmless

    c. Smells strongly of marzipan and therefore can be easily detected

    d. Is colourless and odourless

28. When flying over large bodies of water it is recommended that life jackets:

    a. Should be within easy reach

    b. Should be worn un-inflated

    c. Should be worn inflated

    d. Are not necessary unless flying more than 300 nm from the coast

29. During refuelling the aircraft and the refuelling station must be "bonded" using an earth wire. This is so that:

  a. It is obvious which aircraft is being refuelled

  b. The aircraft and the refuelling station have the same electrical potential

  c. The aircraft and the refuelling station have a different electrical potential

  d. The circuit is made and the counter can register how much fuel is drawn by that aircraft

30. Why should the cabin heat control be set to "off" or "closed" before engine start?

  a. There is no point selecting heat, as this will not function until the engine has warmed up

  b. To ensure all available airflow enters the engine induction to aid starting

  c. The statement is false and the position of the cabin heat control is not specified

  d. The system opens a way through the fire wall, it is closed in case of an engine fire on start.

END OF AIRCRAFT GENERAL PAPER 3

AIRCRAFT GENERAL PAPER 3: ANSWERS

	A	B	C	D
1.				X
2.	X			
3.				X
4.				X
5.		X		
6.			X	
7.	X			
8.	X			
9.			X	
10.		X		
11.			X	
12.			X	
13.				X
14.	X			
15		X		
16.		X		
17.		X		
18.			X	
19.	X			
20.			X	
21.		X		
22.				X
23.			X	
24.				X
25.	X			
26.			X	
27.				X
28.		X		
29.		X		
30.				X

CORRECT ANSWERS: PERCENTAGES							
23	24	25	26	27	28	29	30
76%	80%	83%	86%	90%	93%	96%	100%

1. **(Answer: D)** The green arc on the ASI denotes the normal operating range. It extends from the stall speed at maximum all up weight with gear and flap retracted V_{SI} to V_{NO}, the maximum structural cruising speed, a speed which should not be exceeded except in smooth air. At all speeds within the green arc it will be safe to operate in any conditions.

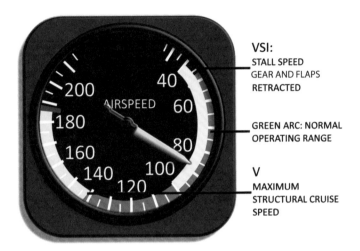

VSI:
STALL SPEED
GEAR AND FLAPS
RETRACTED

GREEN ARC: NORMAL
OPERATING RANGE

V
MAXIMUM
STRUCTURAL CRUISE
SPEED

2. **(Answer: A)** The yellow arc on the ASI denotes the caution range. It extends from V_{NO}, the normal operating limit speed, to V_{NE} the never exceed speed. Operations within the yellow caution range should only be undertaken in smooth air.

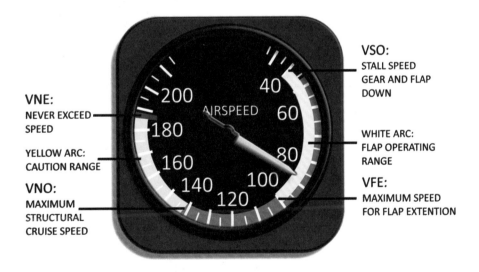

VNE:
NEVER EXCEED
SPEED

YELLOW ARC:
CAUTION RANGE

VNO:
MAXIMUM
STRUCTURAL
CRUISE SPEED

VSO:
STALL SPEED
GEAR AND FLAP
DOWN

WHITE ARC:
FLAP OPERATING
RANGE

VFE:
MAXIMUM SPEED
FOR FLAP EXTENTION

V –SPEEDS:

V_{SO} – stalling speed, gear down, flaps lowered, power off

V_{SI} – stalling speed, gear up, flaps up, power off

V_{FE} – maximum speed for extending flap

V_{NO} – maximum structural cruise speed

V_{NE} – never exceed speed

3.   **(Answer: D)** The pitot tube measures total (or pitot) pressure, that is both dynamic pressure and static pressure. Dynamic pressure is the result of forward motion, but static pressure is omnipresent.

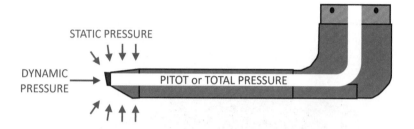

4.   **(Answer: D)** Dynamic pressure is found in the ASI by subtracting static line pressure from pitot pressure. This is achieved by feeding total pressure, the pressure measurement from the pitot, into an expandable diaphragm and static line pressure into the capsule around the diaphragm.

PITOT PRESSURE (dynamic + static) – STATIC PRESSURE = DYNAMIC PRESSURE

As airspeed rises, the dynamic pressure increases, however static pressure remains unchanged. The diaphragm expands with the rise in dynamic pressure and through a series of gears a pointer is positioned to represent the increase in airspeed.

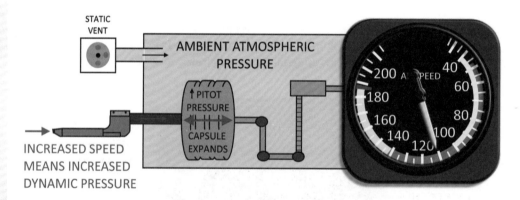

5.   **(Answer: B)** The alternate static source is taken from within the cabin, this pressure is usually slightly lower than external atmospheric pressure. Using alternate static will mean that the instrument readings will not be as accurate.

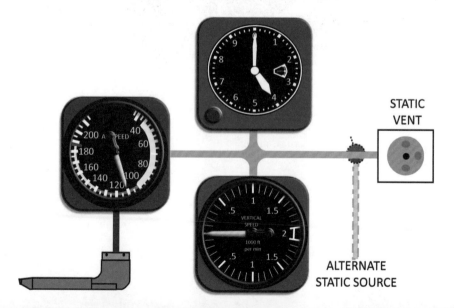

6. **(Answer: C)** As the aircraft descends the aneroid capsule inside the altimeter contracts, pushed inwards by rising ambient pressure around it. The movement is transmitted to a pointer via appropriate linkages which move needles around the scale of the instrument.

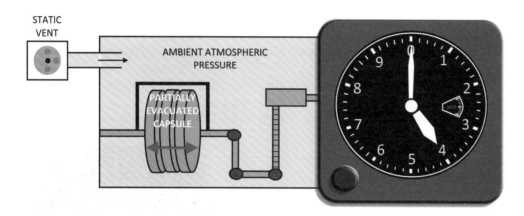

7. **(Answer: A)** During descent the static supply to the altimeter and airspeed indicator becomes blocked. The result is that both the altimeter and ASI will over-read.

Altimeter: will continue to measure the static pressure trapped in the line and so will indicate the level at which the blockage occurred. Thus in a descent it will over-read.

ASI: A blocked static vent would cause the ASI to over-read. The static pressure trapped in the line will be lower than the actual pressure as the aircraft descends. The measured difference between the pitot pressure and the static pressure will be more than actual; hence the ASI will indicate a higher airspeed than is really being achieved.

For the sake of completeness, the VSI will indicate zero should a blockage of the static supply occur during level flight.

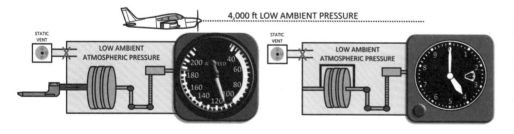

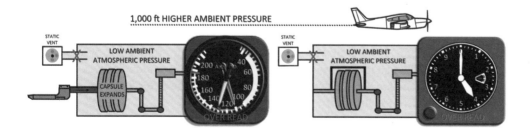

8.   **(Answer: A)** A Vertical Speed Indicator (VSI) indicates rate of change of altitude in feet per minute. Within the VSI is a capsule into which static pressure is fed. Static pressure also enters the instrument casing surrounding the capsule; the difference is that this static source is routed through a restriction so that it is delayed on entering the casing.

In level flight the pressures within and outside the capsule will be equal, there is no pressure differential and the VSI will indicate zero. When a climb is commenced the static pressure inside the capsule will start to fall immediately, however the static pressure outside the capsule is metered and will not change as rapidly. Consequently the capsule will contract slightly as the pressure is now higher outside the capsule than inside. The capsule movement is translated via linkages in the instrument to show a rate of climb.

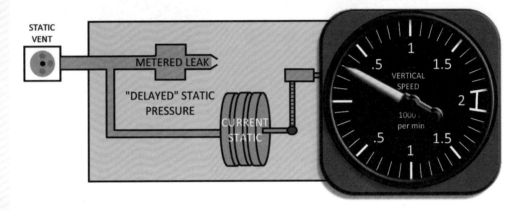

9.   **(Answer: C)** A Vertical Speed Indicator converts rate of change of static pressure to a rate of change of altitude.

10. **(Answer: B)** Gyroscopes are used in the Attitude Indicator, Turn Coordinator and Direction Indicator.

11. **(Answer: C)** A gyroscope is a rotating wheel mounted on gimbals so that it is able to turn freely in one or more directions as required. A rotating mass is able to maintain the same absolute direction in space independent of what is going on around it. This property is called "rigidity in space". In other words the gyroscope remains stable as the aircraft moves around it.

The degree of rigidity depends upon:
- The rotor mass
- The speed of rotation and
- The radius at which the mass is concentrated (its centre of gravity)

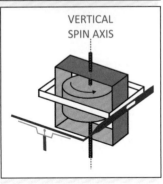

VERTICAL
SPIN AXIS

12. ANSWER C

12. **(Answer: C)** The gyroscope in an Artificial Horizon is an earth gyro rotating in the horizontal plane around the vertical axis. The attitude indicator displays a miniature aircraft and horizon bar, providing the pilot with a picture representing the attitude of the aircraft. The instrument gives an instantaneous indication of changes in attitude. Attitude indicators use a gyroscope (powered either by a vacuum pump or an electrical motor) to establish an inertial reference platform.

The gyro in the attitude indicator is mounted in a horizontal plane and depends upon rigidity in space for its operation. The instrument's horizon bar is fixed to the gyro and represents the true horizon, it remains in an earth horizontal plane as the aircraft is pitched or banked about its lateral or longitudinal axis. In other words, the aircraft actually rotates around the spinning gyro.

13. **(Answer: D)** Apparent wander is caused by the rotation of the earth. The gyroscope is aligned with a point in space, not a point on the earth. As the earth rotates the gyro will continue to point at its original reference point. From the pilot's point of view the DI appears to change heading even though a constant direction is maintained.

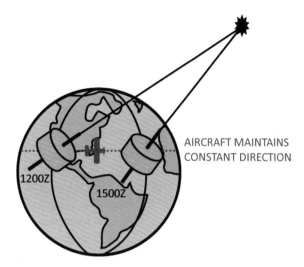

AIRCRAFT MAINTAINS CONSTANT DIRECTION

1200Z

1500Z

Real wander is caused by mechanical imperfections with the instrument; for example worn bearings, friction, or the gyroscope not being in perfect balance.

14. **(Answer: A)** The DI should be periodically checked against the magnetic compass. This should be done when the compass is not experiencing any errors; compass errors will be caused when turning or changing speed. Therefore the DI should be adjusted when the aircraft is in unaccelerated straight and level flight. *(See Aircraft General Paper 4, Question 9, for more on compass errors. Pages 252 and 253)*

15. **(Answer: B)** A compass will be affected not only by the earth's magnetic field, but also any other magnetic field, such as may be generated by radios, engines etc..

The combined effect of these magnetic fields is called deviation; it is a measure of how much the compass is made to deviate from magnetic north. Each aircraft will have a deviation card which will show the correction that needs to be applied to a compass reading to obtain the magnetic heading.

AIRFRAME

---

16. **(Answer: B)** A monocoque structure is one where there is no internal structure and stresses are carried by the skin. The classic example of a monocoque structure is an egg.

17. **(Answer: B)** A semi-monocoque structure is one where there is a light framework covered by an aluminium skin that carries most of the stress.

18. **(Answer: C)** The parts are: 1. Rib 2. Main Spar

19. **(Answer: A)** Flying control locks are used on the ground to ensure that the control surfaces are not damaged in high winds.

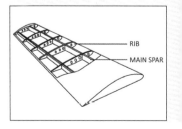

RIB

MAIN SPAR

18. ANSWER C

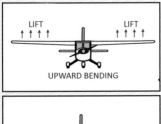

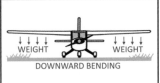

20. ANSWER C

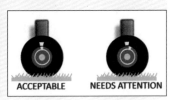

21. ANSWER B

20. (Answer: C) Wing spars carry the major loads experienced by the wing. Upward bending loads are experienced where lift is generated to support the aircraft in flight. These forces are often offset by carrying fuel in the wings or employing wing-tip mounted fuel tanks. Downward bending loads are experienced whilst stationary on the ground due to the weight of the structure, fuel carried in the wings, and possibly wing-mounted engines.

21. (Answer: B) A pilot can identify tyre creep using the two alignment, or "creep" marks, one of which is painted on the tyre side wall and one on the wheel flange. The marks need to be aligned for the tyre to be considered serviceable, if they have moved more than the width of the mark attention is necessary.

22. (Answer: D) During the pre-flight check of the landing gear some of the items a pilot should check are tyre creep, tyre inflation, flat spots caused by skidding and the condition of the side wall.

Flat spots could be due to skidding and are not acceptable as the tyre will be out of balance; the result would be severe vibration during high speed taxi. Additionally the tread around a flat spot could be thin leaving the tyre susceptible to puncturing.

23. (Answer: C) In light aircraft nose wheel steering is usually achieved by push-pull rods operated by cables attached to the rudder pedals

GENERAL FLIGHT SAFETY

24. (Answer: D) BCF extinguishers are suitable for use on all types of fire and so are commonly carried in light aircraft. The extinguishing agent is Halon. If it is necessary to use a BCF extinguisher in the cockpit all vents and windows should be closed before use, once the fire is out all windows and vents should be opened to clear the fumes.

25. (Answer: A) The safest extinguisher to use on a wheel (brake) fire is one containing dry powder. Their use is recommended for fires involving flammable liquids, gases and electrics.

26. (Answer: C) Generically speaking, in the event of a fire in the engine bay during flight, the immediate actions to take would be to close the throttle and turn off the fuel, this will mean the engine will run dry and stop. With no fuel in the engine or induction systems the fire should extinguish. Normally the ignition would now be switched off and preparation for a forced landing commenced. Throughout the procedure close the cabin heat and demister controls to prevent any noxious fumes entering the cabin. Note: your specific aircraft flight manual should be referred to for type-specific procedures.

27. (Answer: D) Carbon monoxide is a colourless, odourless and very dangerous gas. It will combine with haemoglobin in the blood more readily than oxygen and cause headache, dizziness, nausea, deterioration in vision, unconsciousness and eventually death. Defects in the exhaust system and/or heat exchanger may lead to carbon monoxide entering the cabin. Other engine exhaust gases do have an odour and may indicate that they, as well as deadly carbon monoxide, are entering the cockpit. Should this happen shut off all cabin heating and increase the supply of fresh air to the cabin by opening all vents and windows.

28. **(Answer: B)** When flying over large bodies of water it is recommended that life jackets are worn un-inflated. The advice held in a CAA General Aviation Safety Sense leaflet recommends that when flying beyond gliding distance of land life jackets should be worn by all occupants.

29. **(Answer: B)** During refuelling the aircraft and the refuelling station must be "bonded" using an earth wire. This so that the aircraft and the refuelling station have the same electrical potential, preventing the production of a spark which could ignite the fuel vapour.

30. **(Answer: D)** The cabin heat control should be set to "off" or "closed" before engine start because the system opens a way through the fire wall, it is closed in case of an engine fire during the start procedure. Not closing the cabin heat control could lead to poisonous fumes entering the cockpit should a fire occur during start up.

END OF EXPLANATIONS PAPER 3

INTENTIONALLY BLANK

30 Questions; Time allowed 1 hour

SYSTEMS

1. If a fuse blows during flight:

    a. It may be replaced in the air as many times as necessary by one of the same value

    b. It may only be replaced after landing

    c. It may be replaced in the air only once by one of the same value

    d. It may be replaced in the air only once by one of a higher value

2. You are flying a single engine aircraft. Your actions in the event of a generator or alternator failure during flight should be:

    a. To switch off the master switch and continue the flight as normal, but without electrical power

    b. Continue the flight normally as the battery will supply all the electrical needs

    c. To reduce the electrical load and continue the flight normally

    d. To reduce the electrical load and land as soon as practicable

3. In theory a 100 amp/hr battery will be able to supply 25 amps for:

    a. 25 minutes

    b. 100 minutes

    c. 4 hours

    d. 25 hours

4. In theory a 100 amp/hr battery will be able to supply 10 amps for:

    a. 10 minutes

    b. 100 minutes

    c. 5 hours

    d. 10 hours

5. For how long will a 15 amp/hr battery supply 5 amps for?

    a. 15 hours

    b. 5 hours

    c. 15 minutes

    d. 3 hours

6. Two 12 volt 50 amp/hr connected in parallel is equal to a:

    a. 12 volt battery supplying 100 amp/hrs

    b. 24 volt battery supplying 100 amp/hrs

    c. 12 volt battery supplying 50 amp/hours

    d. 24 volt battery supplying 50 amp/hours

7. Two 12 volt 50 amp/hr connected in series is equal to a:

    a. 12 volt battery supplying 100 amp/hrs

    b. 24 volt battery supplying 100 amp/hrs

    c. 12 volt battery supplying 50 amp/hours

    d. 24 volt battery supplying 50 amp/hours

8. During a flight you notice the suction gauge indicating zero. You continue to observe the air driven gyro instruments and after several minutes they still appear to be operating normally. What has happened?

   a.   The vacuum pump has failed
   b.   The suction gauge has failed
   c.   A blockage has occurred in the air filter
   d.   The vacuum warning light has failed to illuminate

9. A lower than normal suction gauge reading may mean:

   a.   That the suction gauge has failed
   b.   That the air filter is blocked
   c.   That the vacuum pump has failed
   d.   That the vacuum pressure is too high

10. The aircraft vacuum system produces:

   a.   A low speed airflow which is directed into the instrument casing of the gyro instruments
   b.   A high speed airflow, which is directed first to a turbine which, in turn, powers the gyros
   c.   A high speed airflow, which is directed onto the gyro rotors to make them spin
   d.   A low speed airflow, which is directed onto the gyro rotors to make them spin

11. The diagram above represents the electrical system associated with a Centre-Zero ammeter. The needle position depicted means that:

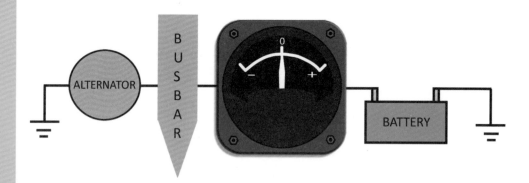

   a.   The battery is fully charged
   b.   Current is flowing into the battery
   c.   Current is flowing out of the battery
   d.   The alternator has failed

12. Refer to the diagram below representing a light aircraft electrical system using a Centre-Zero ammeter. During flight with the battery and alternator switches ON and with the battery fully charged, the ammeter should indicate:

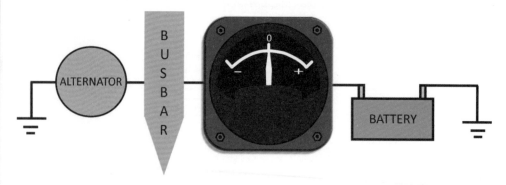

a.   To the right, showing a positive reading

b.   Positioned to the centre-zero

c.   To the right, showing a discharge from the battery

d.   To the left, showing a negative reading

13.   Refer to the diagram below representing a light aircraft electrical system using a Left-Zero ammeter. The most likely cause of the indication above is:

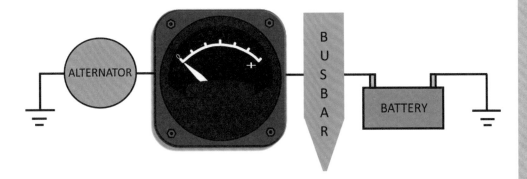

a.   The battery is being charged

b.   The battery is fully charged

c.   The battery is flat

d.   The alternator has failed

14.   When starting the engine all unnecessary electrical equipment and radios should be:

a.   Switched on

b.   Switched off

c.   On or off, it does not matter

d.   Radios should be off, but navigation equipment should be on.

15.   The current flow through the starter switch in the "start" position is .... the current flow through the starter circuit that connects the battery to the starter motor.

a.   The same as

b.   Far lower than

c.   Far higher than

d.   Twice as much as

INSTRUMENTS

16.   The white arc on the airspeed indicator shows the:

a.   Caution range

b.   Normal operating range

c.   Flap operating range

d. V_{NE} range

17. V_{NE} is the:

a.   Stalling speed gear down, flaps lowered and power off

b.   Stalling speed gear up, flaps up and power off

c.   Maximum structural cruise speed

d.   Never exceed speed

18. A Vertical Speed Indicator works by measuring:

    a. The difference between static and dynamic pressure

    b. The rate of change in the difference between static and dynamic pressure

    c. The time between particular levels in a climb or descent

    d. Rate of change of static pressure

19. With regard to a magnetic compass, which of the following statements are true?

    1. A magnetic compass does not suffer from turning or acceleration errors

    2. The fluid within the compass supports the weight of the magnet, decreases friction and dampens oscillations

    3. The aeroplane moves around the compass magnet

    4. When deviation is applied to the compass heading we get the magnetic heading

    5. When variation is applied to the compass heading we get the magnetic heading

    The correct statements are:

    a. 2, 3 and 5

    b. 1, 2 and 4

    c. 2, 3 and 4

    d. 1, 4 and 5

20. Referring to the picture of an ASI below identify X, Y and Z:

    a. X is V_{SO}, Y is V_{NE} and Z is V_{NO}

    b. X is V_{SO}, Y is V_{NO} and Z is V_{NE}

    c. X is V_{SI}, Y is V_{FE} and Z is V_{NE}

    d. X is V_{SI}, Y is V_{NE} and Z is V_{FE}

21. The function of the caging and setting knob on a Direction Indicator is to:

    a. Re-align the heading indicator with the magnetic compass

    b. Re-set the heading indicator to magnetic north

    c. Re-set the heading indication to that on the flight plan

    d. Re-align the magnetic compass with the heading indicator

22. During climb the static supply to the altimeter and airspeed indicator becomes blocked. The result is that:

    a. Both the altimeter and ASI will over-read

    b. The altimeter will over-read and the ASI under-read

    c. Both the altimeter and ASI will under-read

    d. The altimeter will under-read and the ASI will over-read

---

AIRFRAME

---

23. One possible cause of "nose wheel shimmy" is:

    a. Incorrect tyre pressures

    b. Incorrect oleo pressures

    c. Excessive tyre creep

    d. The failure of the torque link

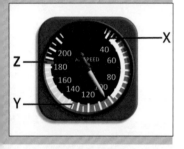

20. IDENTIFY X, Y & Z

24. Load factors for an aircraft in the aerobatic category compared to one certified in the normal or utility category will be:

    a.   Lower

    b.   Higher than normal, but less than utility

    c.   Higher

    d.   Higher than utility, but less than normal

25. On the ground the weight of an aircraft is balanced by the reaction force of the ground on the aircraft which acts:

    a.   Upwards through the tailplane

    b.   Upwards through the wheels

    c.   Downwards through the wheels

    d.   Parallel to the ground through the engine and propeller

26. During a pre-flight inspection of the brakes one important item to check is:

    a.   That the discs are pitted

    b.   The brake assembly is nice and loose

    c.   That the brake discs are not corroded

    d.   There is no need to inspect the brake assembly, it is done during the 50 hour check

PRINCIPLES OF FLIGHT

27. By volume the ratio of oxygen to nitrogen in the air is:

    a.   1:3

    b.   1:4

    c.   3:1

    d.   4:1

28. The major constituents of the atmosphere are:

    a.   Nitrogen, Oxygen and Carbon Dioxide

    b.   Nitrogen, Oxygen and Hydrogen

    c.   Nitrogen, Oxygen and Water vapour

    d.   Nitrogen, Oxygen and Argon

29. Movement about the longitudinal axis is called:

    a.   Rolling

    b.   Yawing

    c.   Pitching

    d.   Spinning

30. A wing stalls at:

    a.   A given speed

    b.   A given angle of incidence

    c.   A given angle of attack

    d.   A given weight

END OF AIRCRAFT GENERAL PAPER 4

	A	B	C	D
1.			X	
2.				X
3.			X	
4.				X
5.				X
6.	X			
7.				X
8.		X		
9.		X		
10.			X	
11.	X			
12.		X		
13.				X
14.		X		
15		X		
16.			X	
17.				X
18.				X
19.			X	
20.		X		
21.	X			
22.			X	
23.				X
24.			X	
25.		X		
26.			X	
27.		X		
28.			X	
29.	X			
30.			X	

CORRECT ANSWERS: PERCENTAGES							
23	24	25	26	27	28	29	30
76%	80%	83%	86%	90%	93%	96%	100%

SYSTEMS

1. **(Answer: C)** If a fuse blows during flight It may be replaced in the air only once by one of the same value. A fuse should not be replaced more than once, as should it blow a second time, it is probably an indication of an electrical problem. The correct amperage must be used; replacing a fuse with one of a higher rating may allow excessive current to flow through the circuit concerned which could lead to a fire hazard. Similarly should a circuit breaker "pop" during flight it should only be reset once.

    In both cases wait a couple of minutes for the circuit to cool and check for any indication of burning or smoke before replacing the fuse or resetting the circuit breaker.

2. **(Answer: D)** In the event of a generator or alternator failure during flight, reduce the electrical load to a minimum and land as soon as practicable. Most aircraft batteries cannot supply all electrical services for an extended time, hence the need to reduce the demand on the battery.

    Thought should be given to landing as soon as it is safe to do so.

3. **(Answer: C)** A battery rated as 100 amp/hr is, in theory, capable of supplying 1 amp for 100 hours; or 25 amps for 4 hours.

    $$\frac{100 \text{ amp}}{1 \text{ amp}} \times \frac{1 \text{ hour}}{25 \text{ amp}} = \frac{100 \text{ amp}}{1 \text{ amp}} \times \frac{1 \text{ hour}}{25 \text{ amp}} = 4 \text{ hours}$$

4. **(Answer: D)** A battery rated as 100 amp/hr is, in theory, capable of supplying 1 amp for 100 hours; or 10 amps for 10 hours.

    $$\frac{100 \text{ amp}}{1 \text{ amp}} \times \frac{1 \text{ hour}}{10 \text{ amp}} = \frac{100 \text{ amp}}{1 \text{ amp}} \times \frac{1 \text{ hour}}{10 \text{ amp}} = 10 \text{ hours}$$

5. **(Answer: D)** A battery rated as 15 amp/hr is, in theory, capable of supplying 1 amp for 15 hours; or 5 amps for 3 hours.

    $$\frac{15 \text{ amp}}{1 \text{ amp}} \times \frac{1 \text{ hour}}{5 \text{ amp}} = \frac{15 \text{ amp}}{1 \text{ amp}} \times \frac{1 \text{ hour}}{5 \text{ amp}} = 3 \text{ hours}$$

6. **(Answer: A)** Connecting two 12 volt 50 amp/hr batteries in parallel will be the equivalent of having a single battery able to produce 12 volts for 100 amp/hours.

    When connected in parallel the voltage output is the average of the two individual battery voltages. Here we have two 12 volt batteries, hence $12 + 12 \div 2 = 12$ Volts.

    The capacity of two batteries connected in parallel is the sum of the two capacities; here we have $50 + 50 = 100$ amp/hr.

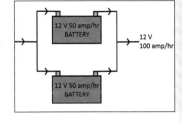

6. ANSWER A

7. **(Answer: D)** Connecting two 12 volt 50 amp/hr batteries in series will be the equivalent of having a single battery able to produce 24 volts for 50 amp/hours. When connected in series the voltage output is the sum of the two individual battery voltages. Here we have two 12 volt batteries, hence $12 + 12 = 24$ Volts.

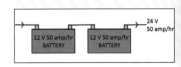

7. ANSWER D

    The capacity of two batteries connected in series is the average of the two individual capacities; here we have $50 + 50 \div 2 = 50$ amp/hr.

8.   **(Answer: B)** The scenario we are presented with is that during a flight you notice the suction gauge indicating zero and that after continuing to observe the air driven gyro instruments for several minutes they still appear to be operating normally. As the instruments are continuing to work as expected it is likely that the suction gauge itself has failed. If it were a failure of the vacuum pump, the suction gauge would indicate zero and after a couple of minutes the gyros will start to run down and the instrument indications will become erroneous.

A blocked air filter would be suspected if the suction gauge was indicating lower than normal. The airflow will be reduced by the blockage meaning the gyroscopes will gradually run slow, and the air operated instruments will start to respond slowly or to indicate wrongly or erratically. Excessive vacuum pressure may cause the gyros to spin too fast and may lead to damage.

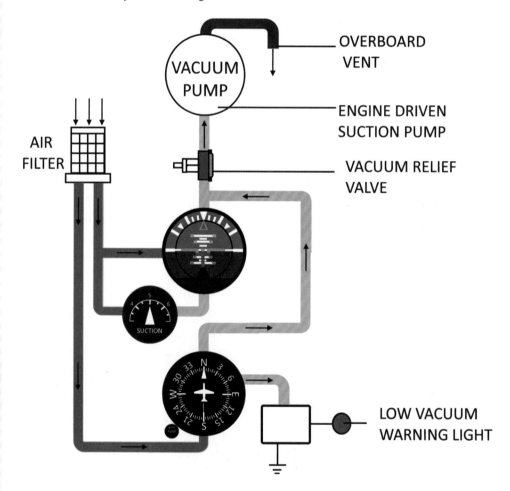

9.   **(Answer: B)** A lower than normal suction gauge reading may mean that the air filter is blocked. The reduced airflow will mean that the gyroscopes will gradually run down and the associated instruments will respond slowly or erratically.

For most light aircraft the required suction is between 3 and 5 inches of mercury (less than atmospheric pressure) this is the normal operating range. Had the vacuum pump failed the suction gauge would indicate zero.

10. **(Answer: C)** The aircraft vacuum system produces a high speed airflow, which is directed onto the gyro rotors to make them spin very fast. The filtered air is directed at high speed through anozzle directed at the gyro buckets making the gyro spin at somewhere in the region of 20,000 RPM.

11. **(Answer: A)** A Centre-Zero ammeter measures current flow to and from the battery.

    With a Centre-Zero ammeter an indication of zero current flow means that current is neither flowing into nor being drawn from the battery.

CHARGE: CURRENT FLOWING INTO BATTERY
With the alternator ON and supplying electrical charge any surplus over the present electrical load is used to charge the battery (if required).

DISCHARGE: CURRENT FLOWING OUT OF BATTERY
With the battery ON, but no output from the alternator. Or the alternator on but incapable of supplying electrical power; in this situation there is danger of flattening the battery.

12. **(Answer: B)** A Centre-Zero ammeter measures current flow to and from the battery. During flight with the battery and alternator switches ON and with the battery fully charged, the ammeter should indicate zero. This means that the alternator is supplying enough power for the present demands and current is not being drawn from the battery. We are told that the battery is fully charged, therefore there will be no current flow into the battery either.

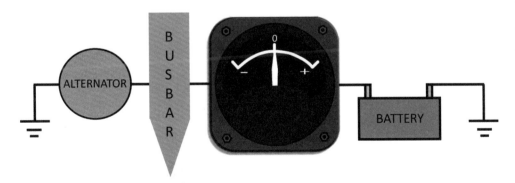

13. **(Answer: D)** A left-centre ammeter measures alternator output. A reading dropping to zero during flight most probably means the alternator has failed.

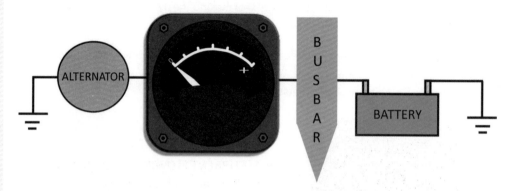

14. **(Answer: B)** When starting the engine all unnecessary electrical equipment and radios should be switched off. Large voltage fluctuations can be experienced when the starter is engaged and may damage sensitive electronic circuits. Similarly the equipment should be switched off again before the engine is shut down.

15. **(Answer: B)** The current flow through the starter switch in the "start" position is far lower than the current flow through the starter circuit that connects the battery to the starter motor. Most light aircraft systems use a low amperage current operated by the starter switch to close a remote relay (solenoid) and complete the much higher amperage circuit between the battery and the starter motor. This arrangement avoids the need to have heavy wiring and high currents running to the switches in the cockpit.

INSTRUMENTS

---

16. **(Answer: C)** The white arc on the airspeed indicator shows the flap operating range.

17. **(Answer: D)** V_{NE} is the never exceed speed.

18. **(Answer: D)** A Vertical Speed Indicator works by measuring the rate of change of static pressure. Within the VSI is a capsule into which static pressure is fed. Static pressure also enters the instrument casing surrounding the capsule; the difference is that this static source is routed through restriction so that it is delayed on entering the casing.

In level flight the pressures within and outside the capsule will be equal, there is no pressure differential and the VSI will indicate zero. When a climb is commenced the static pressure inside the capsule will start to fall immediately. However, the static pressure outside the capsule is metered and will not change as rapidly. Consequently the capsule will contract slightly as the pressure is now higher outside the capsule than inside. The capsule movement is translated via linkages in the instrument to show a rate of climb.

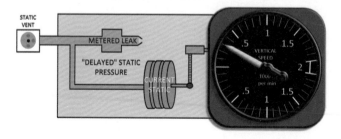

19. (Answer: C) With regard to a magnetic compass, the correct statements are 2, 3 and 4.

   1.   A magnetic compass does not suffer from turning or acceleration errors
   2.   The fluid within the compass supports the weight of the magnet, decreases friction and dampens oscillations
   3.   The aeroplane moves around the compass magnet
   4.   When deviation is applied to the compass heading we get the magnetic heading
   5.   When variation is applied to the compass heading we get the magnetic heading

   1.   The compass suffers from both turning and acceleration errors as a result of magnetic dip leading to the weight of the magnet not being directly underneath the pivot. Magnetic dip is due to the magnet trying to align itself with the earth's magnetic field which is practically horizontal at the equator, but almost vertical at the poles. Arranging the magnet as a pendulum does alleviate some of the problem, but will not eradicate it totally.

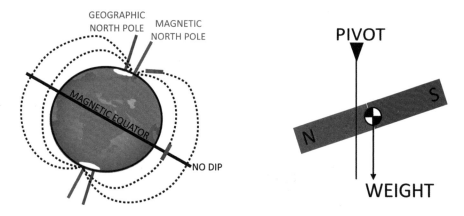

Acceleration errors

As the aircraft changes speed the compass magnet is left behind due to inertia. As the magnet's weight is not directly under the pivot, this lag will mean the compass will swing away from the correct magnetic direction. Acceleration errors are most pronounced on easterly or westerly headings.

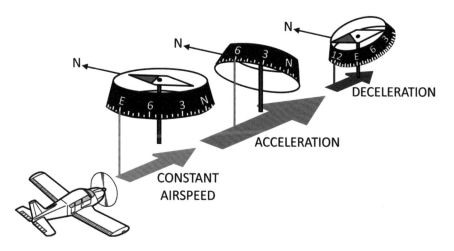

Heading	Acceleration	Deceleration
Easterly	Apparent turn north	Apparent turn south
Westerly	Apparent turn north	Apparent turn south
ANDS: Acceleration gives an apparent turn North; Deceleration gives an apparent turn South.		

COMPASS ACCELERATION ERRORS

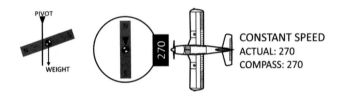

CONSTANT SPEED
ACTUAL: 270
COMPASS: 270

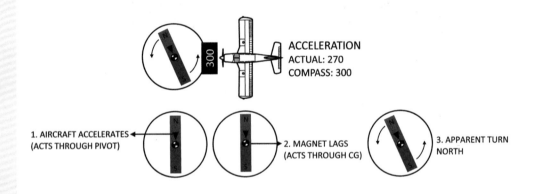

ACCELERATION
ACTUAL: 270
COMPASS: 300

1. AIRCRAFT ACCELERATES
(ACTS THROUGH PIVOT)

2. MAGNET LAGS
(ACTS THROUGH CG)

3. APPARENT TURN
NORTH

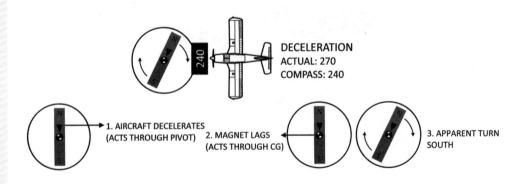

DECELERATION
ACTUAL: 270
COMPASS: 240

1. AIRCRAFT DECELERATES
(ACTS THROUGH PIVOT)

2. MAGNET LAGS
(ACTS THROUGH CG)

3. APPARENT TURN
SOUTH

COMPASS TURNING ERRORS

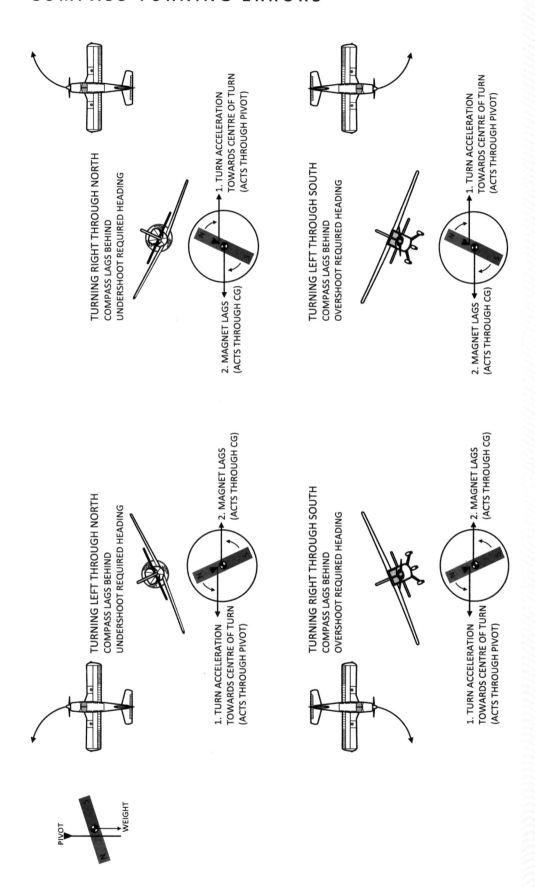

TURNING ERRORS

Turning errors are derived from centripetal force acting towards the centre of the turn. Again the magnet's inertia causes it to lag behind the actual aircraft. This time the errors are at their greatest when turning through north or south. See diagrams on previous page.

2.   The fluid within the compass supports the weight of the magnet, decreases friction and dampens oscillations. This is true. The liquid should be observed before flight to ensure that it is free of bubbles and not discoloured.

3.   The aeroplane moves around the compass magnet. Again, this option is correct.

4.   When deviation is applied to the compass heading we get the magnetic heading. The magnetic compass will not only sense the earth's magnetic field, but also any other field nearby. In anaircraft magnetic fields may be generated by rotating parts of the engine, radio installations and other electronic devices. The combined effect of these magnetic fields is called deviation; it is a measure of how much the compass is made to deviate from magnetic north. Each aircraft will have a deviation card which will show the correction that needs to be applied to a compass reading to obtain the magnetic heading.

TRUE variation MAGNETIC deviation COMPASS
T v M d C

5.   When variation is applied to the compass heading we get the magnetic heading. Variation is the angular difference between true north and magnetic north. It is applied to the true heading to obtain the magnetic heading.

20.   (Answer: B)

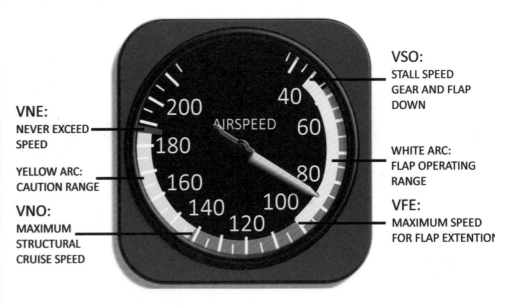

VNE:
NEVER EXCEED SPEED

YELLOW ARC:
CAUTION RANGE

VNO:
MAXIMUM STRUCTURAL CRUISE SPEED

VSO:
STALL SPEED GEAR AND FLAP DOWN

WHITE ARC:
FLAP OPERATING RANGE

VFE:
MAXIMUM SPEED FOR FLAP EXTENTIOI

V –SPEEDS:

V_{SO} –   stalling speed, gear down, flaps lowered, power off
V_{SI} –   stalling speed, gear up, flaps up, power off
V_{FE} –   maximum speed for extending flap
V_{NO} –   maximum structural cruise speed
V_{NE} –   never exceed speed

21. **(Answer: A)** The caging and setting knob on a Direction Indicator is there to allow the pilot to re-align the heading indicator with the magnetic compass. The direction indicator suffers from wander meaning that it will slowly become inaccurate and will need to be readjusted. Apparent wander is caused by the rotation of the earth. The gyroscope is aligned with a point in space, not a point on the earth. As the earth rotates the gyro will continue to point at its original reference point. From the pilot's point of view the DI appears to change heading even though a constant direction is maintained.

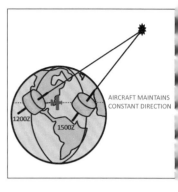

21. ANSWER A

Real wander is caused by mechanical imperfections within the instrument; for example worn bearings, friction, and the gyroscope not being in perfect balance.

The DI should be periodically checked against the magnetic compass. This should be done when the compass is not experiencing any errors; errors will be caused when turning or changing speed.

Therefore the DI should be adjusted when the aircraft is in unaccelerated straight and level flight.

22. **(Answer: C)** During climb the static supply to the altimeter and airspeed indicator becomes blocked. The result is that both the altimeter and ASI will under-read.

Altimeter: will continue to measure the static pressure trapped in the line and so will indicate the level at which the blockage occurred. Thus in a climb it will under-read.

ASI: A blocked static vent would cause the ASI to under-read. The static pressure trapped in the line will be higher than the actual pressure as the aircraft ascends. The measured difference between the pitot pressure and the static pressure will be less than actual; hence the ASI will indicate a lower airspeed than is really being achieved.

For completeness the VSI will indicate zero rate of climb if the static was blocked during level flight.

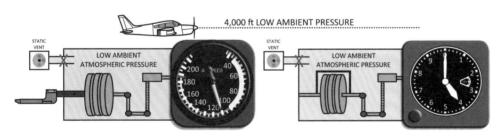

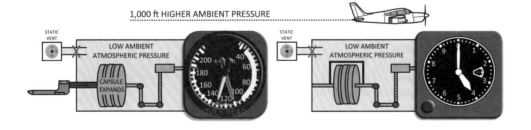

23. **(Answer: D)** One possible cause of "nose wheel shimmy" is the failure of the torque link. Aircraft with oleo-pneumatic units are prone to nose wheel shimmy, where the nose wheel oscillates a few degrees either side of centre as it runs along the ground creating unpleasant and possibly damaging vibrations. Often, to prevent shimmy a "shimmy damper" is fitted to the nose wheel; shimmy could also result if this unit is under pressurised.

24. **(Answer: C)** Load factors for an aircraft certified in the aerobatic category compared to one certified in the normal or utility category will be higher. Aircraft approved for aerobatics are designed to withstand the stresses imposed by aerobatic manoeuvres. Unlike normal and utility category aircraft, aerobatic aeroplanes must undergo rigorous testing to ensure that they remain controllable throughout a wide range of manoeuvres.

JAR 23.3 states:

The normal category is limited to non-aerobatic operations. Non-aerobatic operations include –
(1)   Any manoeuvre incident to normal flying;
(2)   Stalls (except whip stalls); and
(3)   Lazy eights, chandelles and steep turns or similar manoeuvres, in which the angle of bank is not more than 60°.

The utility category is limited to any of the operations covered in the normal category; plus -
(1)   Spins (if approved for the particular type of aeroplane); and
(2)   Lazy eights, chandelles, and steep turns, or similar manoeuvres in which the angle of bank is more than 60° but not more than 90°.

The aerobatic category is without restrictions, other than those shown to be necessary as a result of required flight tests.

25. **(Answer: B)** While on the ground the aeroplane's weight is balanced by the reaction force of the ground on the aircraft, which acts upwards through the wheels.

26. **(Answer: C)** During a pre-flight inspection of the brakes it is important to check that the brake discs are not corroded. Additionally the discs should not be pitted. Other items to inspect are that the assembly is firmly attached and that there are no leaks of hydraulic fluid from the brake lines.

PRINCIPLES OF FLIGHT

---

27. **(Answer: B)** By volume the ratio of oxygen to nitrogen in the air is 1:4. The basic constituents of dry air are:
Nitrogen 78%
Oxygen 21%
Other gases (argon, carbon dioxide etc) 1%

28. **(Answer: C)** In addition to the above, air in the atmosphere always contains water vapour. The actual amount is variable up to a maximum of around 4%.

29. **(Answer: A)** Movement about the longitudinal axis is called rolling. The longitudinal axis runs fore-aft through the centre of gravity.

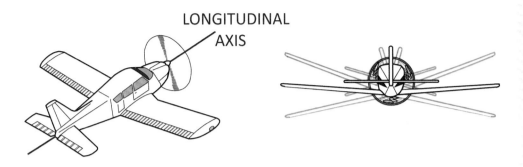

LONGITUDINAL AXIS

30. **(Answer: C)** A wing always stalls at a given angle of attack, the critical angle.

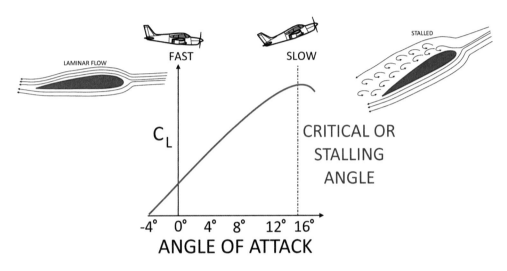

The speed at which the stall will occur varies according to the:
- Lift produced by the aerofoil – any manoeuvre that requires extra lift (e.g. turning) will increase the stalling speed.
- Aircraft's weight – stalling speed will increase with increase in weight.
- Load factor – stall speed increases with load factor
- Power – approaching the stall a vertical component of thrust can support some weight, leading to a lower stall speed
- Bank angle – increases load factor. In a 60° bank you will experience 2g. The stall speed will increase by $\sqrt{2}$ (which equates to approximately a 41% increase)
- Flap selection – use of flap lowers the stall speed, as the aerofoil will have a higher C_L max.

END OF EXPLANATIONS PAPER 4

INTENTIONALLY BLANK

PART 6: FLIGHT PERFORMANCE & PLANNING

The Flight Planning & Performance examination consists of 20 questions; the time allowed is 1 hour.

The pass mark is 75%.

Each question is multiple choice with four possible answers A, B, C and D. You should indicate your chosen answer by placing a cross in the appropriate box on the answer sheet.

Blank answer sheets are to be found at the end of this publication, these may be photocopied.

INTENTIONALLY BLANK

FLIGHT PLANNING AND PERFORMANCE
PAPER 1

1. Aircraft performance tables are often based on:

   a. Cabin altitude

   b. True altitude

   c. True height

   d. Pressure altitude

2. The length of the Take Off Run Available plus the length of any associated clearway is called the:

   a. Accelerate-Stop Distance Available (ASDA)

   b. Maximum Take Off Run Available (MTORA)

   c. Take Off Distance Available (TODA)

   d. Maximum Take Off Distance Available (MTODA)

3. VAT, the target threshold speed, will provide a margin above the stalling speed in the landing configuration of:

   a. 10%

   b. 30%

   c. 50%

   d. 25%

4. From the diagram below: Which profile represents a take off without flap?

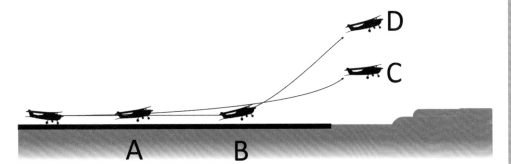

   a. A to C

   b. A to D

   c. B to C

   d. B to D

5. In relation to the position of the Centre of Gravity a light aircraft certified in the "Normal Category" is permitted to undertake:

   a. Normal flying, spinning and angles of bank exceeding 60°

   b. Spinning, but no aerobatic manoeuvres

   c. Normal flying, no spinning or aerobatic manoeuvres and bank angles up to 60°

   d. Manoeuvres exceeding 60° angle of bank and spinning

6. The definition of "Rate of Climb" is: ← *typo? Best RoC*

   a. The amount of height gained in the shortest time

   b. The amount of height gained in the shortest horizontal distance

   c. The amount of height gained with the fastest horizontal speed

   d. The amount of height gained in the shortest vertical distance

7.   Increasing the all up weight of an aircraft will have what effect on its climb performance?

    a. Climb performance will be degraded

    b. Climb performance will improve

    c. Climb performance will improve a great deal

    d. Climb performance will be unaffected

8.   Assume 1 hPa = 30 feet. With an aerodrome elevation of 990 feet and a QFE of 992 hPa, the pressure altitude is:

    a. 1620 ft

    b. 630 ft

    c. 360 ft

    d. 21 ft

9.   With an aerodrome elevation of 600 feet and a QFE of 998 hectopascals, the pressure altitude is:

    a. 450 ft

    b. 1050 ft

    c. 15 ft

    d. 548 ft

10.   In a piston engine aircraft to fly for maximum range a pilot should select:

    a. The minimum drag speed

    b. A speed just above the stalling speed

    c. A speed just above the minimum drag speed

    d. V_{NO}

11.   In a piston engine aircraft to fly for maximum endurance a pilot should select:

    a. The same speed as for maximum range and the lowest safe altitude

    b. A higher speed than for maximum range and the highest altitude possible

    c. A lower speed than for maximum range and the highest altitude possible

    d. A lower airspeed than for maximum range and the lowest safe altitude

12.   With which combination of weight and centre of gravity is it safe to fly?

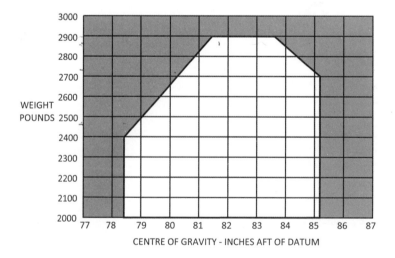

    a. Weight: 2480 C of G position: 78.4

    b. Weight: 2890 C of G position: 81.8

    c. Weight: 2740 C of G position: 80.1

    d. Weight: 2900 C of G position: 85.2

13. An overweight aircraft will:

    a. Have a lower stalling speed, but a higher take off speed
    b. Handle and perform poorly and if flown may suffer structural damage
    c. Have good climb performance and a longer endurance
    d. Have a longer take off run and a lower take off speed

Use the table above to answer the following three questions.

Pressure Altitude Feet	Climb Speed KIAS	Rate of Climb - FPM			
		-20°C	0°C	20°C	40°C
S.L.	80	840	780	720	630
2000	79	740	675	615	555
4000	77	675	595	535	475
6000	75	550	485	435	380
8000	73	430	375	320	260
10000	71	330	275	220	165
12000	69	210	145	---	---

Maximum Rate of Climb at 2300 pounds
Conditions: Full throttle, Flaps up

14. For an aircraft weighing 2300 pounds flying at a pressure altitude of 5,000 feet with an OAT of 0°C the maximum rate of climb will be:

    a. 485 fpm
    b. 540 fpm
    c. 635 fpm
    d. 545 fpm

15. For an aircraft weighing 2300 pounds flying at a pressure altitude of 4,000 feet with an OAT of -10°C the maximum rate of climb will be:

    a. 707 fpm
    b. 565 fpm
    c. 655 fpm
    d. 635 fpm

16. For an aircraft weighing 2300 pounds flying at a pressure altitude of 3,000 feet with an OAT of 20°C the maximum rate of climb will be:

    a. 575 fpm
    b. 485 fpm
    c. 595 fpm
    d. 635 fpm

17. In the UK published take off performance is based on a:

    a. Level and dry short grass surface
    b. Hard surface with an adverse direction of slope
    c. Level and dry hard surface
    d. Level and wet hard surface

18. Complete the following statement: a 2% downslope will ...(i)... the landing distance by approximately ...(ii)...

    a.   i) increase   ii) 20%
    b.   i) decrease   ii) 20%
    c.   i) increase   ii) 10%
    d.   i) decrease   ii) 10%

19. What is the gradient of a 2000 ft runway which has threshold elevations of 415 and 357 feet?

    a.   2.9 %
    b.   4.05 %
    c.   3.2 %
    d.   1.9 %

20. Guidelines published in an AIC recommend that when calculating take off distance, the public transport take off factor should be applied to all flights. The factor is:

    a.   1.5
    b.   1.15
    c.   1.33
    d.   1.43

END OF FLIGHT PLANNING AND PERFORMANCE PAPER 1

INTENTIONALLY BLANK

	A	B	C	D
1.				X
2.			X	
3.		X		
4.				X
5.			X	
6.	X			
7.	X			
8.		X		
9.	X			
10.			X	
11.				X
12.		X		
13.		X		
14.		X		
15				X
16.	X			
17.			X	
18.			X	
19.	X			
20.			X	

CORRECT ANSWERS: PERCENTAGES					
15	16	17	18	19	20
87%	90%	92%	95%	97%	100%

FLIGHT PLANNING AND PERFORMANCE
PAPER 1: EXPLANATIONS

1. **(Answer: D)** Pressure altitude is often used as the datum for measuring aircraft performance. It is the height in the International Standard Atmosphere above the 1013.2 hPa at which the pressure equals that of the aircraft or point in question. Put another way, pressure altitude is the indicated altitude when an altimeter is set to 1013.2 hPa.

2. **(Answer: C)** The Take-Off Distance Available (TODA) is the length of the take-off run available plus the length of any associated clearway. A clearway is a defined rectangular area of ground or water under the control of the appropriate authority, prepared as a suitable area over which an aeroplane may make an initial portion of its climb to a specified height.

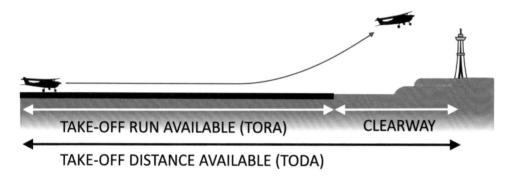

3. **(Answer: B)** V_{AT}, the target threshold speed, will provide a margin above the stalling speed in the landing configuration of 30%. The target threshold speed is that at which the pilot should aim to cross the threshold and is equal to the stalling speed in the landing configuration (V_{SO}) multiplied by 1.3. JAR OPS 1.430(c).

4. **(Answer: D)** Using small flap settings (up to approximately 20°) during take-off decreases the ground run required. If a large flap setting is used drag will greatly increase and no benefit will be gained; small settings, however, will lower the stalling speed enabling both the lift-off and take-off safety speeds to be reduced. Consequently the aircraft will reach its lift-off speed after a shorter ground roll, meaning that shorter runways can be used or runways with a poor surface can be left behind more quickly!

    Although the ground run is reduced due to the increased lift generated by the flaps, the initial rate and angle of climb will both be reduced due to the increase in drag.

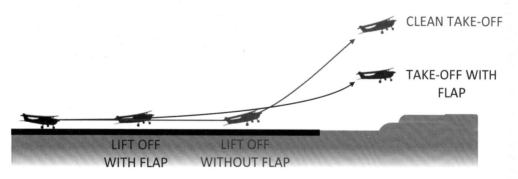

5.   **(Answer: C)** A light aircraft certified in the "Normal Category" is permitted to undertake normal flying; however spinning and aerobatic manoeuvres are not allowed and bank angles may be restricted to 60°.

JAR 23.3 states: The normal category is limited to non-aerobatic operations. Non-aerobatic operations include –
(1)   Any manoeuvre incidental to normal flying;
(2)   Stalls (except whip stalls); and
(3)   Lazy eights, chandelles and steep turns or similar manoeuvres, in which the angle of bank is not more than 60°.

The utility category is limited to any of the operations covered in the normal category; plus -
(1)   Spins (if approved for the particular type of aeroplane); and
(2)   Lazy eights, chandelles, and steep turns, or similar manoeuvres in which the angle of bank is more than 60° but not more than 90°.

The aerobatic category is without restrictions, other than those shown to be necessary as a result of required flight tests.

See also the UK General Aviation Safety Sense Leaflet number 9.

6.   **(Answer: A)** Rate of Climb is defined as the amount of height gained in the shortest time.

7.   **(Answer: A)** Increasing the all up weight of an aircraft will degrade climb performance. The more excess power that is available the greater the rate of climb that can be achieved. Increasing weight will require more lift to balance it, leading to the production of more drag and the necessity to use more power to overcome the drag. As a consequence excess power available will be less and climb performance will degrade.

Factors reducing climb performance:
Weight increased
Altitude increases (lower air density)
Temperature increased (lower air density)

8.   **(Answer: B)** 630 feet. Pressure altitude is often used as the datum for measuring aircraft performance. It is the height in the International Standard Atmosphere above 1013.2 hPa at which the pressure equals that of the aircraft or point in question. Put another way, pressure altitude is the indicated altitude when an altimeter is set to 1013.2 hPa.

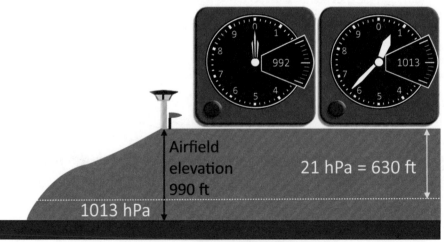

$$\text{SPS - QFE} = 1013 - 992 = 21 \text{ hPa} \times 30 = 630 \text{ ft}$$

9. **(Answer: A)** 450 feet. Pressure altitude is often used as the datum for measuring aircraft performance. It is the height in the International Standard Atmosphere above the 1013.2 hPa at which the pressure equals that of the aircraft or point in question. Put another way, pressure altitude is the indicated altitude when an altimeter is set to 1013.2 hPa.

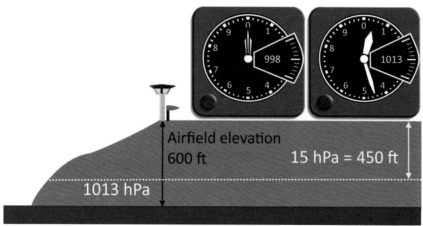

SPS - QFE = 1013 - 998 = 15 hPa x 30 = 450 ft

10. **(Answer: C)** In a piston engine aircraft to fly for maximum range a pilot should select a speed just above the minimum drag speed. To achieve maximum range the aircraft must consume the lowest amount of fuel possible for each nautical mile travelled, this will be where the power to airspeed ratio is the least. To find this point graphically a tangent is drawn from the origin to the power required curve, this is where the power to speed ratio is the smallest and corresponds to the minimum drag speed.

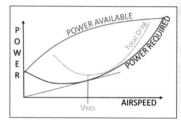

10. ANSWER C

    In practical terms a piston engine is at its most efficient at around 65% power, and taking engine efficiency into account, will give airspeed slightly higher than minimum drag speed. The maximum range speed will be 5 to 10% faster than the minimum drag speed.

11. **(Answer: D)** In a piston engine aircraft, to fly for maximum endurance a pilot should select a lower airspeed than for maximum range and the lowest safe altitude. Maximum endurance means spending the longest possible time airborne, which equates to flying at a speed that will require the minimum amount of power.

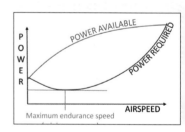

11. ANSWER D

    The second part of the question asks you to select the most desirable altitude. Flying at the lowest safe level means flying at a lower true airspeed which means that the power required to overcome drag is reduced.

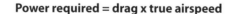

Power required = drag x true airspeed

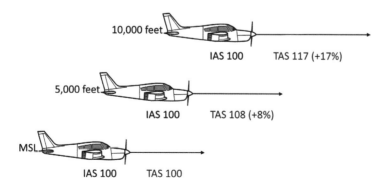

When maintaining a constant indicated airspeed (IAS), true airspeed (TAS) will increase with increase in altitude. The easiest way to picture this is to imagine an aircraft in a climb; to maintain a constant IAS the value of dynamic pressure must remain the same. Dynamic pressure is ½ density x velocity², therefore as the air density decreases with increase in altitude to maintain a constant dynamic pressure the velocity must increase.

12.   **(Answer: B)** In order to be loaded safely, plot the values for mass and centre of gravity on the graph to find whether they fall within the CG envelope. The white area of the graph represents the weight and balance envelope, the only values given that fall within its parameters are: weight 2890 and C of G position 81.8

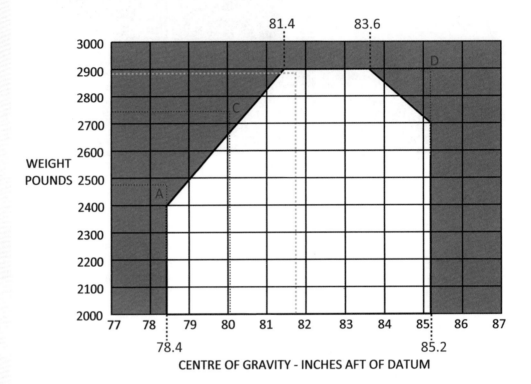

13.   **(Answer: B)** An overweight aircraft will handle and perform poorly, and if flown may suffer structural damage. Other effects of increased weight are:

Higher take off speed
Longer take off run
Higher stalling speed
Reduced climb performance (both rate and angle of climb)
Increased fuel consumption and so less endurance
Shorter range
Higher landing speed and longer landing distance
Reduced manoeuvrability

14. **(Answer: B)** In the performance table pressure altitudes are given at 2,000 ft intervals. Thus to find the maximum rate of climb at 5,000 feet with an OAT of 0°C we must interpolate between the figures given.

Maximum Rate of Climb at 2300 pounds Conditions: Full throttle, Flaps up					
Pressure Altitude Feet	Climb Speed KIAS	Rate of Climb - FPM			
		-20°C	**0°C**	**20°C**	**40°C**
S.L.	80	840	780	720	630
2000	79	740	675	615	555
4000	77	675	**595**	535	475
6000	75	550	**485**	435	380
8000	73	430	375	320	260
10000	71	330	275	220	165
12000	69	210	145	- - -	- - -

At 4,000 feet in the 0°C column we find the maximum rate of climb is 595 fpm; at 6000 feet it is 485 fpm. To find the value at 5,000 feet add these two values together and, as 5,000 feet is exactly half way in between the given values, divide by 2.

$$595 + 485 = 1080 \div 2 = 540 \text{ fpm}$$

15. **(Answer: D)** In the performance table temperatures are given at 20 degree intervals. Thus to find the maximum rate of climb at 4,000 feet with an OAT of -10°C we must interpolate between the figures given.

Maximum Rate of Climb at 2300 pounds Conditions: Full throttle, Flaps up					
Pressure Altitude Feet	Climb Speed KIAS	Rate of Climb - FPM			
		-20°C	**0°C**	**20°C**	**40°C**
S.L.	80	840	780	720	630
2000	79	740	675	615	555
4000	77	**675**	**595**	535	475
6000	75	550	485	435	380
8000	73	430	375	320	260
10000	71	330	275	220	165
12000	69	210	145	- - -	- - -

At 4,000 feet in the 0°C column we find the maximum rate of climb is 595 fpm; in the -20°C column it is 675 fpm. To find the value for -10°C add these two values together and, as -10°C is exactly half way in between the given values, divide by 2.

$$595 + 675 = 1270 \div 2 = 635 \text{ fpm}$$

16. **(Answer: A)** In the performance table pressure altitudes are given at 2,000 ft intervals. Thus to find the maximum rate of climb at 3,000 feet with an OAT of 20°C we must interpolate between the figures given.

Maximum Rate of Climb at 2300 pounds Conditions: Full throttle, Flaps up					
Pressure Altitude Feet	Climb Speed KIAS	Rate of Climb - FPM			
		-20°C	0°C	20°C	40°C
S.L.	80	840	780	720	630
2000	79	740	675	**615**	555
4000	77	675	595	**535**	475
6000	75	550	485	435	380
8000	73	430	375	320	260
10000	71	330	275	220	165
12000	69	210	145	---	---

At 4,000 feet in the 20°C column we find the maximum rate of climb is 535 fpm; at 2000 feet it is 615 fpm. To find the value at 3,000 feet add these two values together and, as 3,000 feet is exactly half way in between the given values, divide by 2.

$$615 + 535 = 1150 \div 2 = 575 \text{ fpm}$$

17. **(Answer: C)** Take off performance data in the UK is based on a hard surface that is level and dry. The friction created by other surfaces, for example grass, will slow acceleration on the ground and increase the take off distance.

   Short dry grass increases the take off distance by 20%, short wet grass by 25%
   Long dry grass increases the take off distance by 25%, long wet grass by 30%
   Soft ground or snow will increase the take off distance by at least 25%, probably more.

18. **(Answer: C)** The landing distance will increase by 10% for each 2% of downhill slope (a factor of x 1.10). AIC 127/2006 (Pink 110)

19. **(Answer: A)** To calculate the runway gradient:

   $$\frac{\text{Higher threshold} - \text{Lower threshold}}{\text{Runway length}} \times \frac{100}{1}$$

   $$\frac{415 - 357}{2000} \times \frac{100}{1} = 2.9\%$$

20. **(Answer: C)** It is recommended that, at least, the public transport factors should be applied for all flights. Unless otherwise specified in the aeroplanes manual, handbook or supplement, as factor of 1.33 for take-off is recommended, and should be applied after other variables have been accounted for. AIC 127/2006 (Pink 110).

END OF EXPLANATIONS PAPER 1

---

1. The airspeed to fly to achieve maximum range is:

    a. The minimum power speed

    b. The speed where power available equals power required

    c. The never exceed speed

    d. The speed where the power: airspeed ratio is least

2. In comparison to a flapless take off, using a small flap setting for take off will:

    a. Increase the stalling, lift off and take off safety speeds

    b. Reduce the stalling and lift off speeds, but will increase the take off safety speed

    c. Reduce the stalling, lift off and take off safety speeds

    d. Reduce the stalling speed, but increase the lift off and take off safety speeds

3. With which combination of weight and centre of gravity is it safe to fly?

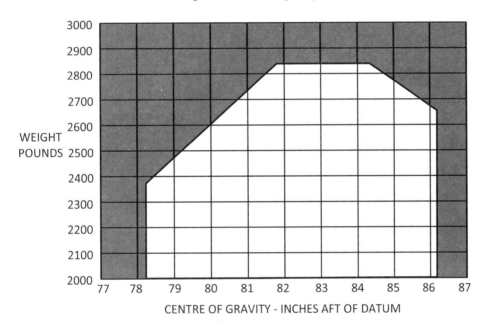

CENTRE OF GRAVITY - INCHES AFT OF DATUM

    a. Weight: 2480 C of G position: 78.4

    b. Weight: 2830 C of G position: 86.2

    c. Weight: 2810 C of G position: 84.4

    d. Weight: 2750 C of G position: 80.5

4. An increase in aircraft weight of 10% will ...(i)... the landing distance by ...(ii)...

    a. i) reduce   ii) a factor of 1.1, or 10%

    b. i) increase   ii) a factor of 1.43, or 43%

    c. i) reduce   ii) a factor of 1.43, or 43%

    d. i) increase   ii) a factor of 1.1, or 10%

5. Using a runway with a down slope will require:

    a. A longer landing distance, and a longer take off distance

    b. A longer landing distance, but a shorter take off distance

    c. A shorter landing distance, and a shorter take off distance

    d. A shorter landing distance, but a longer take off distance

6. Compared to an aerodrome at sea level, when operating from an aerodrome having a high pressure altitude will lead to:

   a.   A longer landing distance, and a longer take off distance

   b.   A longer landing distance, but a shorter take off distance

   c.   A shorter landing distance, and a shorter take off distance

   d.   A shorter landing distance, but a longer take off distance

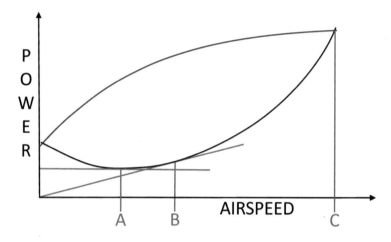

7. Assuming that fuel consumption is directly related to the power delivered by the engine, which point represents the airspeed at which to fly for maximum endurance?

   a.   C or A depending on the aircraft's weight

   b.   C

   c.   B

   d.   A

8. If the stalling speed of a particular aircraft in the landing configuration (V_{so}) is 50 KTS, therefore the minimum approach speed is approximately:

   a.   72 KTS

   b.   65 KTS

   c.   68 KTS

   d.   60 KTS

Refer to the Take Off Performance Graph opposite to answer the following three questions:

9. *Given:*

OAT:	+15°C
Pressure Altitude:	Sea Level
Aircraft Weight:	3100 lbs
Surface Wind:	20 knots Headwind

What is the approximate take off distance required to reach a screen height of 50 ft?

   a.   1,000 feet

   b.   1,500 feet

   c.   900 feet

   d.   1,100 feet

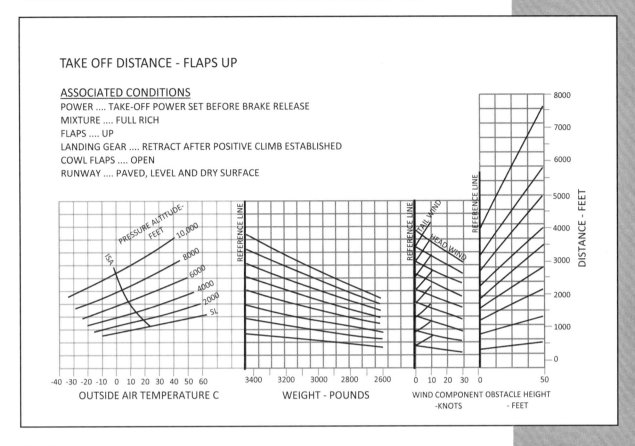

TAKE OFF DISTANCE - FLAPS UP

ASSOCIATED CONDITIONS
POWER .... TAKE-OFF POWER SET BEFORE BRAKE RELEASE
MIXTURE .... FULL RICH
FLAPS .... UP
LANDING GEAR .... RETRACT AFTER POSITIVE CLIMB ESTABLISHED
COWL FLAPS .... OPEN
RUNWAY .... PAVED, LEVEL AND DRY SURFACE

10. *Given:*

OAT:	+20°C
Pressure Altitude:	1,000 feet
Aircraft Weight:	3300 lbs
Surface Wind:	Calm

What is the approximate take off distance required to reach a screen height of 50 ft?

a. 1,950 feet
b. 2,200 feet
c. 1,450 feet
d. 1,700 feet

11. *Given:*

OAT:	-5°C
Pressure Altitude:	Sea Level
Aircraft Weight:	3400 lbs
Surface Wind:	5 knots Tailwind

What is the approximate take off distance required to reach a screen height of 50 ft?

a. 1,350 feet
b. 1,850 feet
c. 2,100 feet
d. 1,050 feet

12. When landing with a tailwind, the ground speed will be:

a. Less than the TAS
b. The same as the TAS
c. Greater than the TAS
d. Slightly less than the TAS

13. With regard to the diagram below showing the variation of power available and power required by a piston engine aircraft over a range of speeds. Assuming that fuel consumption is directly related to the power generated by the engine, which point represents the speed to fly to obtain maximum range?

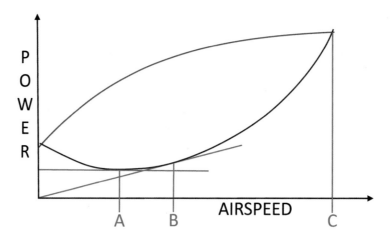

    a.   C or A depending on the aircraft's weight

    b.   C

    c.   B

    d.   A

14. An aircraft having a lift:drag ratio of 6:1 will have a maximum gliding distance from 5,000 feet in still air of approximately:

    a.   6 nm

    b.   5 nm

    c.   4 nm

    d.   3 nm

15. When compared to a lightly loaded aircraft, to achieve the maximum glide range in a heavy aircraft:

    a.   A steeper glide angle must be used

    b.   A shallower glide angle must be used

    c.   A slower speed must be used

    d.   A faster speed must be used

16. Increasing an aircraft's weight by 10% will have what effect on its take off distance?

    a.   Take off distance will increase by 20%

    b.   Take off distance will increase by 33%

    c.   Take off distance will reduce by 20%

    d.   Take off distance will reduce by 43%

17. Which picture represents the Zero Fuel Mass?

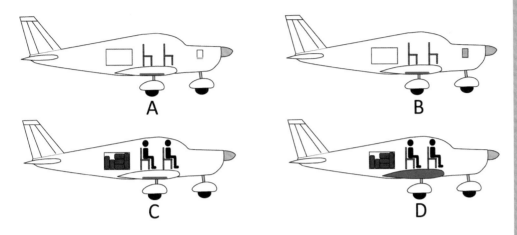

   a.   A
   b.   B
   c.   C
   d.   D

18. Using a higher airspeed than that recommended in the Flight Manual during an approach to landing will have what effect?

   a.   It will have no effect other than you will arrive earlier
   b.   It will increase the landing distance
   c.   It will reduce the landing distance, but increase the braking distance required
   d.   It will reduce the landing distance required

19. Ice on an aircraft's wings will:

   a.   Increase weight, but decrease drag
   b.   Increase weight and drag, and seriously reduce the lift generated
   c.   No change in weight
   d.   Reduce the lift generated, but have no effect on drag

20. With all tanks full an aircraft holds 230 litres of fuel. If the specific gravity (SG) of the fuel is 0.72, what is the approximate weight of the fuel in pounds?

   a.   166 lbs
   b.   364 lbs
   c.   703 lbs
   d.   75 lbs

END OF FLIGHT PLANNING AND PERFORMANCE PAPER 2

FLIGHT PLANNING & PERFORMANCE
PAPER 2: ANSWERS

	A	B	C	D
1.				X
2.			X	
3.			X	
4.				X
5.		X		
6.	X			
7.				X
8.		X		
9.				X
10.	X			
11.		X		
12.			X	
13.			X	
14.		X		
15				X
16.	X			
17.			X	
18.		X		
19.		X		
20.		X		

CORRECT ANSWERS: PERCENTAGES					
15	16	17	18	19	20
87%	90%	92%	95%	97%	100%

1. **(Answer: D)** In a piston engine aircraft to fly for maximum range a pilot should select a speed just above the minimum drag speed. To achieve maximum range the aircraft must consume the lowest amount of fuel possible for each nautical mile travelled, this will be where the power: airspeed ratio is the least. To find this point graphically a tangent is drawn from the origin to the power available curve, this is where the power: speed ratio is the smallest and corresponds to the minimum drag speed.

    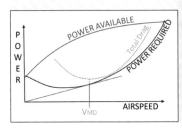

    1. ANSWER D

    In practical terms a piston engine is at its most efficient at around 65% power, and taking engine efficiency into account, will give airspeed slightly higher than minimum drag speed. The maximum range speed will be 5 to 10% faster than the minimum drag speed.

2. **(Answer: C)** Using small flap settings (up to approximately 20°) during take-off will generate extra lift with a relatively small increase in drag. As a consequence an aircraft will be able to take off at a slower speed and with a shorter ground run.

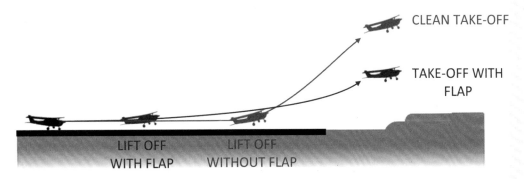

Extending flap changes the shape of the aerofoil to one with a higher C$_L$MAX, meaning that the same weight can be supported at a lower speed.

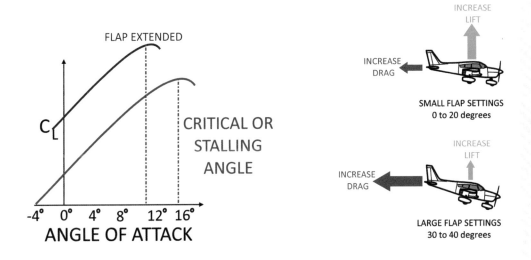

3. **(Answer: C)** In order to be loaded safely, plot the values for mass and centre of gravity on the graph to find whether they fall within the CG envelope. The white area of the graph represents the weight and balance envelope: the only values given that fall within its parameters are: weight 2810 and C of G position 84.4

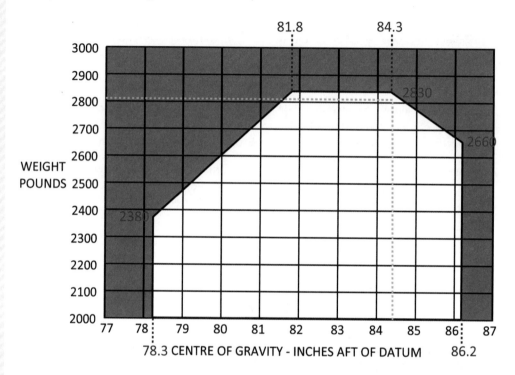

4. **(Answer: D)** Increased weight will increase the landing distance, because the stalling speed will increase and consequently the minimum approach speed (1.3 x V_{so}) will increase. A higher landing speed means that the aircraft will require more distance to stop. Additionally the higher kinetic energy must be absorbed by the brakes which will also increase the landing run.

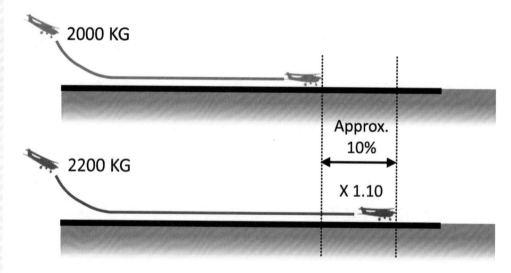

From AIC 127/2006 (Pink 110): Guide line factor: landing distance will be increased by 10% for each 10% increase in aeroplane weight (a factor of x 1.10).

5.   **(Answer: B)** A runway with a downhill slope will increase the landing distance and will decrease the take off distance as the aircraft will accelerate faster. A 2% down slope will increase the landing distance by 10%, a factor of 1.1. AIC 127/2006 (Pink 110)

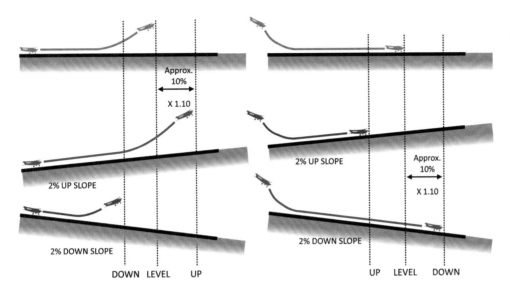

6.   **(Answer: A)** Aircraft performance deteriorates with an increase in altitude and the pressure altitude at the aerodrome should be used for calculations. This equates to the height shown on the altimeter on the ground at the aerodrome with the sub-scale set at 1013 hPa. Take-off distance will be increased by 10% for each 1000 ft increase in aerodrome altitude (a factor of x 1.10).

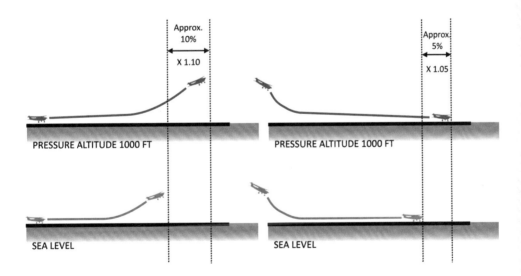

Landing distance will be increased by 5% for each 1000 ft increase in aerodrome pressure altitude (a factor of x 1.05).

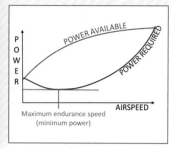

7. ANSWER D

7.   **(Answer: D)** Maximum endurance means spending the longest possible time airborne, it equates to flying at a speed that will require the minimum amount of power.

8.   **(Answer: B)** 65 knots. V_{AT}, the target threshold speed, will provide a margin above the stalling speed in the landing configuration of 30%. The target threshold speed is that at which the pilot should aim to cross the threshold and is equal to the stalling speed in the landing configuration (V_{SO}) multiplied by 1.3. JAR OPS 1.430(c).

9.   **(Answer: D)** 1,100 feet

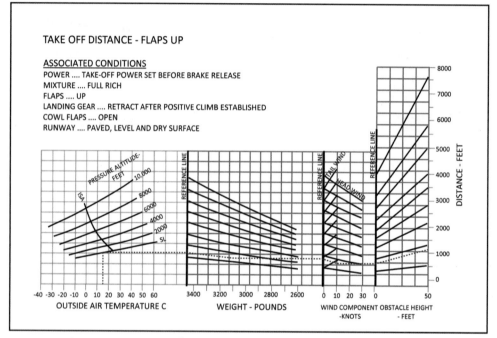

TAKE OFF DISTANCE - FLAPS UP

ASSOCIATED CONDITIONS
POWER .... TAKE-OFF POWER SET BEFORE BRAKE RELEASE
MIXTURE .... FULL RICH
FLAPS .... UP
LANDING GEAR .... RETRACT AFTER POSITIVE CLIMB ESTABLISHED
COWL FLAPS .... OPEN
RUNWAY .... PAVED, LEVEL AND DRY SURFACE

OAT: +15 PA: Sea Level A/C Weight: 3100 lbs Wind: H/W 20 Knots OBSTACLE: 50 FT

1.   Enter the graph from the bottom at +15°C and draw a line vertically upwards to the actual pressure altitude, in this case sea level.

2.   Draw a horizontal line to the first reference line

3.   Follow the direction of the nearest "weight" lines until the take-off weight, 3100 lbs, is reached.

4.   From this point draw a horizontal line to the second reference line.

5.   Parallel the nearest lines representing headwind remembering, unless otherwise stated, to use only **50% of the reported headwind**. In this case use 10 knots.

6.   Again, draw a horizontal line this time to the third reference line.

7.   Finally, follow the nearest lines to obtain the 50 ft screen height figure.

NOTE: TO THIS FIGURE WE SHOULD THEN ADD THE TAKE OFF SAFETY FACTOR OF 1.33, TOGETHER WITH ANY ADDITIONAL FACTORS FOR RUNWAY SURFACE, SLOPE ETC.. THAT MAY BE NECESSARY.

10.   (Answer: A) 1,950 feet.

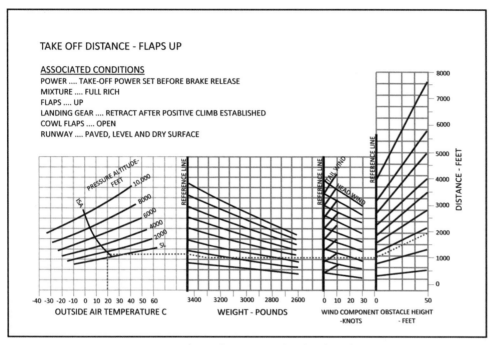

OAT: +20 PA: 1000 A/c Weight: 3300 Wind: Calm Obstacle: 50 FT

1.   Enter the graph from the bottom at +20°C and draw a line vertically upwards to the actual pressure
      altitude, in this case 1,000 feet.
2.   Draw a horizontal line to the first reference line
3.   Follow the direction of the nearest "weight" lines until the take-off weight, 3300 lbs, is reached.
4.   From this point draw a horizontal line to the second reference point.
5.   As the wind is calm continue this horizontal line all the way to the third reference line.
6.   Finally, parallel the nearest lines to obtain the 50 ft screen height figure.

NOTE: TO THIS FIGURE WE SHOULD THEN ADD THE TAKE OFF SAFETY FACTOR OF 1.33, TOGETHER WITH ANY
ADDITIONAL FACTORS FOR RUNWAY SURFACE, SLOPE ETC.. THAT MAY BE NECESSARY.

11.   (Answer: B) 1,850 feet

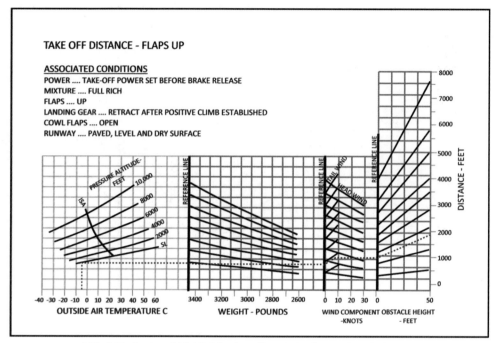

OAT: -5 PA: Sea Level A/c Weight: 3400 lbs Wind: 5 knot tailwind Obstacle: 50 FT

1.   Enter the graph from the bottom at -5°C and draw a line vertically upwards to the actual pressure altitude, in this case sea level.
2.   Draw a horizontal line to the first reference line
3.   Follow the direction of the nearest "weight" lines until the take-off weight, 3400 lbs, is reached.
4.   From this point draw a horizontal line to the second reference point.
5.   Parallel the nearest lines representing tailwind remembering, unless otherwise stated, to use **150% of the reported tailwind**. In this case use 7.5 knots.
6.   Again, draw a horizontal line this time to the third reference line.
7.   Finally, follow the nearest lines to obtain the 50 ft screen height figure.

NOTE: TO THIS FIGURE WE SHOULD THEN ADD THE TAKE OFF SAFETY FACTOR OF 1.33, TOGETHER WITH ANY
ADDITIONAL FACTORS FOR RUNWAY SURFACE, SLOPE ETC.. THAT MAY BE NECESSARY.

---

12.   (Answer: C) A tailwind means that the ground speed will be greater than the TAS. The consequences of this are a higher touchdown speed and a longer landing run.

13.   (Answer: C) In a piston engine aircraft to fly for maximum range a pilot should select a speed just above the minimum drag speed. To achieve maximum range the aircraft must consume the lowest amount of fuel possible for each nautical mile travelled, this will be where the power: airspeed ratio is the least. To find this point graphically a tangent is drawn from the origin to the power required curve, this is where the power: speed ratio is the smallest and corresponds to the minimum drag speed.

In practical terms a piston engine is at its most efficient at around 65% power, and taking engine efficiency into account, will give airspeed slightly higher than minimum drag speed. The maximum range speed will be 5 to 10% faster than the minimum drag speed.

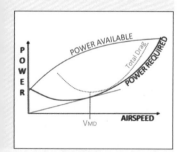

13. ANSWER C

14.   (Answer: B) A lift: drag ratio of 6:1 will glide 6 times as far as it descends. For each 1,000 feet of height lost the aircraft will travel 6,000 feet horizontally.

Therefore from 5,000 feet:
6 x 5,000 = 30,000 feet
30,000 ÷ 6,000 = 5 nm

I nm is equal to 6080 feet (near enough 6,000 feet), so the aircraft will glide approximately 5 nm.

15.   (Answer: D) Aircraft weight does not affect the gliding range, the best lift: drag ratio is achieved at a particular angle of attack. The factor that does alter is the glide speed; a heavier aircraft will need to have a higher airspeed at any given angle of attack than a lighter aircraft. This is because more lift is required to balance the greater weight. For a heavier aircraft both lift and drag will need to increase but the proportions will remain the same.

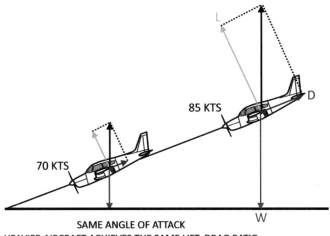

SAME ANGLE OF ATTACK
HEAVIER AIRCRAFT ACHIEVES THE SAME LIFT: DRAG RATIO
AT A HIGHER SPEED

16.   (Answer: A) Increased weight on departure will mean slower acceleration and increased friction from the extra weight on wheels – leading to more distance being used up.

From AIC 67/2002 (Pink 36): Guide line factor: take off distance will be increased by 20% for each 10% increase in aeroplane weight (a factor of x 1.20).

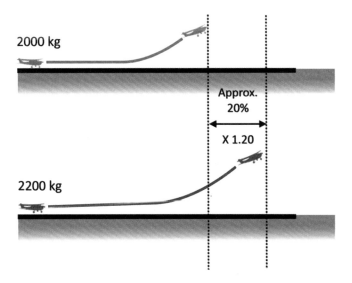

17. **(Answer: C)**

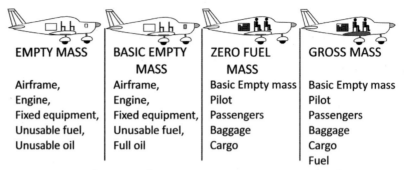

EMPTY MASS	BASIC EMPTY MASS	ZERO FUEL MASS	GROSS MASS
Airframe, Engine, Fixed equipment, Unusable fuel, Unusable oil	Airframe, Engine, Fixed equipment, Unusable fuel, Full oil	Basic Empty mass Pilot Passengers Baggage Cargo	Basic Empty mass Pilot Passengers Baggage Cargo Fuel

NOTE: "PAYLOAD" means Passengers, Cargo and Ballast

18. **(Answer: B)** Landing performance charts are based on flying the specified approach speed. If a faster speed is adopted the landing distance will exceed that predicted by the chart.

19. **(Answer: B)** Ice accretion on wings adds a great deal of weight and significantly increases drag. Additionally it can drastically reduce the lift generated by a wing; this is especially true when ice forms on the upper surface.

20. **(Answer: B)** There are two ways to tackle these problems either mathematically or using the CPR Flight Computer.

    Mathematically: a specific gravity of 0.72 means that Avgas weighs only 0.72 times as much as an equal volume of water. One litre of water weighs 1 kg, so one litre of Avgas weighs 0.72 kg. **230 litres x 0.72 = 165.6 kg**

    However we are asked for an answer in pounds: **165.6 x 2.2 = 364.3 lbs**

    CRP-1: Set the number of litres (230 lt) under the litres index on the fixed outer scale. Notice on the fixed outer scale are two scales for specific gravity (Sp. G) one in kg and one in lbs. Below 72 on the Imperial Sp. G scale read off 364 lb on the INNER rotating scale.

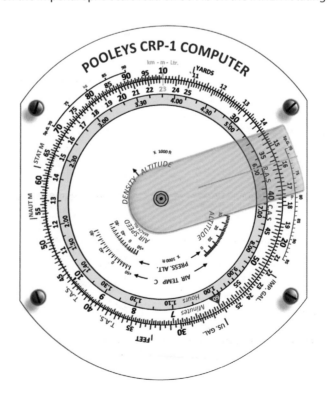

FLIGHT PLANNING AND PERFORMANCE
PAPER 3

1. Using a runway with an up slope will require:

   a. A longer landing distance, and a longer take off distance

   b. A longer landing distance, but a shorter take off distance

   c. A shorter landing distance, and a shorter take off distance

   d. A shorter landing distance, but a longer take off distance

2. You are completing the following loading form:

   Max Take off Mass Authorised 2400 lbs
   Max Landing Mass Authorised 2300 lbs
   CG limits: 18 to 22 inches aft of datum

Item	Mass (lb)	Arm	Moment (lb In)
Basic Mass	1600	+27	+43,200
Pilot & Front Passenger	320	−6	−1,920
Oil (SG 0.8)	30	−17	−510
Rear Passengers	140	+24	+3,360
Baggage	10	+42	+420
Fuel (SG 0.72)		+20	
TOTAL			

   What is the maximum amount of fuel in litres that may be safely loaded?

   a. 136 l

   b. 189 l

   c. 416 l

   d. 317 l

3. If the aircraft is fuelled with 250 lbs of fuel, of which 200 lbs will be burned during the flight, what is the CG position on departure and on landing?

   Max Take off Mass Authorised 2400 lbs
   Max Landing Mass Authorised 2300 lbs
   CG limits: 18 to 22 inches aft of datum

Item	Mass (lb)	Arm	Moment (lb In)
Basic Mass	1600	+27	+43,200
Pilot & Front Passenger	320	−6	−1,920
Oil (SG 0.8)	30	−17	−510
Rear Passengers	140	+24	+3,360
Baggage	10	+42	+420
Fuel (SG 0.72)		+20	
TOTAL			

   a. CG position on departure: 21.08 CG position on landing: 21.18

   b. CG position on departure: 20.4 CG position on landing: 28.91

   c. CG position on departure: 21.18 CG position on landing: 21.68

   d. CG position on departure: 22.01 CG position on landing: 22.10

4.   Given:

Aircraft planned take-off weight: 2300 lb
CG on departure: 85.75 inches aft of datum
Fuel burn: 300 lb (position 82 inches aft of datum)

On landing what is the calculated CG position?

   a.   86.31 inches aft of datum
   b.   110.9 inches aft of datum
   c.   75.05 inches aft of datum
   d.   66.39 inches aft of datum

5.   Given:

Aircraft planned take-off weight: 2200 lb
CG on departure: 84.75 inches aft of datum
Fuel burn: 200 lb (position 81 inches aft of datum)

On landing what is the calculated CG position?

   a.   70.94 inches aft of datum
   b.   101.3 inches aft of datum
   c.   88.225 inches aft of datum
   d.   85.125 inches aft of datum

6.   Given:

Aircraft planned take-off weight: 2300 lb
CG on departure: 90.75 inches aft of datum
Fuel burn: 170 lb (position 87 inches aft of datum)

On landing what is the calculated CG position?

   a.   78.52 inches aft of datum
   b.   91.05 inches aft of datum
   c.   89.88 inches aft of datum
   d.   90.49 inches aft of datum

7.   Before refuelling an aircraft weighs 1800 lbs, the total moment was 151,200 lb in. 310 lb of fuel are then loaded having an arm 90 inches aft of the datum. The total moment is...(i)... and the aircraft's CG will now be ...(ii)...:

   a.   i) 123,300 lb in   ii) 82.75 inches aft of the datum
   b.   i) 155,200 lb in   ii) 73.55 inches aft of the datum
   c.   i) 133,400 lb in   ii) 83.01 inches aft of the datum
   d.   i) 179,100 lb in   ii) 84.88 inches aft of the datum

8.   Before refuelling an aircraft weighs 1900 lbs, the total moment was 162,200 lb in. 400 lb of fuel are then loaded having an arm 12 ft aft of the datum. The aircraft's CG will now be:

   a.   72.60 inches aft of the datum
   b.   95.56 inches aft of the datum
   c.   69.73 inches aft of the datum
   d.   111.33 inches aft of the datum

9. Selecting full flap on approach allows a pilot to adopt a ... (i)... approach path and/or a ...(ii)...approach speed.

   a.   i) more shallow   ii) faster

   b.   i) steeper   ii) slower

   c.   i) steeper   ii) faster

   d.   i) more shallow   ii) slower

10. An overloaded aircraft:

   a.   May have a longer take-off run but will have good climb performance

   b.   Will have a lower stalling speed and be more manoeuvrable

   c.   Will handle and perform badly and, if flown, may suffer structural damage

   d.   May have a lower take-off speed and a shorter range

11. By how much should you expect the landing distance to increase when landing on very short, wet grass with firm soil?

   a.   60%

   b.   50%

   c.   40%

   d.   30%

12. An aircraft is loaded as follows:

Departure mass: 1010 kg
Total moment: 930 kg.m

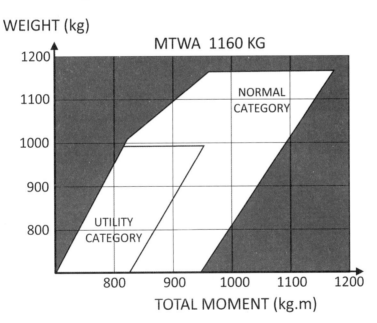

With reference to the centre of gravity envelope chart below which of the following statements is correct?

   a.   The aircraft centre of gravity lies within the utility category and angles of bank exceeding 60° are permitted

   b.   The aircraft centre of gravity lies within the normal category and angles of bank exceeding 60° are permitted

   c.   The aircraft centre of gravity lies within the utility category and angles of bank exceeding 60° are not permitted

   d.   The aircraft centre of gravity lies within the normal category and angles of bank exceeding 60° are not permitted

13. One important reason for taking off into a headwind is:

a. To enable the aircraft to lift off at a higher speed and have a longer ground run

b. To enable the aircraft to lift off at a higher speed and have a shorter ground run

c. To enable the aircraft to lift off at a lower speed and have a shorter ground run

d. To enable the aircraft to lift off at a lower speed and have a longer ground run

14. When operating from a grass runway pilots can expect:

a. The Landing Distance Required to increase due to reduced braking efficiency

b. The Landing Distance Required to be unaffected, especially if the grass is short

c. The Landing Distance Required to decrease if the grass is wet

d. The Landing Distance Required to reduce due to increased friction from the grass

15. Taking off from sea level you intend to climb to 6,000 feet. Assuming a standard atmosphereand that you adopt the recommended climb speed, from the table below determine:

i) the time it will take to reach 6,000 feet

ii) the fuel used from start up; and

iii) the distance flown during the climb

TIME, FUEL AND DISTANCE TO CLIMB
AT 2390 POUNDS
CONDITIONS: FLAPS UP, FULL THROTTLE, STANDARD TEMPERATURE

PRESSURE ALTITUDE FT	TEMP °C	CLIMB SPEED KIAS	RATE OF CLIMB FPM	FROM SEA LEVEL		
				TIME IN MINUTES	FUEL USED GAL	DISTANCE NM
SEA LEVEL	15	82	760	0	0.0	0
1000	13	81	710	1	0.5	2
2000	11	80	670	3	0.9	4
3000	9	79	630	4	1.3	6
4000	7	78	595	6	1.7	9
5000	5	77	550	8	2	12
6000	3	76	505	10	2.4	15
7000	1	75	475	14	2.9	19
8000	-1	74	420	18	3.4	23
9000	-3	73	380	22	4	25
10000	-5	72	315	25	5.4	30

NOTES:
1. Add 1.3 gallons of fuel for engine start, taxi and take-off
2. Increase time, fuel and distance by 10% for each 10°C above standard temperature
3. Distances based on zero wind
4. Mixture leaned above 3,000 feet for maximum RPM

a. i) 10   ii) 2.4   iii) 15

b. i) 14   ii) 2.9   iii) 19

c. i) 10   ii) 3.7   iii) 15

d. i) 10   ii) 2.4   iii) 19

16. An aircraft is cruising at 4,000 feet, the pilot decides to climb to 8,000 feet. From the table above determine:

     i)   the time it will take to reach 8,000 feet
     ii)   the fuel used; and
     iii)   the distance flown during the climb

     Assume a standard atmosphere and that the recommended climb speed is used.
     a.   i) 18   ii) 3.4   iii) 23
     b.   i) 12   ii) 1.7   iii) 14
     c.   i) 6   ii) 1.7   iii) 9
     d.   i) 10   ii) 2.4   iii) 15

17. Carburettor icing is more likely:

     a.   At high level
     b.   In the winter
     c.   At high power settings, when the throttle butterfly is fully open
     d.   At low power settings, when the throttle butterfly is only partially open

18. Any ice accretion on an aircraft's wing will cause:

     a.   Weight and drag to increase, and lift to reduce significantly
     b.   Weight, drag and lift to reduce significantly
     c.   Weight and drag to decrease, but lift to increase
     d.   Weight and drag to increase, but will have no effect on the lift generated

19. Compared with gliding in still air, gliding with a tailwind will ... (i)... the distance covered over the ground and will ...(ii)... the rate of descent:

     a.   i) reduce   ii) reduce
     b.   i) increase   ii) not change
     c.   i) increase   ii) increase
     d.   i) not change   ii) reduce

MAXIMUM RATE OF CLIMB AT 2300 POUNDS

CONDITIONS:
Full Throttle
Flaps Up

PRESSURE ALTITUDE FEET	CLIMB SPEED KIAS	RATE OF CLIMB - FPM			
		-20°C	0°C	20°C	40°C
S.L.	80	840	780	720	630
2000	79	740	675	615	555
4000	77	675	595	535	475
6000	75	550	485	435	380
8000	73	440	375	320	260
10000	71	330	275	220	165
12000	69	210	145	- - -	- - -

20. Using the table on the facing page. For an aircraft weighing 2300 pounds flying at a pressure altitude of 7,000 feet with an OAT of minus 10°C the maximum rate of climb will be:

    a.   460 fpm

    b.   490 fpm

    c.   430 fpm

    d.   510 fpm

END OF FLIGHT PLANNING AND PERFORMANCE PAPER 3

INTENTIONALLY BLANK

FLIGHT PLANNING & PERFORMANCE
PAPER 3: ANSWERS

	A	B	C	D
1.				X
2.		X		
3.	X			
4.	X			
5.				X
6.		X		
7.				X
8.		X		
9.		X		
10.			X	
11.	X			
12.				X
13.			X	
14.	X			
15			X	
16.		X		
17.				X
18.	X			
19.		X		
20.	X			

CORRECT ANSWERS: PERCENTAGES					
15	16	17	18	19	20
87%	90%	92%	95%	97%	100%

FLIGHT PLANNING AND PERFORMANCE
PAPER 3: EXPLANATIONS

1. **(Answer: D)** A runway with a uphill slope will decrease the landing distance and will increase the take off distance as the aircraft will accelerate faster. A 2% up slope will increase the take off distance by 10%, a factor of 1.1. AIC 127/2006 (Pink 110)

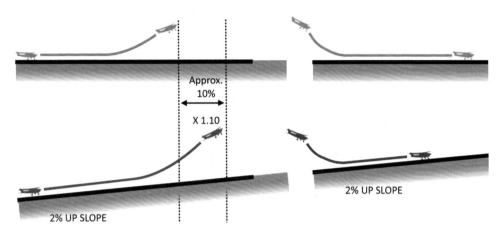

2. **(Answer: B)** 189 l

   The first thing to do is find out the weight available to use for fuel:
   2400 - (1600 + 320 + 30 + 140 + 10) = 300 lbs

   Max Take off Mass Authorised 2400 lbs
   Max Landing Mass Authorised 2300 lbs
   CG limits: 18 to 22 inches aft of datum

Item	Mass (lb)	Arm	Moment (lb In)
Basic Mass	1600	+27	+43,200
Pilot & Front Passenger	320	−6	−1,920
Oil (SG 0.8)	30	−17	−510
Rear Passengers	140	+24	+3,360
Baggage	10	+42	+420
Fuel (SG 0.72)	300	+20	
TOTAL	**2400**		

   Next we need to find out how many litres weigh 300 lb. There are two ways to tackle these problems either mathematically or using the CPR Flight Computer.

   Mathematically: 300 lb ÷ 2.2 = 136.4 kg
   We are told in the loading graph that the specific gravity of the fuel is 0.72. A specific gravity of 0.72 means that Avgas weighs only 0.72 times as much as an equal volume of water. One litre of water weighs 1 kg, so one litre of Avgas weighs 0.72 kg.
   136.4 ÷ 0.72 = 189.3 lt

CRP-1: Set the 300 on the rotating inner scale below 72 on the Imperial specific gravity scale. Below the km-m-ltr index on the fixed outer scale, we can read off 190 on the inner scale. Obviously this is jolly close to 189 lt!

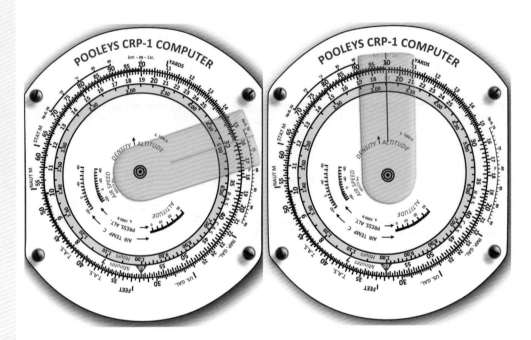

3.   **(Answer: A)** CG position on departure: 21.08 inches aft of datum.

CG position on landing: 21.18 inches aft of datum

Load sheet for departure:

Item	Mass (lb)	Arm	Moment (lb ln)
Basic Mass	1600	+27	+43,200
Pilot & Front Passenger	320	−6	−1,920
Oil (SG 0.8)	30	−17	−510
Rear Passengers	140	+24	+3,360
Baggage	10	+42	+420
Fuel (SG 0.72)	250	+20	+5,000
TOTAL	**2400**		**+49,550**

CG position on departure $= \dfrac{49550}{2,350} = 21.08$ inches aft of datum

Load sheet for landing:

Item	Mass (lb)	Arm	Moment (lb ln)
Basic Mass	1600	+27	+43,200
Pilot & Front Passenger	320	−6	−1,920
Oil (SG 0.8)	30	−17	−510
Rear Passengers	140	+24	+3,360
Baggage	10	+42	+420
Fuel (SG 0.72)	50	+20	+1,000
TOTAL	**2150**		**+45,550**

CG position on landing $= \dfrac{45,550}{2,150} = 21.18$ inches aft of datum

4.   **(Answer: A)** 86.31 inches aft of datum

Given:

Aircraft planned take-off weight: 2300 lb
CG on departure: 85.75 inches aft of datum
Fuel burn: 300 lb (position 82 inches aft of datum)

Method:

1. Find the aircraft moment on departure = weight X moment arm = 2300 x 85.75   = 197,225 lb in
2. Find the moment arm of the fuel used: 300 x 82 = 24,600 lb in
3. Find the landing moment by subtracting the fuel used moment from the departure moment: 197,225 – 24,600 = 172,625 lb in
4. Find the landing weight: 2300 – 300 = 2000 lb
5. Finally divide the landing moment by the landing weight to find the CG position on landing: $\frac{172,625}{2000} = 86.31$ inches aft of datum

5.   **(Answer: D)** 85.125 inches aft of datum

Given:

Aircraft planned take-off weight: 2200 lb
CG on departure: 84.75 inches aft of datum
Fuel burn: 200 lb (position 81 inches aft of datum)

Method:

1. Find the aircraft moment on departure = weight X moment arm = 2200 x 84.75 = 186,450 lb in
2. Find the moment arm of the fuel used: 200 x 81 = 16,200 lb in
3. Find the landing moment by subtracting the fuel used moment from the departure moment: 186,450 – 16,200 = 170,250 lb in
4. Find the landing weight: 2200 – 200 = 2000 lb
5. Finally divide the landing moment by the landing weight to find the CG position on landing: $\frac{170,250}{2000} = 85.125$ inches aft of datum

6.   **(Answer: B)** 91.05 inches aft of datum

Given:

Aircraft planned take-off weight: 2300 lb
CG on departure: 90.75 inches aft of datum
Fuel burn: 170 lb (position 87 inches aft of datum)

Method:

1. Find the aircraft moment on departure = weight X moment arm = 2300 x 90.75 = 208,725 lb in
2. Find the moment arm of the fuel used: 170 x 87 = 14,790 lb in
3. Find the landing moment by subtracting the fuel used moment from the departure moment: 208,725 – 14,790 = 193,935 lb in
4. Find the landing weight: 2300 – 170 = 2130 lb
5. Finally divide the landing moment by the landing weight to find the CG position on landing: 193,935 ÷ 2130 = 91.05 inches aft of datum

7.   **(Answer: D)** Total moment: 179,100 lb in; CG position: 84.88 inches aft of the datum

Given:

Before refuelling aircraft weight: 1800 lbs
Total moment: 151,200 lb in.
Weight of fuel: 310 lb of fuel (position 90 inches aft of the datum)

	Weight	Moment Arm	Moment
Aircraft	1800		151,200
Fuel	310	90	27,900
TOTAL	**2110**		**179,100**

CG position = total moment ÷ total weight = 179,100 ÷ 2110 = 84.88 inches aft of the datum

8.   **(Answer: B)** CG position: 95.56 inches aft of the datum

Given:

Before refuelling aircraft weight: 1900 lbs
Moment: 162,200 lb in.
Weight of fuel: 400 lb (position 12 ft aft of the datum)

Note the catch here, the fuel CG position is given in feet. This must be converted to inches for the calculation:
12 x 12 = 144 inches

	Weight	Moment Arm	Moment
Aircraft	1900		162,200
Fuel	400	144	57,600
TOTAL	**2300**		**219,800**

CG position= total moment ÷ total weight = 219,800 ÷ 2300 = 95.56 inches aft of the datum

9.   **(Answer: B)** The use of flap on approach allows a steeper approach path to be flown (providing better forward vision) and a slower approach speed to be adopted.

Lift = CL ½pV2S

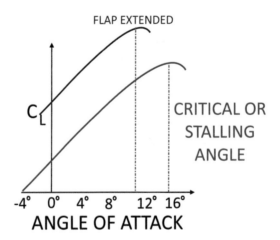

Flaps enable the lift required to oppose the aircraft's weight to be generated at a lower speed and the aircraft will stall at a lower indicated airspeed. Since the approach speed is calculated on the stalling speed in the landing configuration ($V_{AT} = V_{SO}$ x 1.3) the approach speed will be reduced.

10. **(Answer: C)** An overweight aircraft will handle and perform badly and, if flown, may sufferstructural damage.

Other effects of increased weight are:
Higher take off speed
Longer take off run
Higher stalling speed
Reduced climb performance (both rate and angle of climb)
Increased fuel consumption and so less endurance
Shorter range
Higher landing speed and longer landing distance
Reduced manoeuvrability

11. **(Answer: A)** A low friction surface such as grass or snow increase the ground roll, as despite the increased rolling resistance of the surface brake effectiveness is reduced and this is the more significant factor.

Guide line factors:
Dry grass (under 8 inches) the landing distance will be increased by 15% (a factor of x 1.15).
Wet grass (under 8 inches) the landing distance will be increased by 35% (a factor of x 1.35).
When the grass is very short, the surface may be slippery and distances may increase by up to 60%
(a factor of x 1.60)
For snow, the landing distance will be increased by 25% or more (a factor of at least x 1.25).
AIC 127/2006 (Pink 110)

12. **(Answer: D)** The aircraft centre of gravity lies within the normal category and angles of bank exceeding 60° are not permitted.

Departure mass: 1010 kg
Total moment: 930 kg.m

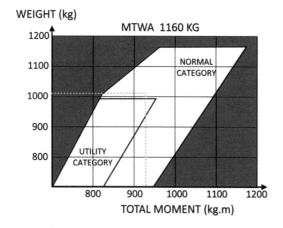

JAR 23.3 states:
The normal category is limited to non-aerobatic operations. Non-aerobatic operations include –
(1) Any manoeuvre incident to normal flying;
(2) Stalls (except whip stalls); and
(3) Lazy eights, chandelles and steep turns or similar manoeuvres, in which the angle of bank is not more than 60°.
The utility category is limited to any of the operations covered in the normal category; plus -
(1) Spins (if approved for the particular type of aeroplane); and
(2) Lazy eights, chandelles, and steep turns, or similar manoeuvres in which the angle of bank is more than 60° but not more than 90°.

See also the UK General Aviation Safety Sense Leaflet number 9.

13. **(Answer: C)** One important reason for taking-off into a headwind is to enable the aircraft to lift off at a lower speed and have a shorter ground run. A headwind can be considered as free airspeed towards that required to lift off; also once airborne the climb gradient relative to the ground is improved giving better obstacle clearance. A tailwind has the opposite effect; a tailwind component of 10% of the lift off speed will increase the take off distance by 20%.

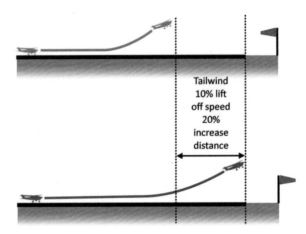

14. **(Answer: A)** When operating from a grass runway pilots can expect the Landing Distance Required to increase due to reduced braking efficiency. (Part of graph from Safety leaflet)

15. **(Answer: C)**

   i) the time it will take to reach 6,000 feet = 10 minutes
   ii) the fuel used from start up = 3.7 (From the notes section do not forget to " Add 1.3 gallons of fuel for engine start, taxi and take-off")
   iii) the distance flown during the climb = 15 nm

TIME, FUEL AND DISTANCE TO CLIMB
AT 2390 POUNDS
CONDITIONS: FLAPS UP, FULL THROTTLE, STANDARD TEMPERATURE

PRESSURE ALTITUDE FT	TEMP °C	CLIMB SPEED KIAS	RATE OF CLIMB FPM	TIME IN MINUTES	FUEL USED GAL	DISTANCE NM
SEA LEVEL	15	82	760	0	0.0	0
1000	13	81	710	1	0.5	2
2000	11	80	670	3	0.9	4
3000	9	79	630	4	1.3	6
4000	7	78	595	6	1.7	9
5000	5	77	550	8	2	12
6000	3	76	505	10	2.4	15
7000	1	75	475	14	2.9	19
8000	-1	74	420	18	3.4	23
9000	-3	73	380	22	4	25
10000	-5	72	315	25	5.4	30

NOTES:
1. Add 1.3 gallons of fuel for engine start, taxi and take-off
2. Increase time, fuel and distance by 10% for each 10°C above standard temperature
3. Distances based on zero wind
4. Mixture leaned above 3,000 feet for maximum RPM

16. (Answer: B)

   i)   the time it will take to reach 8,000 feet = 12 minutes
   ii) the fuel used = 1.7 gallons
   iii) the distance flown during the climb = 14 nm

The table is compiled as if the aircraft is climbing from sea level; intermediate data must be interpolated. Begin by entering the table at the level to which the aircraft will climb, 8,000 feet in this case and note the details; next obtain the values for the level from which climb is commenced, in this instance 4,000 feet and subtract them from the 8,000 feet numbers.

TIME, FUEL AND DISTANCE TO CLIMB
AT 2390 POUNDS
CONDITIONS: FLAPS UP, FULL THROTTLE, STANDARD TEMPERATURE

PRESSURE ALTITUDE FT	TEMP °C	CLIMB SPEED KIAS	RATE OF CLIMB FPM	FROM SEA LEVEL		
				TIME IN MINUTES	FUEL USED GAL	DISTANCE NM
SEA LEVEL	15	82	760	0	0.0	0
1000	13	81	710	1	0.5	2
2000	11	80	670	3	0.9	4
3000	9	79	630	4	1.3	6
4000	7	78	595	6	1.7	9
5000	5	77	550	8	2	12
6000	3	76	505	10	2.4	15
7000	1	75	475	14	2.9	19
8000	-1	74	420	18	3.4	23
9000	-3	73	380	22	4	25
10000	-5	72	315	25	5.4	30

NOTES:
1. Add 1.3 gallons of fuel for engine start, taxi and take-off
2. Increase time, fuel and distance by 10% for each 10°C above standard temperature
3. Distances based on zero wind
4. Mixture leaned above 3,000 feet for maximum RPM

	Time in Minutes	Fuel used Gal	Distance NM
8,000 feet	18	3.4	23
4,000 feet	6	1.7	9
8,000 – 4,000 feet	12	1.7	14

17. (Answer: D) Throttle icing: occurs when the fuel/air mix accelerates past the throttle butterfly valve leading to a temperature drop, and to the possibility of ice forming on the throttle valve. At small throttle openings the acceleration and temperature drop are at their greatest, a situation exacerbated by the fact that at small throttle openings not a great deal of ice is necessary to from a blockage. For this reason there is a greater likelihood of carburettor icing at reduced power settings.

18. (Answer: A) Ice accretion on wings adds a great deal of weight and significantly increases drag. Additionally it can drastically reduce the lift generated by a wing; this is especially true when ice forms on the upper surface.

19. **(Answer: B)** Compared with gliding in still air, gliding with a tailwind will increase the distance covered over the ground but will not change the rate of descent.

When gliding with a tailwind, the aircraft is moving over the ground at its TAS plus the speed of the moving airmass, it will therefore travel further over the ground than in still air. The glide angle is considered relative to the airmass and is thus unaffected by the wind. The aircraft has the same TAS, the same nose attitude, the same angle of attack and the same rate of descent whether flying in still air or a head/tailwind. Rate of descent refers to time, so the aircraft will remain airborne for the same amount of time regardless of wind, but will travel further in that time with a tailwind.

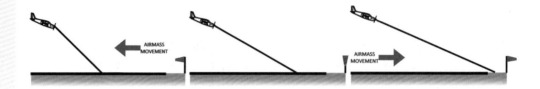

20. **(Answer: A)** 460 fpm

PRESSURE ALTITUDE FEET	CLIMB SPEED KIAS	RATE OF CLIMB - FPM			
		-20°C	0°C	20°C	40°C
S.L.	80	840	780	720	630
2000	79	740	675	615	555
4000	77	675	595	535	475
6000	75	550	485	435	380
8000	73	440	375	320	260
10000	71	330	275	220	165
12000	69	210	145	- - -	- - -

MAXIMUM RATE OF CLIMB AT 2300 POUNDS
CONDITIONS: Full Throttle, Flaps Up

This is a two-stage process. First we must find the values at 7,000 feet for both -20°C and at 0°C and then interpolate between our results.

In the performance table pressure altitudes are given at 2,000 ft intervals, thus to find the maximum rate of climb at 7,000 feet with an OAT of -20°C and 0°C we must interpolate between the figures given.

The 7,000 ft rate of climb at -20°C = (550 + 440) ÷ 2 = 490 fpm
The 7,000 ft rate of climb at -0°C = (485 + 375) ÷ 2 = 430 fpm

To find the 7,000 ft rate of climb at -10°C interpolate between these answers. As the temperature is exactly half way between the values we have: (490 + 430) ÷ 2 = 460 fpm

FLIGHT PLANNING AND PERFORMANCE
PAPER 4

1. Given:

   Aircraft planned take-off weight: 2450 lb
   CG on departure: 88.7 inches aft of datum
   Fuel burn: 240 lb (position 85 inches aft of datum)

   On landing what is the calculated CG position?
   a. 107.5 inches aft of datum
   b. 89.1 inches aft of datum
   c. 73.2 inches aft of datum
   d. 80.37 inches aft of datum

2. Before refuelling an aircraft weighs 2100 lbs, the total moment was 170,800 lb in. 350 lb of fuel are then loaded having an arm 86.7 inches aft of the datum. The aircraft's CG will now be:

   a. 80.26 inches aft of datum
   b. 57.32 inches aft of datum
   c. 95.7 inches aft of datum
   d. 82.1 inches aft of datum

3. When compared to still air conditions, with a strong tailwind the best range speed will be:

   a. Slower
   b. Faster
   c. Higher or lower, depending upon the cruise altitude
   d. Unaffected

4. You have planned an early morning departure. The aircraft requires a measured take off distance to a height of 50 feet of 350 m and you calculated the TODR as 512 m using a 2% upslope runway, a 1900 lb aircraft, and an OAT of +10°C.

   Poor visibility prevents your planned early departure, and by the time departure is possible the OAT is +20°C and your friend weighing 190lb can now make the trip. What is the new TODR?
   a. 614 m
   b. 676 m
   c. 898 m
   d. 563 m

5. Using small flap settings (up to 20°) on take-off will:

   a. Provide a large increase in lift and a large increase in drag. The take-off run will not be affected
   b. Provide a small increase in lift and a large increase in drag. The take-off run will be reduced
   c. Provide a large increase in lift and a small increase in drag. The take-off run will be reduced
   d. Provide a small increase in lift and a small increase in drag. The take-off run will be reduced

6. V_2, the take-off safety speed is:

   a. V_{S1} x 1.2 and should provide at least a 20% margin above the stalling speed
   b. V_{S1} x 1.33 and should provide at least a 33% margin above the stalling speed
   c. V_{NO} x 1.2 and should provide at least a 20% margin above the stalling speed
   d. V_{NE} x 1.33 and should provide at least a 33% margin above the stalling speed

7. An increase in gross weight will ... (i) ... the speed at which the aircraft rotates and ... (ii) ... the take-off safety speed:

     a.   i) increase   ii) increase

     b.   i) increase   ii) decrease

     c.   i) decrease   ii) increase

     d.   i) decrease   ii) decrease

8. Using the table above determine the i) % BHP ii) TAS and iii) fuel burn for an aircraft cruising in an atmosphere 20°C above standard at 6,000 feet with a constant RPM of 2100.

     a.   i) 69 ii) 117 iii) 9.0

     b.   i) 61 ii) 107 iii) 8.1

     c.   i) 65 ii) 109 iii) 8.5

     d.   i) 59 ii) 105 iii) 7.9

9. Using the table above determine the i) % BHP ii) TAS and iii) fuel burn for an aircraft cruising in a standard atmosphere at 4,000 feet with a constant RPM of 2200.

     a.   i) 69 ii) 115 iii) 9.0

     b.   i) 68 ii) 114 iii) 8.9

     c.   i) 72 ii) 115 iii) 9.4

     d.   i) 77 ii) 117 iii) 9.9

CRUISE PERFORMANCE

CONDITIONS: 2500 POUNDS, RECOMMENDED LEAN MIXTURE AT ALL ALTITUDES

PRESSURE ALTITUDE	RPM	20°C BELOW STANDARD TEMPERATURE			STANDARD TEMPERATURE			20°C ABOVE STANDARD TEMPERATURE		
		% BHP	KTAS	GPH	% BHP	KTAS	GPH	% BHP	KTAS	GPH
2000	2300	- - -	- - -	- - -	81	119	10.3	76	120	9.8
	2250	81	116	10.4	76	116	9.8	72	115	9.3
	2150	71	111	9.2	67	110	8.8	64	109	8.4
	2050	63	105	8.3	60	103	7.9	57	101	7.7
	1950	56	100	7.5	53	95	7.2	52	93	7.1
4000	2350	- - -	- - -	- - -	81	121	10.4	77	121	9.9
	2300	82	119	10.5	77	118	9.9	72	118	9.4
	2200	77	117	9.9	72	115	9.4	68	114	8.9
	2100	68	110	8.9	64	109	8.4	61	107	8.1
	2000	60	104	8	57	102	7.7	55	99	7.5
	1900	54	96	7.3	52	94	7.1	51	97	6.9
6000	2400	- - -	- - -	- - -	82	124	10.5	77	123	9.9
	2350	82	121	10.5	77	121	9.9	72	120	9.4
	2300	78	119	10	73	118	9.4	69	117	9
	2200	73	116	9.4	69	115	9	66	113	8.6
	2100	65	109	8.5	62	108	8.2	59	105	7.9
	2000	58	102	7.7	55	100	7.5	54	97	7.3

10. Whilst flying in the vicinity of a broken layer of cumulus cloud, you notice ice building on the wings. The most appropriate action to take is to:

    a.   Climb above the cloud

    b.   Continue your current flight path, but closely monitor the situation

    c.   Descend into warmer air, or make a 180° turn

    d.   Climb into warmer air

11. Overloading an aircraft will:

    a.   Improve both the range and endurance

    b.   Slow acceleration and increase the take-off run

    c.   Reduce the rate of climb, but will not affect the maximum operating altitude

    d.   Increase the aircraft's manoeuvrability

12. Advice is contained in a Safety Sense Leaflet regarding the effect of runway surface on distances required. It states that when landing on dry grass (less than 8 inches long) will ... (i) ... the landing distance by ... (ii) ...; landing on very short wet grass will ... (iii) ... the landing distance by up to ... (iv) ...:

    a.   i) increase ii) 10% iii) increase iv) 30%

    b.   i) increase ii) 20% iii) decrease iv) 50%

    c.   i) decrease ii) 10% iii) decrease iv) 30%

    d.   i) increase ii) 20% iii) increase iv) 60%

13. If an aircraft is loaded so that the CG is at the forward limit, the aircraft will:

    a.   Experience a decrease in longitudinal stability

    b.   Be very stable in pitch and require high elevator forces during the flare

    c.   Experience a reduction in the stalling speed

    d.   Be very stable in pitch and require only small elevator forces during the flare

14. If an aircraft is loaded so that the CG is at the aft limit, the aircraft will:

    a.   Be more stable in pitch

    b.   Have a higher stalling speed

    c.   Require a reduction in elevator force required during the flare

    d.   Require an increase in elevator force required during the flare

15. With all tanks full an aircraft holds 380 litres of fuel. If the specific gravity (SG) of the fuel is 0.72, what is the approximate weight of the fuel in pounds?

    a.   602 lbs

    b.   274 lbs

    c.   158 lbs

    d.   699 lbs

PRESSURE ALTITUDE FEET	CLIMB SPEED KIAS	RATE OF CLIMB - FPM			
		-20°C	0°C	20°C	40°C
S.L.	80	840	780	720	630
2000	79	740	675	615	555
4000	77	675	595	535	475
6000	75	550	485	435	380
8000	73	430	375	320	260
10000	71	330	275	220	165
12000	69	210	145	---	---

MAXIMUM RATE OF CLIMB AT 2300 POUNDS
CONDITIONS: Full Throttle, Flaps Up

16. Use the table above to determine the following:

    For an aircraft weighing 2300 pounds flying at a pressure altitude of 2,000 feet with an OAT of minus 10°C the maximum rate of climb will be:

    a.   635 fpm
    b.   810 fpm
    c.   642 fpm
    d.   705 fpm

17. If the aircraft below is fuelled with 200 lbs of fuel, of which 120 lbs will be burned during the flight what is the CG position on departure and on landing?

    Max Take off Mass Authorised 2400 lbs
    Max Landing Mass Authorised 2300 lbs
    CG limits: 18 to 22 inches aft of datum

Item	Mass (lb)	Arm	Moment (lb In)
Basic Mass	1600	+27	+43,200
Pilot & Front Passenger	320	–6	–1,920
Oil (SG 0.8)	30	–17	–510
Rear Passengers	140	+24	+3,360
Baggage	10	+42	+420
Fuel (SG 0.72)	200	+20	
TOTAL			

    a.   CG position on departure: 22.2 CG position on landing: 22.1
    b.   CG position on departure: 21.10 CG position on landing: 21.17
    c.   CG position on departure: 20.5 CG position on landing: 27.9
    d.   CG position on departure: 21.18 CG position on landing: 21.68

18. What is the gradient of a 2500 ft runway which has threshold elevations of 355 and 460 feet?

    a.   4.2 %
    b.   32.6 %
    c.   6.5 %
    d.   3.7 %

19. Refer to the Take Off Performance Graph to answer the following:

Given:

OAT: +30°C
Pressure Altitude: 3,000 feet
Aircraft Weight: 2900 lbs
Surface Wind: 30 knots Headwind

What is the approximate take off distance required to reach a screen height of 50ft?

a.　　1000 feet
b.　　1540 feet
c.　　990 feet
d.　　1380 feet

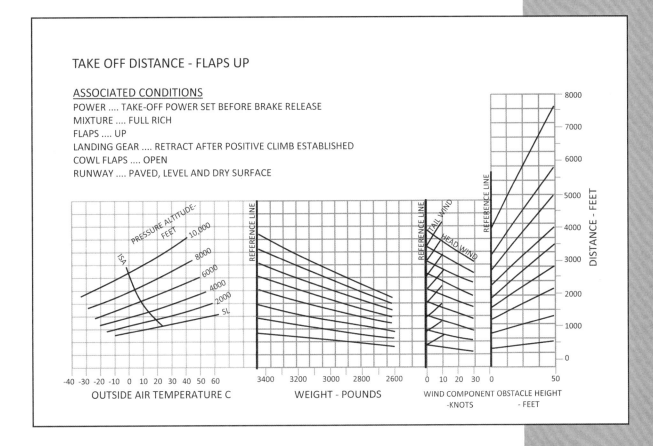

20. The best rate of climb:

a.　　Gains the greatest amount of height in the shortest time
b.　　Gains the greatest amount of height in the shortest distance over the ground
c.　　Gains the greatest amount of height with the greatest horizontal speed
d.　　Gains the greatest amount of height in the greatest distance over the ground

END OF FLIGHT PLANNING AND PERFORMANCE PAPER 4

FLIGHT PLANNING AND PERFORMANCE
PAPER 4: ANSWERS

	A	B	C	D
1.		X		
2.				X
3.	X			
4.		X		
5.			X	
6.	X			
7.	X			
8.				X
9.			X	
10.			X	
11.		X		
12.				X
13.		X		
14.			X	
15	X			
16.				X
17.		X		
18.	X			
19.				X
20.	X			

CORRECT ANSWERS: PERCENTAGES					
15	16	17	18	19	20
87%	90%	92%	95%	97%	100%

1. **(Answer: B)** 89.1 inches aft of datum

   Given:

   Aircraft planned take-off weight: 2450 lb
   CG on departure: 88.7 inches aft of datum
   Fuel burn: 240 lb (position 85 inches aft of datum)

   Method:
   1. Find the aircraft moment on departure = weight X moment arm = 2450 x 88.7 = 217,315 lb in
   2. Find the moment arm of the fuel used: 240 x 85 = 20,400 lb in
   3. Find the landing moment by subtracting the fuel used moment from the departure moment:
      217,315 – 20,400 = 196,915 lb in
   4. Find the landing weight: 2450 – 240 = 2210 lb
   5. Finally divide the landing moment by the landing weight to find the CG position on landing:
      196,915 ÷ 2210 = 89.1 inches aft of datum

2. **(Answer: D)** 82.1 inches aft of the datum

   Before refuelling, an aircraft weighs 2100 lbs, the total moment was 170,800 lb in. 350 lb of fuel are then loaded having an arm 86.7 inches aft of the datum. The aircraft's CG will now be:

   Given:

   Before refuelling aircraft weight: 2100 lbs
   Moment: 170,800 lb in.
   Weight of fuel: 350 lb (position 86.7 inches aft of the datum)

	Weight	Moment Arm	Moment
Aircraft	2100		170,800
Fuel	350	86.7	30,345
TOTAL	**2450**		**201,145**

   CG position= total moment ÷ total weight = 201,145 ÷ 2450 = 82.1 inches aft of the datum

3. **(Answer: A)** When compared to still air conditions, with a strong tailwind to help progress, the best range speed will be slower. As the tailwind is assisting progress over the ground, we can reduce the power and consequently the fuel consumption and still achieve the best range. In headwind conditions the best range speed is faster than the still air best range, as even though fuel consumption will be greater flying faster will give the headwind less time to act on the aircraft.

4. **(Answer: B)** Any factors applied to the calculated take-off distance must be multiplied.

   Originally the TODR: 350 x 1.1 (2% upslope) x 1.33 (safety factor) = 512 m
   The new TODR for the later departure: 350 x 1.1 (2% upslope) x 1.2 (10% increase weight) x 1.1 (10°C increase temp) x 1.33 (safety factor) = 676 m

5.   **(Answer: C)** Using small flap settings (up to 20°) on take-off will provide a large increase in lift and a small increase in drag. The take-off run will be reduced.

Take-off flap refers to relatively small flap settings up to around 20°. Extra lift is generated by altering the effective camber of the wing, this happens with a fairly small drag penalty. The result is a slower lift off speed, a slower take-off safety speed and a shorter take-off ground run required. However, once airborne flap will reduce both the rate and angle of climb so the take-off distance (the distance to reach 50 ft) may not be significantly reduced.

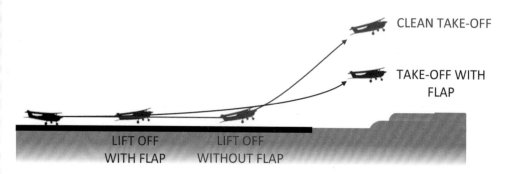

Landing flap is the term used to describe flap settings between 20° and 40°. These settings create large amounts of drag with relatively little increase in lift.

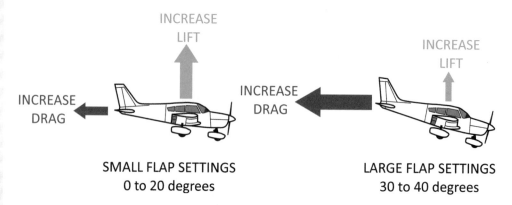

6.   **(Answer: A)** V_2, the take-off safety speed is V_{S1} x 1.2 and should provide at least a 20% margin above the stalling speed.

7.   **(Answer: A)** An increase in gross weight will increase the speed at which the aircraft rotates and increase the take-off safety speed.

The lift generated by a wing is proportional to speed for a given angle of attack, should the aircraft's weight increase more lift is required to balance the extra weight and this must be generated by increasing speed. The speed at which the aircraft lifts off will therefore be higher. A heavier aircraft will also have a higher stalling speed.

The Take-Off Safety Speed is a function of V_{S1}, so, if the stall speed is higher the TOSS must also be higher. The take-off safety speed is V_{S1} x 1.2 and should provide at least a 20% margin above the stalling speed. The Take-Off Safety Speed is the speed that is assumed in performance calculations to be flown from lift off to a 50 ft screen height.

8.   **(Answer: D)** i) % BHP 59 ii) TAS 105 knots iii) Fuel burn 7.9 GPH

Enter the table at the appropriate level, in this question 6,000 feet, then move along to the second column which is the RPM and select the row for 2100 RPM. Finally select the last 3 columns of data, those for ISA +20°C.

CRUISE PERFORMANCE

CONDITIONS: 2500 POUNDS, RECOMMENDED LEAN MIXTURE AT ALL ALTITUDES

PRESSURE ALTITUDE	RPM	20°C BELOW STANDARD TEMPERATURE			STANDARD TEMPERATURE			20°C ABOVE STANDARD TEMPERATURE		
		% BHP	KTAS	GPH	% BHP	KTAS	GPH	% BHP	KTAS	GPH
2000	2300	- - -	- - -	- - -	81	119	10.3	76	120	9.8
	2250	81	116	10.4	76	116	9.8	72	115	9.3
	2150	71	111	9.2	67	110	8.8	64	109	8.4
	2050	63	105	8.3	60	103	7.9	57	101	7.7
	1950	56	100	7.5	53	95	7.2	52	93	7.1
4000	2350	- - -	- - -	- - -	81	121	10.4	77	121	9.9
	2300	82	119	10.5	77	118	9.9	72	118	9.4
	2200	77	117	9.9	72	115	9.4	68	114	8.9
	2100	68	110	8.9	64	109	8.4	61	107	8.1
	2000	60	104	8	57	102	7.7	55	99	7.5
	1900	54	96	7.3	52	94	7.1	51	97	6.9
6000	2400	- - -	- - -	- - -	82	124	10.5	77	123	9.9
	2350	82	121	10.5	77	121	9.9	72	120	9.4
	2300	78	119	10	73	118	9.4	69	117	9
	2200	73	116	9.4	69	115	9	66	113	8.6
	2100	65	109	8.5	62	108	8.2	**59**	**105**	**7.9**
	2000	58	102	7.7	55	100	7.5	54	97	7.3

9.   **(Answer: C)** i) 72 % BHP ii) TAS 115 knots iii) Fuel burn 9.4 GPH

CRUISE PERFORMANCE

CONDITIONS: 2500 POUNDS, RECOMMENDED LEAN MIXTURE AT ALL ALTITUDES

PRESSURE ALTITUDE	RPM	20°C BELOW STANDARD TEMPERATURE			STANDARD TEMPERATURE			20°C ABOVE STANDARD TEMPERATURE		
		% BHP	KTAS	GPH	% BHP	KTAS	GPH	% BHP	KTAS	GPH
2000	2300	- - -	- - -	- - -	81	119	10.3	76	120	9.8
	2250	81	116	10.4	76	116	9.8	72	115	9.3
	2150	71	111	9.2	67	110	8.8	64	109	8.4
	2050	63	105	8.3	60	103	7.9	57	101	7.7
	1950	56	100	7.5	53	95	7.2	52	93	7.1
4000	2350	- - -	- - -	- - -	81	121	10.4	77	121	9.9
	2300	82	119	10.5	77	118	9.9	72	118	9.4
	2200	77	117	9.9	72	**115**	9.4	68	114	8.9
	2100	68	110	8.9	64	109	8.4	61	107	8.1
	2000	60	104	8	57	102	7.7	55	99	7.5
	1900	54	96	7.3	52	94	7.1	51	97	6.9
6000	2400	- - -	- - -	- - -	82	124	10.5	77	123	9.9
	2350	82	121	10.5	77	121	9.9	72	120	9.4
	2300	78	119	10	73	118	9.4	69	117	9
	2200	73	116	9.4	69	115	9	66	113	8.6
	2100	65	109	8.5	62	108	8.2	59	105	7.9
	2000	58	102	7.7	55	100	7.5	54	97	7.3

10.   **(Answer: C)** Whilst flying in the vicinity of a broken layer of cumulus cloud, you notice ice building on the wings. The most appropriate action to take is to descend into warmer air (if terrain permits) or reverse course to an area where you know icing conditions were not present. Ice accumulations on the wings will increase weight and disrupt laminar flow over the lift generating surfaces.

11.   **(Answer: B)** Overloading an aircraft will slow acceleration and increase the take-off run. Additionally, an overweight aircraft will handle and perform badly and, if flown, may suffer structural damage.

Other effects of increased weight are:
Higher take off speed
Longer take off run Higher stalling speed
Reduced climb performance (both rate and angle of climb)
Increased fuel consumption and so less endurance
Shorter range
Higher landing speed and longer landing distance
Reduced manoeuvrability

12. **(Answer: D)** Landing on dry grass (less than 8 inches long) will increase the landing distance by 20%; landing on very short wet grass will increase the landing distance by up to 60%.

Extract from Safety Sense Leaflet – Aeroplane performance:

Condition	Take Off		Landing	
	INCREASE IN DISTANCE TO HEIGHT 50 FEET	FACTOR	INCREASE IN LANDING DISTANCE FROM 50 FEET	FACTOR
Dry Grass – up to 8 in	20%	1.2	20%	1.2
Wet Grass – up to 8 in	30%	1.3	30%	1.3 When the grass is very short, the surface may be slippery and distances may increase by up to 60%

Rather annoyingly the AIC relating to light aircraft performance (127/2006 Pink 110) quotes slightly different figures:

Guide line factors from Pink 110:
For dry grass (under 8 inches) the landing distance will be increased by 15% (a factor of x 1.15).
For wet grass (under 8 inches) the landing distance will be increased by 35% (a factor of x 1.35).

NOTE 1: WHEN THE GRASS IS VERY SHORT, THE SURFACE MAY BE SLIPPERY AND DISTANCES
MAY INCREASE BY UP TO 60% (A FACTOR OF X 1.60)

At least both agree on the effect of very short, wet grass! Make sure you read the question carefully to determine exactly which source you are asked to quote.

13. **(Answer: B)** If the centre of gravity is at or close to its forward limit the aircraft's longitudinal stability is increased, i.e. it becomes more stable in pitch. This is because the tailplane has a very long moment arm (moment = force x distance).

The aircraft will feel extremely nose-heavy and resistant to changes in pitch. It is probable that the pilot may not be able to prevent the nose pitching down at low speed, for instance when landing, even with the control column fully aft.

Exceeding the forward limit may lead to:
Difficulty during rotation
Increased stall speed
Greater induced drag leading to increased fuel consumption and consequently reduced range
Difficulty in flying a stable approach
Difficulty in flaring during landing

14. **(Answer: C)** If the centre of gravity is at or close to its aft limit the aircraft's longitudinal stability is reduced, i.e. it becomes less stable in pitch. In this case the tailplane has its minimum moment arm; hence its effectiveness is reduced. With an aft C of G, lift generated from the wing will give a nose-up pitching moment, even a slight increase in angle of attack will cause the lift to increase and a greater nose-up pitching moment to be experienced. This cycle would repeat and eventually the aircraft would become uncontrollable in pitch leading to a stall from which recovery would be doubtful.

With an aft C of G it is the aircraft's natural tendency to pitch up meaning that only very slight elevator forces will be required in the flare. The danger here would be to over pitch and stall onto the runway.

Exceeding the aft limit may lead to:
Rotating early on take off
The danger of stalling during climb
Longitudinal instability
Degraded stall recovery

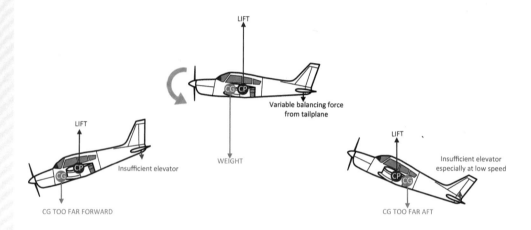

15. **(Answer: A)** There are two ways to tackle these problems - either mathematically or using the Pooleys CRP-1 Flight Computer.

Mathematically: a specific gravity of 0.72 means that Avgas weighs only 0.72 times as much as an equal volume of water. One litre of water weighs 1 kg, so one litre of Avgas weighs 0.72 kg. 380 litres x 0.72 = 273.6 kgs

However we are asked for an answer in pounds:
273.6 x 2.2 = 601.9 lbs

15. ANSWER A

CRP: Set the number of litres (380) under the litres index on the fixed outer scale. Also on the fixed outer scale are two scales for specific gravity (Sp. G) one in kgs and one in lbs. Below 72 on the Imperial Sp. G scale read off approximately 600 lb on the INNER rotating scale.

16.   (Answer: D) 705 fpm

PRESSURE ALTITUDE FEET	CLIMB SPEED KIAS	RATE OF CLIMB - FPM			
		-20°C	0°C	20°C	40°C
S.L.	80	840	780	720	630
2000	79	740	675	615	555
4000	77	675	595	535	475
6000	75	550	485	435	380
8000	73	430	375	320	260
10000	71	330	275	220	165
12000	69	210	145	- - -	- - -

MAXIMUM RATE OF CLIMB AT 2300 POUNDS
CONDITIONS: Full Throttle, Flaps Up

In the performance table temperatures are given at 20 degree intervals. Thus to find the maximum rate of climb at 2,000 feet with an OAT of -10°C we must interpolate between the figures given.

At 2,000 feet in the 0°C column we find the maximum rate of climb is 670 fpm; in the -20°C column it is 740 fpm. To find the value for -10°C add these two values together and, as -10°C is exactly half way in between the given values, divide by 2.
670 + 740 = 1410 ÷ 2 = 705 fpm

17.   (Answer: B)
CG position on departure: 21.10 inches aft of datum
CG position on landing: 21.17 inches aft of datum

Max Take off Mass Authorised 2400 lbs
Max Landing Mass Authorised 2300 lbs
CG limits: 18 to 22 inches aft of datum

Load sheet for departure:

Item	Mass (lb)	Arm	Moment (lb In)
Basic Mass	1600	+27	+43,200
Pilot & Front Passenger	320	−6	−1,920
Oil (SG 0.8)	30	−17	−510
Rear Passengers	140	+24	+3,360
Baggage	10	+42	+420
Fuel (SG 0.72)	200	+20	+4,000
TOTAL	**2,300**		**+48,550**

CG position on departure = 48,550 ÷ 2,300 = 21.10 inches aft of datum

Load sheet for landing:

Item	Mass (lb)	Arm	Moment (lb In)
Basic Mass	1600	+27	+43,200
Pilot & Front Passenger	320	−6	−1,920
Oil (SG 0.8)	30	−17	−510
Rear Passengers	140	+24	+3,360
Baggage	10	+42	+420
Fuel (SG 0.72)	200	+20	+1,600
TOTAL	**2,180**		**+46,150**

CG position on arrival = 46,150 ÷ 2,180 = 21.17 inches aft of datum

18. (Answer: A) 4.2%

To calculate the runway gradient:

$$\frac{\text{Higher threshold} - \text{Lower threshold}}{\text{Runway length}} \times \frac{100}{1}$$

$$\frac{460 - 355}{2500} \times \frac{100}{1} = 4.2\,\%$$

19. (Answer: D) 1,380 feet

1. Enter the graph from the bottom at +30°C and draw a line vertically upwards to the actual pressure altitude, in this case 3,000 feet.
2. Draw a horizontal line to the first reference line
3. Follow the direction of the nearest "weight" lines until the take-off weight, 2900 lbs, is reached.
4. From this point draw a horizontal line to the second reference point.
5. Parallel the nearest lines representing headwind remembering to use only 50% of the reported headwind. If you are to use the full wind speed it should state this in the flight manual. In this case use 15 knots.
6. Again, draw a horizontal line this time to the third reference line.
7. Finally, follow the nearest lines to obtain the 50 ft screen height figure, 1,380 feet.

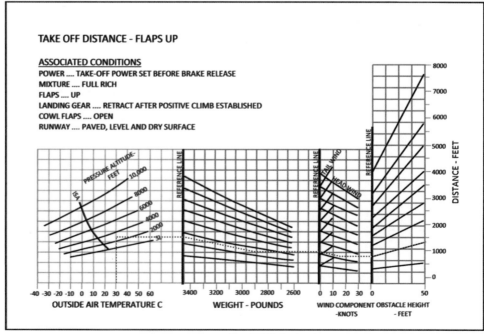

TAKE OFF DISTANCE - FLAPS UP

<u>ASSOCIATED CONDITIONS</u>
POWER ..... TAKE-OFF POWER SET BEFORE BRAKE RELEASE
MIXTURE ..... FULL RICH
FLAPS ..... UP
LANDING GEAR ..... RETRACT AFTER POSITIVE CLIMB ESTABLISHED
COWL FLAPS ..... OPEN
RUNWAY ..... PAVED, LEVEL AND DRY SURFACE

OAT: +30 PA: 3,000 ft A/C Weight: 2900 lbs Wind: H/W 30 Knots OBSTACLE: 50 FT

NOTE: TO THIS FIGURE WE SHOULD THEN ADD THE TAKE OFF SAFETY FACTOR OF 1.33, TOGETHER WITH ANY ADDITIONAL FACTORS FOR RUNWAY SURFACE, SLOPE ETC.. THAT MAY BE NECESSARY TO OBTAIN THE TAKE-OFF DISTANCE REQUIRED.

---

20.   **(Answer: A)** The best rate of climb is used to gain the greatest altitude in the shortest time. The greater the excess power the greater the rate of climb, hence the best rate of climb speed generally occurs near the best lift/drag ratio. The best angle of climb is used to gain the most altitude in the shortest distance travelled. Best angle depends upon excess thrust available and is usually slightly slower than the best rate of climb speed.

END OF EXPLANATIONS PAPER 4

INTENTIONALLY BLANK

PART 7: NAVIGATION

The Navigation examination consists of 25 questions; the time allowed is 1 hour 30 minutes. You will need a 1:500,000 chart of South England and Wales, a protractor, a navigation scale ruler and a CRP-1 Computer.

The pass mark is 75%.

Each question is multiple choice with four possible answers A, B, C and D. You should indicate your chosen answer by placing a cross in the appropriate box on the answer sheet.

Blank answer sheets are to be found at the end of this publication, these may be photocopied.

INTENTIONALLY BLANK

RADIO NAVIGATION

1. A VOR is a radio navigation aid that operates in which radio band?

   a. MF
   b. LF
   c. UHF
   d. VHF

2. The airborne VOR receiver:

   a. Measures the range from the ground station. It measures the time taken for the interrogation pulse to return to the aircraft.
   b. Measures the magnetic direction of the signal transmitted by the ground station.
   c. Measures the true direction of the signal transmitted by the ground station.
   d. Measures the phase difference between two signals transmitted by the VOR beacon.

3. A VOR radial is:

   a. The true bearing from the station
   b. The magnetic bearing from the station
   c. The true bearing to the station
   d. The magnetic bearing to the station

4. When flying towards a VOR on the 125 radial. In order to obtain CDI indications in the correct sense the OBS should be set to:

   a. 125° with a FROM indication
   b. 125° with a TO indication
   c. 305° with a TO indication
   d. 305° with a FROM indication

5. Which aircraft is on the 060 radial tracking towards a VOR beacon and receiving correct sense indications?

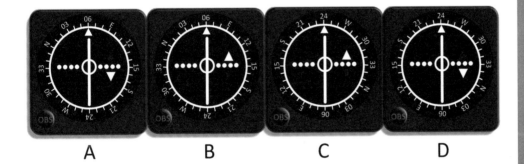

A   B   C   D

   a. A
   b. B
   c. C
   d. D

NAVIGATION

6.   Assume that conditions allow the aircraft to be operated at MTWA. Given the following what is the maximum payload that can be carried?

Given:

MTWA	2,650 lbs
Aircraft Basic Empty Weight	1,660 lbs
Pilot's Weight	190 lbs
Fuel Required 45 USG (Sp.G 0.72)	?

127 KS ⇒ 270lb

2120lbs

a.   530 lbs
b.   476 lbs
c.   678 lbs
d.   654 lbs

7.   Given the following what is the minimum amount of fuel required?

Start Up, Taxi, Run up and Take Off	2 USG
Fuel Consumption	9 USG per Hour
Flight Planned Time	1 Hour
Diversion	20 Minutes
Approach and Landing (or missed approach)	2 USG
Reserve at Diversion Airfield	6 USG

9 uSG

3uSG

a.   20 USG
b.   24 USG
c.   22 USG
d.   25 USG

You are planning the following VFR flight:

From: **Leicester (52 36 28N 001 01 55W)**
To: **Thruxton (51 12 38N 001 36 00W)**
Via: **Westcott NDB (WCO 51 51 18N 000 57 75W)**
Alternate: **Popham (51 11 63N 001 14 08W)**

Complete the Flight Plan opposite before answering questions 8 to 25
Note: The AIP entry for Thruxton can be found on pages 411 to 416.

8.   What is the magnetic heading from Leicester to Westcott?

a.   169°
b.   187°
c.   175°
d.   181°

9.   What is the ground speed in knots from Leicester to Westcott?

a.   100 kt
b.   87 kt
c.   134 kt
d.   96 kt

PLOG FOR NAVIGATION PAPER 1

TAKE OFF:

LAND:

FLIGHT TIME:

FROM	TO	ALT/FL	SAFE ALT	TAS	W/V	TRK T	DRIFT	HDG T	VAR	HDG M	GS	DIST	TIME	ETA
LEICESTER	**WCO**													
52 36 28N	51 51 18N	As Reqd.	1300	110	150/25	176.5	6	170	3W	173	87	46	31:30	
001 01 55W	000 57 75W													
WCO	**THRUXTON**													
51 51 18N	51 12 38N	As Reqd.	1300	110	150/25	212.5	-12	200.5	3W	203.5	96	45.5	28	
000 57 75W	001 36 00W													
										TOTAL		91	Setting	
ALTERNATE	**POPHAM**													
THRUXTON	51 11 63N	As Reqd.	1300	110	160/20	093	+10	103	3W	106	100	14	8:30	
51 12 38N	001 14 08W													
001 36 00W														

Note: Safety Altitude is calculated from the higher of: i) the highest ground plus 1,299 feet; or ii) the highest structure plus 1,000 feet. Within 5 nm of track rounded up to the next 100 feet

10. What is the magnetic heading from Westcott to Thruxton?

    a.   225°

    b.   201°

    c.   218°

    d   204°

11. What is the distance from Westcott to Thruxton?

    a.   28 nm

    b.   23 nm

    c.   45 nm

    d.   39 nm

12. What is the flight time from Westcott to Thruxton?

    a.   31 minutes

    b.   44.1 minutes

    c.   28.1 minutes

    d.   40.6 minutes

13. What is the magnetic heading from Thruxton to the alternate airfield, Popham?

    a.   105°

    b.   108°

    c.   098°

    d.   088°

14. What is the aerodrome elevation of Thruxton?

    a.   319 ft

    b.   420 ft

    c.   604 ft

    d.   130.45 ft

15. To the south west of Westcott what is the meaning of the following chart symbol and in relation to such areas what action are you strongly advised to take?

    a.   It is a Danger Area and should be avoided unless Benson ATC approve transit

    b.   It is a Restricted Area and may be crossed with caution

    c.   It is controlled airspace Class E and permission to enter must be obtained from Brize Radar on 124.275

    d.   It is an Area of Intense Aerial Activity and it is recommended to contact Brize Radar on 124.475

16. What is the meaning of the group of symbols at Westcott?

    a.   A GPS Validation Station, a VOR and an airfield

    b.   A GPS Validation Station, an NDB and an airfield

    c.   A Gas Venting Station, a DME and an airfield

    d.   A symbol denoting Gas Venting Operations, an NDB and a disused airfield

17. What type of activity takes place at Drayton St Leonard, to the NNW of Benson?

    a.   Free fall parachuting

    b.   Paragliding or hang-gliding with winch launching up to a maximum altitude of 2,200 feet AMSL

    c.   Gliding with winch launching up to a maximum of 2,200 feet AMSL

    d.   Paragliding or hang-gliding with winch launching up to a maximum altitude of 180 feet AMSL

18. When north of Thruxton which agency should you contact:

    a. Thruxton Radio 130.450 to request join

    b. Thruxton Information 130.450 to request MATZ penetration

    c. Boscombe Down 126.7 to request join

    d. Either Boscombe Down 126.7 to request MATZ penetration, or Thruxton Radio ensuring that the MATZ is avoided

19. What is the maximum level at which to enter the Thruxton ATZ?

    a. Not above 1,400 feet aal, as this ensures that the aircraft is below the MATZ stub

    b. Not above 900 feet aal, as this ensures that the aircraft is below the MATZ stub

    c. Not above 1,200 feet aal, as this is the procedure promulgated for Thruxton traffic

    d. Not above 2,000 feet aal, as this is the top of the Thruxton ATZ

20. With reference to the UK AIP Thruxton (Attachment 2) what is the ATS unit call sign and its hours of operation during the summer?

    a. Thruxton Radar operating between 0800 and 1600

    b. Thruxton Radio operating between 0900 and 1700

    c. Thruxton Radio operating between 0800 and 1600

    d. Thruxton Information operating between 0900 and 1700

21. To the south west of Thruxton is an area denoted §127/12.0. What does this mean?

    a. A Danger Area number 127 which is active 12 months of the year and controlled by Boscombe Down.

    b. A Danger Area number 127 which is active from the surface to 12,000 feet AMSL and pre-flight information is available.

    c. A Danger Area number 127 which is active from the surface to 12,000 feet AMSL and a Danger Area Crossing Service is available

    d. A Danger Area number 127 which is active from the surface to 12,000 feet AMSL and a Danger Area Information Service is available

22. The maximum demonstrated cross wind for your aircraft is 18 kt. With a surface wind speed of 23 kt, by how many degrees can the surface wind differ from the runway direction before the crosswind component equals 18 kt?

    a. 50°

    b. 60°

    c. 40°

    d. 75°

23. On the 1:500,000 chart, within each quadrangle of the graticule of latitude and longitude is a blue two digit group. These figures represent the:

    a. Safe altitude within that quadrilateral in hundreds of metres

    b. Safe altitude within that quadrilateral in hundreds of feet

    c. Maximum elevation figure (MEF) within that quadrilateral in hundreds of metres

    d. Maximum elevation figure (MEF) within that quadrilateral in hundreds of feet

24. A fuel check over WCO reveals that you have 20 USG remaining. Assume a fuel consumption rate of 9 USG per hour. Allowing for the flight planned time to Thruxton, plus 10 minutes to the alternate Popham and for a reserve of 6 USG; what will be the safe endurance remaining on arrival at the alternate Popham?

    a. 1 hour 35 minutes

    b. 55 minutes

    c. 20 minutes

    d. 1 hour 9 minutes

25. To the WSW of Westcott by approximately 12 nm is Oxford airfield, it shows this symbol.

What does the symbol represent and what action are you advised to take?

a.   It represents a busy airfield and you are advised to remain at least 10 nm away

b.   It represents an instrument approach procedure outside controlled airspace, pilots are strongly advised to avoid the area

c.   It represents an instrument approach procedure outside controlled airspace, pilots are strongly advised to contact the appropriate ATSU when operating within 10 nm of the aerodrome

d.   It represents an airfield where aircraft will be radar vectored along the fan line, pilots must be in contact with an appropriate radar unit, in this instance Brize.

END OF NAVIGATION PAPER 1

INTENTIONALLY BLANK

NAVIGATION PAPER 1: ANSWERS

	A	B	C	D
1.				X
2.				X
3.		X		
4.			X	
5.			X	
6.	X			
7.			X	
8.			X	
9.		X		
10.				X
11.			X	
12.			X	
13.		X		
14.	X			
15				X
16.				X
17.		X		
18.				X
19.			X	
20.			X	
21.				X
22.	X			
23.				X
24.		X		
25.			X	

CORRECT ANSWERS: PERCENTAGES						
19	20	21	22	23	24	25
76%	80%	84%	88%	92%	96%	100%

RADIO NAVIGATION

1. **(Answer: D)** The VOR operates in the VHF frequency band. VOR is an abbreviation for very high frequency omni-directional radio range. VORs are allocated frequencies between 108.0 MHz and 117.95 Mhz.

2. **(Answer: D)** The VOR operates on the principle of phase comparison. The ground station transmits two VHF radio signals:

    1. A reference signal: which is the same in all directions; and
    2. A variable signal: the phase of this signal is made to vary at a constant rate throughout 360°.

    The phase difference – the difference between the peaks of the radio waves - experienced by the receiver varies according to the aircraft's position around the station. When the aircraft is due north of the station the signals are in phase, i.e. they peak and trough at the same time.

    The signals are then out of phase as follows:
    090°M the signals are 90° out of phase
    180°M the signals are 180° out of phase (anti-phase)
    270°M the signals are 270° out of phase

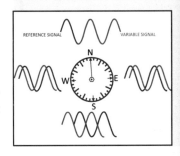

2. ANSWER D

Reference Signal (blue)
and Variable Signal (red)

3. **(Answer: B)** A VOR radial is the magnetic bearing from the station. A radial can also be thought of as a track away from a VOR beacon. The 360 tracks away from a VOR are separated from each other by 1° and are each related to magnetic north. A radial may also be called a QDR.

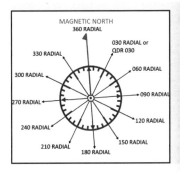

3. ANSWER B

A VOR Radial is the magnetic
bearing from the station.

4. **(Answer: C)** The cockpit display for the VOR is referred to as the OBS – omni bearing selector, it displays on a course card the radial selected by the pilot. The needle is referred to as the course deviation indicator, or CDI. If the aircraft is on the selected radial the needle will be in the centre. If it is not the needle will be deflected to the left or right as appropriate.

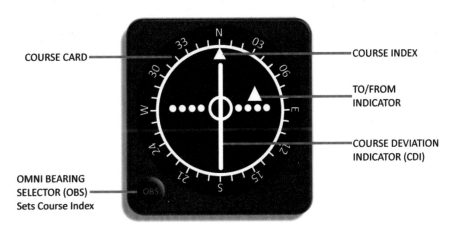

In this question we are told that the aircraft is on the 125 radial, i.e. it is to the south east of the beacon. In order to fly to the beacon with correct sense indications the OBS should be set to 305 with a TO indication.

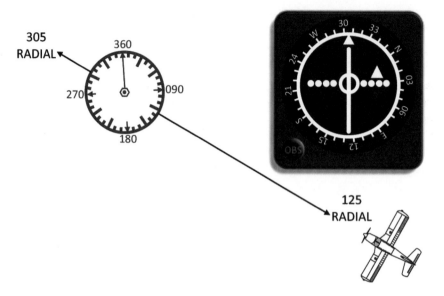

One way to think about the orientation is to remember that all the radio waves are emanating from the beacon and travelling away from it. For the OBS to work in the correct sense the TO/FROM indication should match the direction in which the selected radio wave is moving.

5.   **(Answer: C)** The radio waves are being emitted by the VOR beacon and moving away from it. In order to receive correct sense indications you need to be following a radial, or radio wave, travelling in the same direction as your aircraft. A TO indication shows that the selected course is on the other side of the VOR beacon. A FROM indication shows that the OBS selection and the aircraft are on the same side of the VOR.

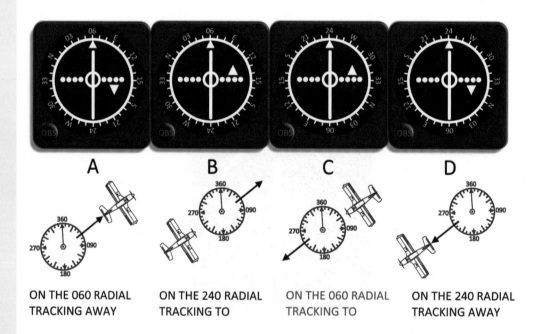

A	B	C	D
ON THE 060 RADIAL TRACKING AWAY	ON THE 240 RADIAL TRACKING TO	ON THE 060 RADIAL TRACKING TO	ON THE 240 RADIAL TRACKING AWAY

NAVIGATION

---

6. **(Answer: A)** To find the payload (which is the weight of passengers, cargo and baggage), first find the weight of the fuel that is needed for the flight. This can be done either using the CRP, or by using 6 lb per USG. This is a handy figure to commit to memory: one USG with a Specific Gravity of 0.72 weighs 6 lb.

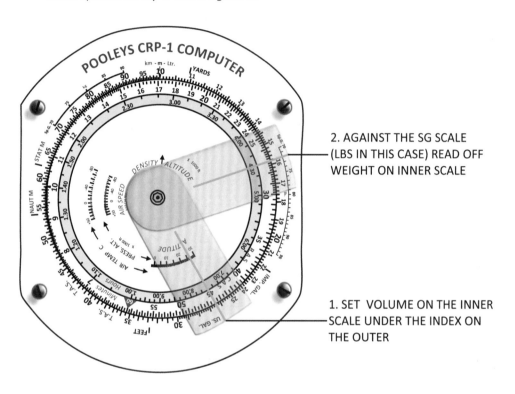

2. AGAINST THE SG SCALE (LBS IN THIS CASE) READ OFF WEIGHT ON INNER SCALE

1. SET VOLUME ON THE INNER SCALE UNDER THE INDEX ON THE OUTER

MTWA	2,650 lbs
Aircraft Basic Empty Weight	1,660 lbs
Pilot's Weight	190 lbs
Fuel Required 45 USG (Sp.G 0.72)	**270 lbs**

Next, find the sum of the weight used so far: 1,660 + 190 + 270 = 2,120 lbs
Finally, subtract this figure from the MTWA:
Payload available = 2,650 – 2,120 = 530 lbs

7. **(Answer: C)** The minimum fuel required is 22 USG.

Start Up, Taxi, Run up and Take Off	2 USG	2 USG
Fuel Consumption	9 USG per Hour	
Flight Planned Time	1 Hour	9 USG
Diversion	20 Minutes	3 USG
Approach and Landing (or missed approach)	2 USG	2 USG
Reserve at Diversion Airfield	6 USG	6 USG
Total		**22 USG**

TAKE OFF:

LAND:

FLIGHT TIME:

FROM	TO	ALT/FL	SAFE ALT	TAS	W/V	TRK T	DRIFT	HDG T	VAR	HDG M	GS	DIST	TIME	ETA
LEICESTER	**WCO**													
52 36 28N	51 51 18N													
001 01 55W	000 57 75W	As Reqd. 2300		110	150/25	178	6S	172	3W	175	87	45	31	
WCO	**THRUXTON**													
51 51 18N	51 12 38N													
000 57 75W	001 36 00W	As Reqd. 2300		110	150/25	213	12S	201	3W	204	96	45	28	
										TOTAL		90	59	
ALTERNATE														
THRUXTON	**POPHAM**													
51 12 38N	51 11 63N													
001 36 00W	001 14 08W	As Reqd. 1800		110	160/20	095	10P	105	3W	108	100	13.7	8	

Note: Safety Altitude is calculated from the higher of: i) the highest ground plus 1,299 feet; or ii) the highest structure plus 1,000 feet; Within 5 nm of track rounded up to the next 100 feet

8.   **(Answer: C)** The magnetic heading from Leicester to Westcott is 175°M.

Method:

1.   Place the centre of the protractor over the track drawn on the map near the mid-point between the two ends of the track.

2.   Align the grid marks on the protractor with the vertical meridian lines on the chart. Read off the True Track, in this case 178°.

3.   Next, find the effect of the wind on the aircraft. So, using your CRP computer set the wind direction (150) on the rotating inner scale under the Index on the fixed outer scale.

4.   Set the centre circle on a convenient speed arc – 100 is a handy round number. Mark down the wind speed, 25 knots for this question.

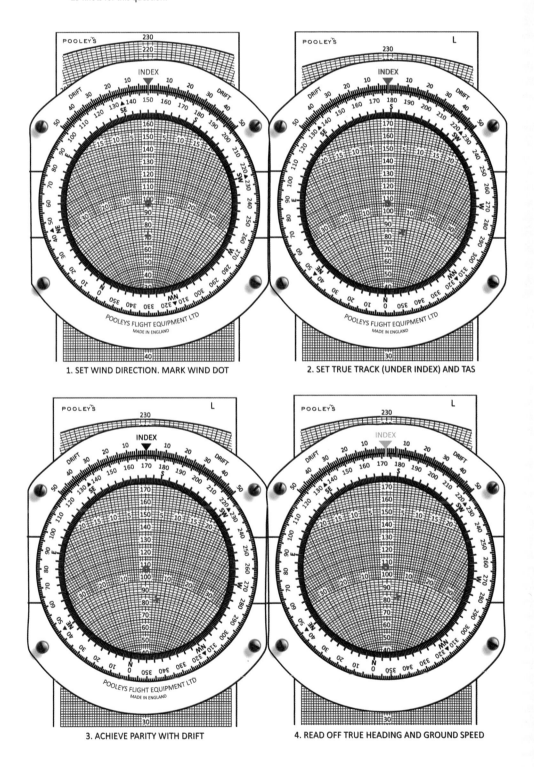

1. SET WIND DIRECTION. MARK WIND DOT

2. SET TRUE TRACK (UNDER INDEX) AND TAS

3. ACHIEVE PARITY WITH DRIFT

4. READ OFF TRUE HEADING AND GROUND SPEED

5. Move the sliding scale so that the centre circle is over the TAS 110.
6. Rotate the inner scale so that the measured true track, 178, is now below the index. Note the wind mark is now displaced 8° to the right.
7. Rotate the inner scale 8° to the right, 178 is now below 8° on the right hand side of the fixed drift scale. However, now the pencil mark indicates 6° of starboard drift. What we are aiming for is parity, so move the rotating scale so that 178 is below 6° on the fixed drift scale and still right of the index. In so doing the drift remains at 6° and we have parity – the track is offset 6° and the wind mark still shows 6°.
8. Read off the true heading under the Index = 172°.
9. Finally apply the variation, in this case 3°W. Remember "East is Least, West is Best", the variation is West, hence we add it giving a magnetic heading of 175°.

9. **(Answer: B)** Keeping the CRP as in picture 4 with the last question, read the ground speed under the wind dot – 87 knots. The CRP can be very easy to misread, drawing a small sketch of the route will give you a rough idea of the answers you expect to obtain and ensure that any amendments are applied correctly.

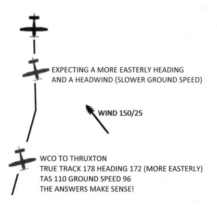

10. **(Answer: D)** The magnetic heading from Westcott to Thruxton is 204°. Following the same method as in question 8, we find a true heading of 201 to which we add the variation of 3°W to obtain the magnetic heading.

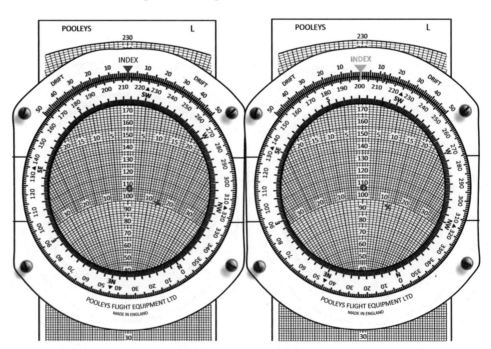

11. **(Answer: C)** 45 nm. The distance is found by measuring the track drawn on the chart. As we are using a 1:500,000 chart ensure that you are measuring with the correct scale.

12. **(Answer: C)** 28.1 minutes. Set the "60" mark on the rotating inner scale under the ground speed, here 96 knots. Re-set the moving lubber line to 45 (the distance) on the outer scale – here it helps to remember from school "speed = distance over time" i.e. distance is set on the outer scale OVER time on the inner. Read off on the top of the inner scale 28.1 minutes.

Again, it is useful to have an idea of the answer we are expecting to get so that we can be confident that we have read the computer correctly. Very roughly a ground speed of 96 knots is almost 90, which would give us a rate over the ground of 1.5 nm per minute. The distance 45 divided by 1.5 gives an answer of 30, so we are anticipating an answer in the region of 30 minutes.

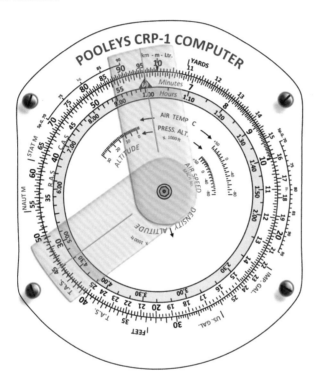

Outer Scale:	Distance	Speed
Inner Scale:	Time	60

13. **(Answer: B)** The magnetic heading from Thruxton to Popham is 108°. Follow the same method as in question 8, however notice for this leg that the wind is different.

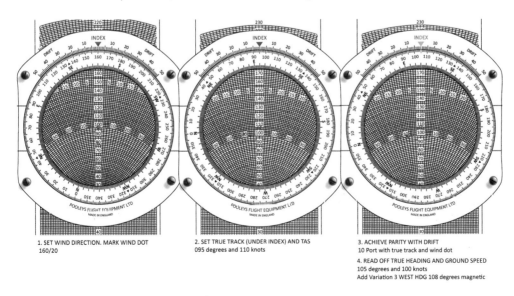

1. SET WIND DIRECTION. MARK WIND DOT
160/20

2. SET TRUE TRACK (UNDER INDEX) AND TAS
095 degrees and 110 knots

3. ACHIEVE PARITY WITH DRIFT
10 Port with true track and wind dot

4. READ OFF TRUE HEADING AND GROUND SPEED
105 degrees and 100 knots
Add Variation 3 WEST HDG 108 degrees magnetic

14.   **(Answer: A)** The aerodrome elevation of Thruxton is 319 ft. This can either be found on the chart, or in the AIP details.

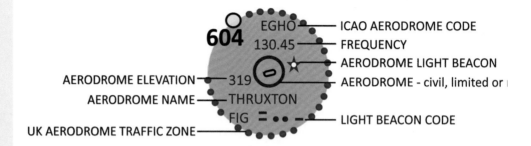

15.   **(Answer: D)** This chart symbol denotes an Area of Intense Aerial Activity, in this instance the Oxford AIAA from the surface to 5,000 feet. It is strongly recommended that you contact Brize Radar 124.275 for a service. In the case of this particular flight the necessity to transit the Benson MATZ will probably take priority.

From the UK AIP:

Area of Intense Aerial Air Activity (AIAA) - Airspace within which the intensity of civil and/or military flying is exceptionally high or where aircraft, either singly or in combination with others, regularly participate in unusual manoeuvres. Intense civil and/or military air activity takes place within the areas listed in ENR 5.2. Pilots of non-participating aircraft who are unable to avoid AIAAs are to keep a good lookout and are strongly advised to make use of a radar service if available.

16.   **(Answer: D)** The symbols in the vicinity of Westcott are symbols denoting Gas Venting Operations, an NDB and a disused airfield.

GAS VENTING OPERATIONS GVS/2.8

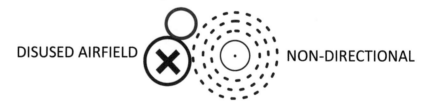

17.   **(Answer: B)** Drayton St Leonard, to the NNW of Benson is a hang- gliding or paragliding site with winch launching taking place up to a maximum altitude of 2,200 feet AMSL

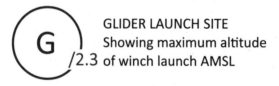

GLIDER LAUNCH SITE
Showing maximum altitude of winch launch AMSL

FREE FALL PARACHUTE DROP ZONE

HAND/PARA GLIDING
Showing maximum altitude of winch launch AMSL

MICROLIGHT FLYING SITES

18. **(Answer: D)** When north of Thruxton pilots should contact either Boscombe Down 126.7 to request MATZ penetration, or Thruxton Radio ensuring that the MATZ is avoided.

   From the Thruxton AIP entry:
   During Boscombe Down/Middle Wallop CMATZ hours of operation, it is a condition of use of Thruxton aerodrome that the flight procedures set out below are complied with. Information on the CMATZ activity status may be obtained from the A/G station.

   i. Arriving aircraft
   1. Contact Boscombe Down on frequency 126.700 MHz for a MATZ penetration service (in accordance with ENR 2.2). To reduce the possibility of inadvertent CMATZ or ATZ penetration, arriving traffic may be routed via a point 1 nm north of Andover. Once an aircraft has reported at this point it will be advised to free-call Thruxton A/G. Remain outside the Thruxton ATZ and contact 'Thruxton Radio' (130.450 MHz) for ATZ entry information. ATZ entry should be at 1200 ft aal, or a maximum height to remain in VMC, not above 1200 ft aal; or
   2. Avoid the Boscombe Down CMATZ, contact Thruxton Radio for ATZ entry information. ATZ entry should be not above 1200 ft aal. If contact with the A/G Station is not possible, ATZ entry must be not above 1200 ft aal.

19. **(Answer: C)** From the Thruxton AIP entry reproduced above, we can see that the procedure promulgated for arrival has a maximum level at which to enter the ATZ of 1,200 feet.

20. **(Answer: C)** The call sign is Thruxton Radio operating between 0800 and 1600 during the summer. AD 2.18 ATS COMMUNICATION FACILITIES

21. **(Answer: D)** The symbol denotes a Danger Area with the number 127 which is active from the surface to 12,000 feet AMSL and that there is a Danger Area Information Service is available. From the Chart legend we can find that DAIS is available from Boscombe Down.

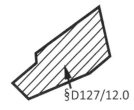

§D127/12.0

DANGER AREA SYMBOLS

✝ CROSSING SERVICE (DACS)

§ DANGER AREA INFORMATION SERVICE (DAIS)

¶ PREFLIGHT INFORMATION AVAILABLE

✳ BY LAWS PROHIBIT ENTRY DURING HOURS OF ACTIVITY

22. **(Answer: A)** 50°. To find the crosswind component use the wind triangle side of the CRP and the square grid at the bottom of the low speed side of the sliding plate.

   Set the rotating inner scale to North, and place the centre dot at the zero speed point at the top of the square grid. Make a mark to represent the wind speed – 23 knots for this question.

   Rotate the inner scale until your pencil mark reaches the maximum cross wind limit of 18 knots. Now read off on the inner scale the number directly below the index, this represents the degrees from runway heading at which the crosswind component will be 18 knots.

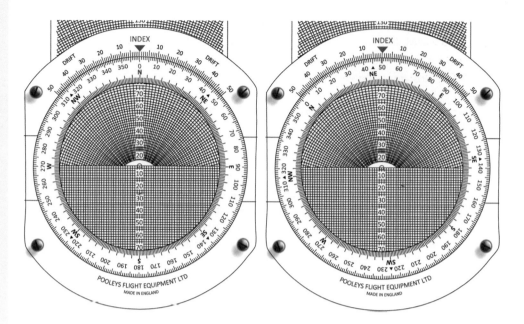

23. **(Answer: D)** The figure represents the maximum elevation figure (MEF) within that quadrilateral in hundreds of feet. It is based on the highest known feature in each quadrangle, be that either terrain or an obstacle. The MEF is NOT a safety height.

24. **(Answer: B)** The safe endurance on arrival at Popham will be 55 minutes.

   The reserve of 6 USG must not be taken into account, so we are left with 14 USG for the remainder of the route and flight to the diversion airfield. From the plog Westcott to Thruxton will take 28 minutes and for the diversion we are told to allow 10 minutes; so we need to calculate how much fuel this will use and subtract it from the 14 USG we have available to use.

   On the CRP set the 60 index below "90" to represent the 9 USG per hour fuel burn. A rough estimate is that our flight time is nearly 40 minutes (⅔ of an hour) and ⅔ of 9 USG is 6 USG; so we are expecting the remaining flight time to use approximately 6 USG. Read off against the 38 minute flight time on the inner scale 57 on the outer.

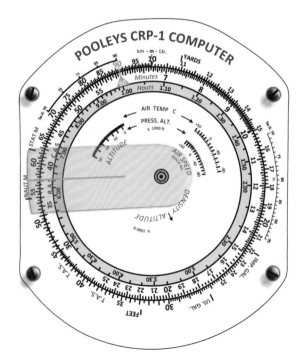

Outer Scale:	Fuel Flow	Fuel Required
Inner Scale:	60 ▲	Time

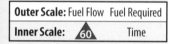

This gives us an answer of 5.7 USG. Subtracting this from the 14 USG available to use gives 8.3 USG. Keeping the CRP set to "90" above the index to represent the fuel flow, now read off how long 8.3 USG on the outer scale will last on the inner. Expecting roughly an hour, we see the answer on the inner scale is 55, so 55 minutes.

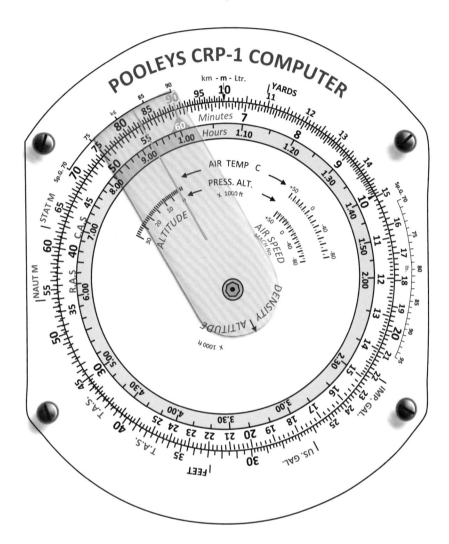

25. **(Answer: C)** This symbol represents an instrument approach procedure outside controlled airspace, pilots are strongly advised to contact the appropriate ATSU when operating within 10 nm of the aerodrome.

END OF EXPLANATIONS PAPER 1

INTENTIONALLY BLANK

NAVIGATION PAPER 2

1. The correct Q code for a true bearing from a VDF station is:

   a. QDM
   b. QDR
   c. QUJ
   d. QTE

2. A Class B VDF bearing is accurate to:

   a. ± 5°
   b. ± 2°
   c. ± 10°
   d. ± 8°

3. The accuracy of a VDF may be decreased by:

   a. Night effect
   b. Thunderstorms
   c. Coastal effect
   d. Site and propagation errors

4. How may the range of primary radar be increased?

   a. By increasing the rate of rotation of the radar head
   b. By increasing the width of the radar head antenna which will produce a long and narrow beam
   c. By locating the radar head at an elevation above surrounding obstacles
   d. By reducing the width of the radar head antenna which will produce a long and narrow beam

5. With regard to the illustration below, which of the following statements is correct?

   a. "A" is a primary radar return
   b. "B" is a primary and secondary radar return
   c. "C" is a primary and secondary radar return with Mode Charlie information
   d. "B" is a primary return, secondary information is provided on a separate screen

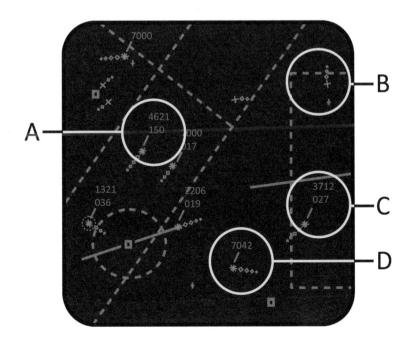

PLOG FOR NAVIGATION PAPER 2

TAKE OFF:

LAND:

FLIGHT TIME: 1.35:20

FROM	TO	ALT/FL	SAFE ALT	TAS	W/V	TRK T	DRIFT	HDG T	VAR	HDG M	GS	DIST	TIME	ETA
CAERNAFON 53 06 27N 004 20 42W	ABERYSTWYTH 52 25 02N 004 05 00W	As req.	4300	110	230/30	167	−14°	181	3.5W	185	92	42	27:20	
ABERYSTWYTH 52 25 02N 004 05 00W	SWANSEA 51 36 04N 004 04 20W	As req.	4300	110	230/30	179	−13°	192	3.5W	196	88	49	33	
SWANSEA 51 36 04N 004 04 20W	EXETER 50 44 05N 003 24 84W	As req.	3500	110	230/30	154	−16°	170	3W	173	98	57.5	35	
EXETER 50 44 05N 003 24 84W	DUNKESWELL 50 51 60N 003 14 08W	As req.	2200	110	250/20	042	4°	038	3W	041	128	9.5	4:30	
ALTERNATE									TOTAL				28:30	

Note: Safety Altitude is calculated from the higher of: i) the highest ground plus 1,299 feet; or ii) the highest structure plus 1,000 feet; within 5 nm of track rounded up to the next 100 feet

NAVIGATION

6. Given the following what is the minimum amount of fuel required? (round up to the nearest gallon). Given:

Start Up, Taxi, Run up and Take Off	2 USG
Fuel Consumption	10 USG per Hour
Flight Planned Time	55 Minutes
Diversion	15 Minutes
Approach and Landing (or missed approach)	2 USG
Reserve at Diversion Airfield	8 USG

(handwritten: { 12 USG)

 a. 24 USG
   b. 16 USG
   c. 22 USG
   d. 26 USG

7. Assume that conditions allow the aircraft to be operated at MTWA. Given the following what is the maximum payload that can be carried? Given:

MTWA	2,220 lbs
Aircraft Basic Empty Weight	1,360 lbs
Pilot's Weight	170 lbs
Fuel Required 45 USG (Sp.G 0.72)	? *(handwritten: = 270 lb)*

   a. 374 lbs
   b. 426 lbs
   c. 376 lbs
   d. 450 lbs

(handwritten: 1800 lb)
(handwritten: ⇒ 420 lb)

You are planning the following VFR flight:
From: Caernarfon (53 06 27N 004 20 42W)
To: Exeter (50 44 05N 003 24 84W)
Via: Aberystwyth (52 25 02N 004 05 00W) and
Swansea aerodrome (51 36 04N 004 04 20W)
Alternate: Dunkeswell (50 51 60N 003 14 08W)

Complete the Flight Plan before answering questions 8 to 25

8. What is the magnetic heading from Caernarfon to Aberystwyth?
   a. 168°
   b. 185°
   c. 180°
   d. 194°

9. What is the ground speed between Caernarfon and Aberystwyth?
   a. 83 kt
   b. 89 kt
   c. 93 kt
   d. 99 kt

10. What is the magnetic heading from Swansea to Exeter?

   a.   156°
   b.   171°
   c.   194°
   d.   174°

11. What is the total flight plan time for the flight from Caernarfon to Exeter?

   a.   90 minutes
   b.   1 hour and 25 minutes
   c.   99 minutes
   d.   1 hour and 35 minutes

12. What is the magnetic heading and ground speed for the diversion leg from Exeter to Dunkeswell?

   a.   041° and 128 knots
   b.   041° and 140 knots
   c.   038° and 140 knots
   d.   038° and 128 knots

13. What is the meaning of the symbol at 53 04 07N 004 04 32W?

   a.   It is a spot height
   b.   It is an exceptionally high lighted obstacle
   c.   It is the highest known point on the entire chart
   d.   It is an exceptionally high unlit obstacle

14. To the west of Aberystwyth is a marked area with the following text **D201/↑UNL** What does this mean?

   a.   A Prohibited Area with an information service available, it is activated by NOTAM and has no upper limit
   b.   A Danger Area with a crossing service available, it is active during scheduled hours and has no upper limit
   c.   A Danger Area with an information service available, it is active during scheduled hours and has no upper limit
   d.   A Danger Area with a crossing service available, it is activated by NOTAM and has no upper limit

15. You check your fuel state overhead Swansea and you have 22 USG remaining. Assume a constant fuel consumption of 9 USG per hour and flight planned times for the subsequent legs. What will be your safe endurance on arrival at the alternate airfield, Dunkeswell? Allow a reserve of 6 USG.

   a.   1 hour and 7 minutes
   b.   1 hour and 47 minutes
   c.   12 minutes
   d.   1 hour and 27 minutes

Refer to the extract from the UK AIP in the back of the book (pages 403 to 410) to answer the next two questions:

16. What is the call sign of the ATS unit at Caernarfon, the type of service provided and its summer hours of operation?

    a.   Caernarfon Information, Flight Information Service and 0800 to 1700

    b.   Caernarfon Radio, Air Ground Communication Service and 0800 to 1700

    c.   Caernarfon Tower, Air Traffic Control and 0900 to 1630

    d.   Caernarfon Radio, Air Ground Communication Service and 0900 to 1630

17. Unless otherwise instructed which frequency should be contacted immediately after take- off from Caernarfon?

    a.   Pilots must remain with Caernarfon Radio 122.250 MHz until outside the ATZ

    b.   Pilots must contact Llanbedr ATC on 122.5 MHz immediately after take-off

    c.   Pilots should contact Swanwick (Mil) 128.7 MHz

    d.   Pilots should contact Valley ATC 125.225 MHz immediately after take-off

18. What type of aeronautical activity takes place at Rhigos (position 51 45N 003 35W) and what is the maximum winch launch altitude?

    a.   Parachuting up to 28,000 feet

    b.   Gliding up to 7,800 feet

    c.   Gliding up to 2,800 feet

    d.   Paragliding up to 2,800 feet

19. What is the base of controlled airspace immediately above Rhigos and what class of airspace is it?

    a.   Altitude 7,500 feet, Class B

    b.   Altitude 750 feet, Class A

    c.   Flight Level 75, Class B

    d.   Flight Level 75, Class A

20. On a 1:500,000 chart what is the meaning of the following symbol:

    a.   A Class E controlled airspace boundary

    b.   An isogonal line

    c.   The boundary between Altimeter Setting Regions

    d.   An FIR boundary

Your ATA overhead Swansea was 1020; at 1030 you fix your position on track and 15nm from Swansea

21. What is the revised groundspeed?

    a.   90 knots

    b.   99 knots

    c.   80 knots

    d.   105 knots

22. What is your revised ETA at Exeter?

    a.   1054

    b.   1102

    c.   1044

    d.   1058

23. Fifteen nm north of Exeter, at altitude 4,500 feet you wish to commence a descent to 1,500 feet to be level five nm north of Exeter. What rate of descent is required assuming a ground speed of 100 knots in the descent?

   a.   500 fpm
   b.   333 fpm
   c.   650 fpm
   d.   450 fpm

24. The maximum demonstrated cross wind for your aircraft is 15 kt. With a surface wind speed of 25 kt, by how many degrees can the surface wind differ from the runway direction before the crosswind component equals 15 kt?

   a.   38°
   b.   26°
   c.   12°
   d.   51°

25. What type of activity takes place at Upottery approximately 5 nm to the north east of Dunkeswell?

   a.   Gliding up to a maximum of 2,900 feet AMSL
   b.   Parachuting from 29,000 feet AMSL
   c.   Hang-gliding or Paragliding with winch launching up to a maximum of 2,900 feet AMSL
   d.   Paragliding up to a maximum of 2,900 feet AMSL

END OF NAVIGATION PAPER 2

INTENTIONALLY BLANK

	A	B	C	D
1.				X
2.	X			
3.				X
4.			X	
5.			X	
6.	X			
7.		X		
8.		X		
9.			X	
10.				X
11.				X
12.	X			
13.			X	
14.		X		
15	X			
16.		X		
17.				X
18.			X	
19.				X
20.			X	
21.	X			
22.				X
23.	X			
24.	X			
25.			X	

CORRECT ANSWERS: PERCENTAGES						
19	20	21	22	23	24	25
76%	80%	84%	88%	92%	96%	100%

NAVIGATION PAPER 2: EXPLANATIONS

RADIO NAVIGATION

1. **(Answer: D)** QTE is the true bearing of the aircraft from the station.

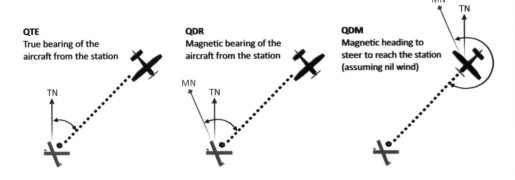

QTE
True bearing of the aircraft from the station

QDR
Magnetic bearing of the aircraft from the station

QDM
Magnetic heading to steer to reach the station (assuming nil wind)

2. **(Answer: A)**
Accuracy of VDF Bearings
Class A +/- 2 degrees
Class B +/- 5 degrees
Class C +/- 10 degrees
Class D accuracy less than class C

3. **(Answer: D)** VDF accuracy can be decreased by:

   a. Site errors: caused by reflections from buildings, uneven ground etc..
   b. Propagation errors: caused by the radio wave scalloping over differing terrain, these are particularly noticeable at long range from the VDF station

4. **(Answer: C)** Primary radar uses UHF (ultra- high frequency) transmissions which are line of sight; buildings, high ground and the curvature of the earth can cause radar shadows, meaning that objects in these areas are not detected. One way to try to lessen these effects is to site the radar antenna on high ground above surrounding obstacles.

   An approximate range can be calculated using one of the following formulae:
   Radar range = √1.5 x height above ground level in ft (nm)
   Or
   Radar range = 1.22 √ height above ground level in ft (nm)

5. **(Answer: C)**

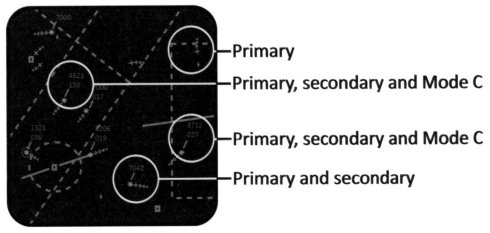

—Primary

—Primary, secondary and Mode C

—Primary, secondary and Mode C

—Primary and secondary

NAVIGATION

---

6. **(Answer: A)** The minimum fuel required is 24 USG

Start Up, Taxi, Run up and Take Off	2 USG	2 USG
Fuel Consumption	10 USG per Hour	
Flight Planned Time	55 Minutes	9.2 USG
Diversion	15 Minutes	2.5 USG
Approach and Landing (or missed approach)	2 USG	2 USG
Reserve at Diversion Airfield	8 USG	8 USG
Total		**23.7 USG**

The fuel used en-route can either be calculated mathematically, or using the CRP:

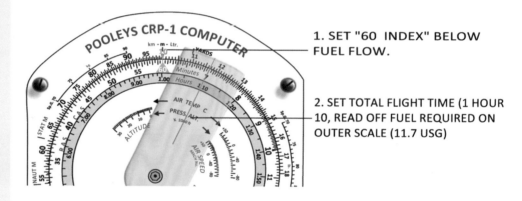

1. SET "60 INDEX" BELOW FUEL FLOW.

2. SET TOTAL FLIGHT TIME (1 HOUR 10, READ OFF FUEL REQUIRED ON OUTER SCALE (11.7 USG)

7. **(Answer: B)** 426 lbs. To find the payload, which is the weight of passengers, cargo and baggage, we first find the weight of the fuel that is needed for the flight. This can be done either using the CRP, or by using 6 lb per USG. This is a handy figure to commit to memory: one USG with a Specific Gravity of 0.72 weighs 6 lb.

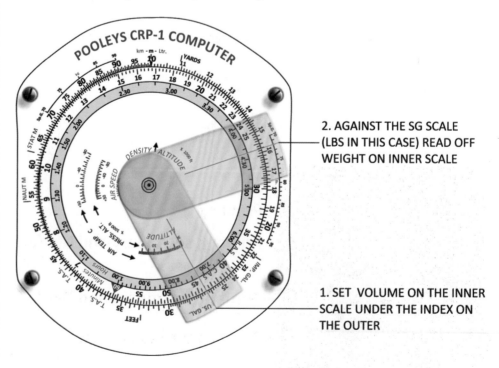

2. AGAINST THE SG SCALE (LBS IN THIS CASE) READ OFF WEIGHT ON INNER SCALE

1. SET VOLUME ON THE INNER SCALE UNDER THE INDEX ON THE OUTER

MTWA	2,220 lbs
Aircraft Basic Empty Weight	1,360 lbs
Pilot's Weight	170 lbs
Fuel Required 44 USG (Sp.G 0.72)	**264 lbs**

Next find the sum of the weight used so far: 1,360 + 170 + 264 = 1,794 lbs
Finally subtract this figure from the MTWA: Payload available = 2,220 – 1,794 = **426 lbs**

8.   **(Answer: B)** The magnetic heading between Caernarfon and Aberystwyth is 185°

Method:

1.   Place the centre of the protractor over the track drawn on the map near the mid-point between the two ends of the track.
2.   Align the grid marks on the protractor with the vertical meridian lines on the chart. Read off the True Track, in this case 168°
3.   Next we need to find the effect of the wind on the aircraft. So, using your CRP computer set the wind direction (230) on the rotating inner scale under the Index on the fixed outer scale.

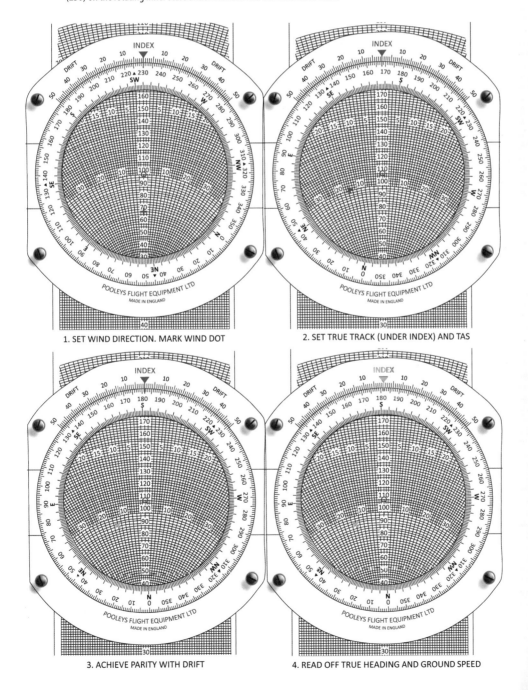

1. SET WIND DIRECTION. MARK WIND DOT

2. SET TRUE TRACK (UNDER INDEX) AND TAS

3. ACHIEVE PARITY WITH DRIFT

4. READ OFF TRUE HEADING AND GROUND SPEED

TAKE OFF:

LAND:

FLIGHT TIME:

FROM	TO	ALT/FL	SAFE ALT	TAS	W/V	TRK T	DRIFT	HDG T	VAR	HDG M	GS	DIST	TIME	ETA
CAERNARFON 53 06 27N 004 20 42W	ABERYSTWYTH 52 25 02N 004 05 00W	As req.	4900	110	230/30	168	14 P	182	3W	185	93	42.3	27.2	
ABERYSTWYTH 52 25 02N 004 05 00W	SWANSEA 51 36 04N 004 04 20W	As req.	4900	110	230/30	180	11 P	191	3W	194	89	49.0	33	
SWANSEA 51 36 04N 004 04 20W	EXETER 50 44 05N 003 24 84W	As req.	3500	110	230/30	156	15 P	171	3W	174	99	57.6	34.9	
										TOTAL		148.9	95.1	
ALTERNATE EXETER 50 44 05N 003 24 84W	DUNKESWELL 50 51 60N 003 14 08W	As req.	2200	110	250/20	043	5 S	038	3W	041	128	10.2	4.8	

Note: Safety Altitude is calculated from the higher of: i) the highest ground plus 1,299 feet; or ii) the highest structure plus 1,000 feet; within 5 nm of track rounded up to the next 100 feet

4. Set the centre circle on a convenient speed arc – 100 is a handy round number. Mark down the wind speed, 30 knots for this question.

5. Move the sliding scale so that the centre circle is over the TAS 110.

6. Rotate the inner scale so that the measured true track, 168, is now below the index. Note the wind mark that was drawn is now displaced 15° to the left

7. Now rotate the inner scale 15° to the left, 168 is now below 15° on the left hand side of the fixed drift scale. However, now the pencil mark indicates 14° of port drift. What we are aiming for is parity, so move the rotating scale so that 168 is below 14° on the fixed drift scale and still left of the index. In so doing the drift remains at 14° and we have parity – the track is offset 14° and the wind mark still shows 14°.

8. Read off the true heading under the Index = 182°

9. Finally apply the variation, in this case 3°W. Remember "East is Least, West is Best", the variation is West, hence we add it giving a magnetic heading of 185°

9. **(Answer: C)** Keeping the CRP as above read the ground speed under the wind dot – 93 knots. The CRP can be very easy to misread, when using it drawing a small sketch of the route is a good way to get a rough idea of the answer you expect to obtain and to ensure that any amendments are applied correctly.

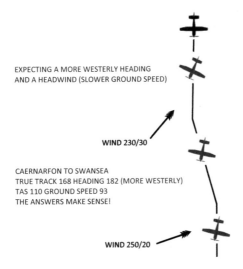

EXPECTING A MORE WESTERLY HEADING
AND A HEADWIND (SLOWER GROUND SPEED)

WIND 230/30

CAERNARFON TO SWANSEA
TRUE TRACK 168 HEADING 182 (MORE WESTERLY)
TAS 110 GROUND SPEED 93
THE ANSWERS MAKE SENSE!

WIND 250/20

10. **(Answer: D)** The magnetic heading from Swansea to Exeter is 174°. Following the same method as in question 8, we find a true heading of 171° to which we add the variation of 3°W to obtain the magnetic heading.

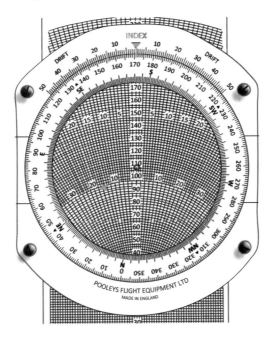

11. **(Answer: D)** The sum of the three legs gives an expected flight time of 95 minutes or 1 hour and 35 minutes. *(see the completed plan on page 352)*

12. **(Answer: A)** The magnetic heading for the diversion is 041° and the ground speed is 128 knots.

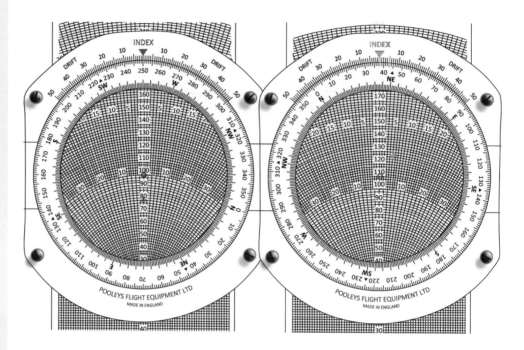

13. **(Answer: C)** The highest spot elevation on each chart is marked in slightly larger print than other spot elevations and is displayed in a white rectangle with a black outline. In this instance we are looking at Mount Snowdon. In the bottom right hand corner of the chart you can find the "relief portrayal" where the highest known elevation is mentioned again.

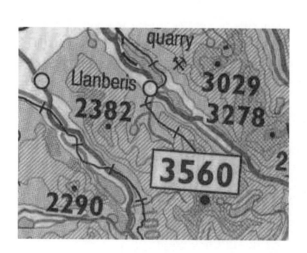

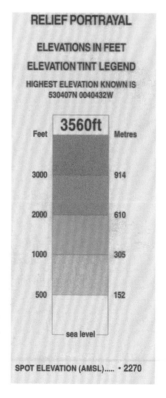

14. **(Answer: B)** D201 is a Danger Area number 201 with a Danger Area Crossing Service (DACS) available, it is active during scheduled hours and has no upper limit.

The solid outline denotes a Danger Area that is active during scheduled hours, areas activated by NOTAM have a pecked outline. After the oblique the level is stated, in this instance UNL meaning unlimited, i.e. there is no upper level.

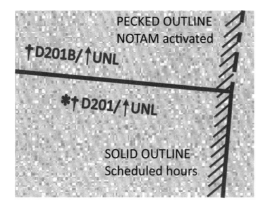

DANGER AREA SYMBOLS

† CROSSING SERVICE (DACS)

§ DANGER AREA INFORMATION SERVICE (DAIIS)

¶ PREFLIGHT INFORMATION AVAILABLE

✱ BY LAWS PROHIBIT ENTRY DURING HOURS OF ACTIVITY

15. **(Answer: A)** The flight planned times for the subsequent legs are:

Swansea to Exeter: 34.9 minutes
Exeter to Dunkeswell: 4.8 minutes
Total: 39.7 minutes

Firstly, find out how much fuel the remaining flight time requires, using the CRP set the 60 index below 9 for the fuel flow. Read off above the time (39.7 minutes) on the inner scale a fuel requirement of 5.95 USG. A rough calculation will confirm whether we have the decimal point in the correct place: 40 minutes is ⅔ of an hour, ⅔ of 9 USG is 6.

Overhead Swansea we had 22 USG of fuel and from this we need to subtract the 5.95 USG we are going to use and the 6 USG that we are told in the question must be held in reserve: 22 – 5.95 – 6 = 10.05 USG

Keeping the CRP as above with the 60 index below the 9, this time read off below 10.05 on the outer scale a time of 67 minutes on the inner scale. Therefore the endurance remaining is 1 hour and 7 minutes.

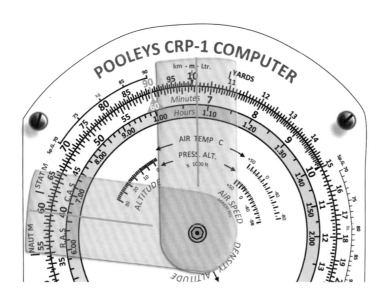

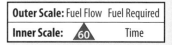

16.   (Answer: B) Caernarfon Radio, Air Ground Communication Service and 0800 to 1700

EGCK AD 2.18 - ATS COMMUNICATION FACILITIES

Service Designation	Callsign	Channel MHz	Hours of Operation		Remarks
			Winter	**Summer**	
1	2	3	4		5
A/G	Caernarfon Radio	122.250	0900-1630	0800-1700	ATZ hours co-incident with A/G hours, but not by arrangement

17.   (Answer: D) EGCK AD 2.22 - FLIGHT PROCEDURES

   a.   The aerodrome is in the vicinity of the Valley MATZ. Civil aircraft are to fly at 1500 ft or below Holyhead QNH in the Menai Straits area.

   b.   Arriving aircraft From the south and southeast should call Llanbedr ATC on 122.500 MHz at least 5 minutes before abeam Llanbedr aerodrome. Unless otherwise instructed, these aircraft should subsequently call Valley ATC on 125.225 MHz at least 15 minutes before ETA Caernarfon ATZ boundary. All other aircraft should call Valley ATC on 125.225 MHz at least 15 minutes before ETA Caernarfon ATZ boundary

   c.   Departing Aircraft Unless otherwise instructed, departing aircraft should call Valley ATC on 125.225 MHz immediately after take-off

   d.   Circuit height 800 ft aal. Aircraft are requested to join overhead not above 1300 ft aal. Circuit direction 02 and 26 RH

18.   (Answer: C) Gliding takes place at Rhigos up to 2,800 feet

19.   (Answer: D) Airway Lima 9 (L9) is Class A controlled airspace extending from FL 75. The annotation FL 75(+) means that the airspace extends to an upper limit of FL 195.

20.   (Answer: C) This symbol denotes the boundary between Altimeter Setting Regions.

21.   (Answer: A) 90 knots. Your ATA overhead Swansea was 1020; at 1030 you fix your position on track and 15 nm from Swansea.

To find the new ground speed: Speed = distance ÷ time

$$\frac{15 \text{ nm}}{10 \text{ minutes}} \times 60 \text{ minutes} = 90 \text{ knots}$$

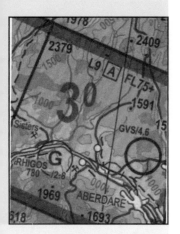

18. ANSWER C

21. ANSWER A

Alternatively using the CRP set 10 minutes on the rotating inner scale under the distance 15 nm on the outer scale; you may then read the speed above the 60 index.

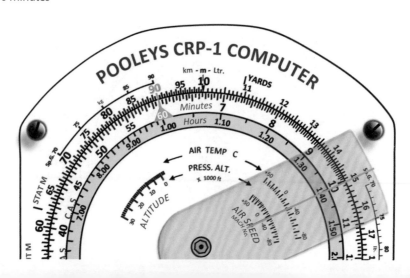

22. **(Answer: D)** 1058. The distance remaining to Exeter is 57.6 – 15 = 42.6 nm.

Time to Exeter = $\dfrac{\text{Distance remaining}}{\text{Ground speed}} = \dfrac{42.6}{90} \times 60$ minutes = 28.4 minutes

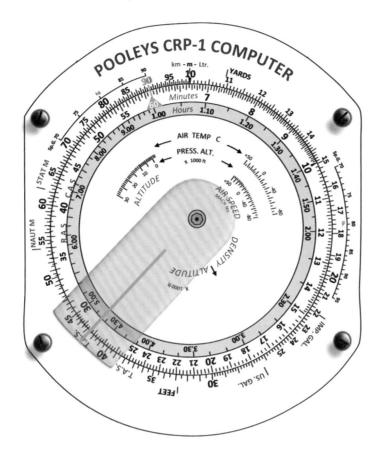

22. ANSWER D

Or, using the CRP set the 60 index below the ground speed (90), beneath distance 42.6 on the outer scale, read off the time on the inner scale, 28.4 minutes. The ETA at Exeter is therefore 1030 plus 28.4 minutes – 1058 and 24 seconds.

Outer Scale:	Distance	Speed
Inner Scale:	Time	60

23. **(Answer: A)** 500 fpm.

First we need to find the time it will take from the TOD to 1,500 feet:

Time = $\dfrac{\text{Distance}}{\text{Ground speed}} = \dfrac{10 \text{ nm}}{100 \text{ knots}} \times 60$ minutes = 6 minutes

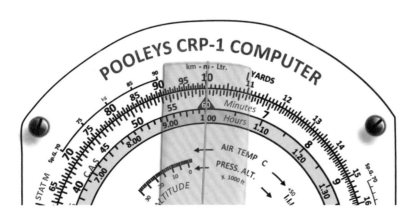

23. ANSWER A

Using the CRP, set the 60 index below the ground speed on the outer scale (10 representing 100 knots). Read off below 10 nm 6 (minutes) on the inner scale. Be careful, as in this case, you are in essence reading from exactly what you have set, but changing the position of the decimal place.

Using the CRP, set the 60 index below 30 to represent the 3,000 ft altitude reduction. Above 10 on the rotating inner scale you can read off 50 which represents 500 fpm.

Rate of Descent = $\dfrac{\text{Altitude reduction}}{\text{Time}} = \dfrac{(4{,}500 - 1{,}500) \text{ ft}}{6 \text{ minutes}} = \dfrac{3{,}000}{6} = 500$ fpm

24. **(Answer: A)** The wind can vary 38° from the runway direction.

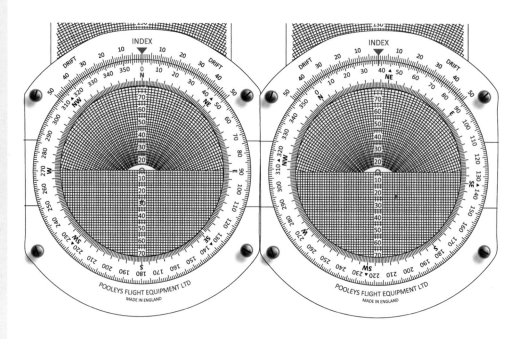

25. **(Answer: C)** Upottery is a hang-gliding or paragliding site with winch launching up to a maximum of 2,900 feet.

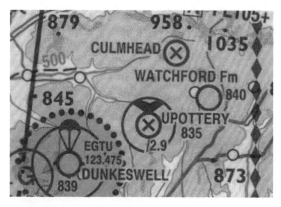

 UPOTTERY
/ 835
/2.9

 GLIDER LAUNCH SITE
Showing maximum altitude of winch launch AMSL

 FREE FALL PARACHUTE DROP ZONE

 HAND/PARA GLIDING
Showing maximum altitude of winch launch AMSL

 MICROLIGHT FLYING SITES

INTENTIONALLY BLANK

PLOG FOR NAVIGATION PAPER 3

TAKE OFF:

LAND:

FLIGHT TIME:

FROM	TO	ALT/FL	SAFE ALT	TAS	W/V	TRK T	DRIFT	HDG T	VAR	HDG M	GS	DIST	TIME	ETA
BODMIN 50 30 06N 004 39 96W	**MELKSHAM** 51 22 45N 002 08 30W	As req.	2800	100	330/35	061	20R	041	3W	044	95	108.5	68m30	
MELKSHAM 51 22 45N 002 08 30W	**WYCOMBE** 51 36 70N 000 48 49 W	As req.	3300	100	320/25	074	13R	061	2W	063	108	51.5	28m30	
										TOTAL		160	97m00	
ALTERNATE **WYCOMBE** 51 36 70N 000 48 49W	**BLACKBUSHE** 51 19 42N 000 50 90W	As req.	1300	100	320/25	184	10.5L	194.5	2W	196.5 =197	116	17	8m45	

Note: Safety Altitude is calculated from the higher of: i) the highest ground plus 1,299 feet; or ii) the highest structure plus 1,000 feet; Within 5 nm of track rounded up to the next 100 feet

You are planning the following VFR flight:

From:	Bodmin (50 30 06N 004 39 96W)
To:	Wycombe (51 36 70N 000 48 49W)
Via:	Melksham (51 22 45N 002 08 30W)
Alternate:	Blackbushe (51 19 42N 000 50 90W)

Complete the Flight Plan before answering questions 6 to 20

1. What is the magnetic heading from Bodmin to Melksham?

    a. 049°
    b. 044°
    c. 041°
    d. 063°

2. What is the groundspeed from Bodmin to Melksham?

    a. 102 knots
    b. 107 knots
    c. 99 knots
    d. 95 knots

3. What is the magnetic heading from Melksham to Wycombe?

    a. 063°
    b. 057°
    c. 061°
    d. 054°

4. What is the magnetic heading from Wycombe to Blackbushe?

    a. 195°
    b. 197°
    c. 185°
    d. 187°

5. What is the flight plan time from Bodmin to Wycombe?

    a. 1 hour 38 minutes
    b. 1 hour 47 minutes
    c. 108 minutes
    d. 1 hour 28 minutes

6. Assume that controlled airspace is not an issue. The leg between Melksham and Wycombe is to be conducted at the lowest available quadrantal level above the Transition Altitude of 3,000 feet; the Regional QNH is 1016 hectopascals. What level should be adopted? (FL graph)

    a. FL 30
    b. FL 35
    c. FL50
    d. FL40

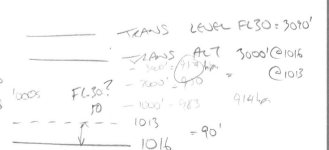

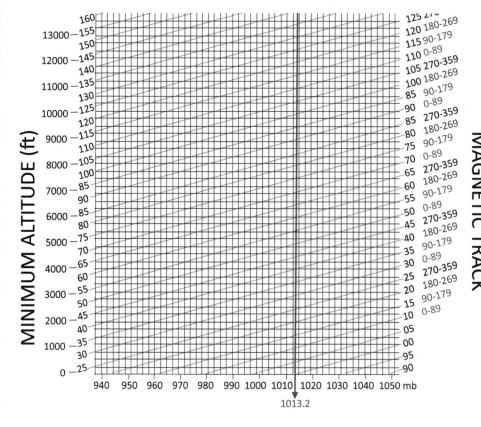

7.   You establish your position south of track over Glastonbury (51 08.87N 00242.90W). What would be the lowest permissible level to overfly Glastonbury in order to conform to the flight rules regarding flight over congested areas?

   a.   1,600 feet
   b.   1,000 feet
   c.   1,300 feet
   d.   900 feet

8.   62 nm along the first leg, you fix your position overhead Culmhead disused airfield, 5½ nm right of track. What correction needs to be made to route directly to Melksham? Assume that a constant heading has been flown from Bodmin.

   a.   066°M
   b.   039°M
   c.   037°M
   d.   032°M

9.   9 nm east of Bodmin is the following symbol: What does it mean?

   a.   Multiple unlit obstacles
   b.   An exceptionally high obstacle which is lit
   c.   A single high obstacle which is lit
   d.   Multiple obstacles which are lit

10. What feature can be seen at 51 01.11N 003 06.03W?

   a.   A town
   b.   A disused airfield
   c.   A large town or city
   d.   A large industrial area

11. What activity takes place at 50 21.90N 003 42.52W?

    a. Motor glider flying

    b. Gliding

    c. Paragliding or hang gliding

    d. Microlight flying

12. What does the symbol at Benson Aerodrome (51 36.85N 001 05.85W) represent?

    a. A Civil Aerodrome with limited facilities

    b. A Government Aerodrome

    c. A Government Aerodrome available for Civil use

    d. A Government Heliport

13. Looking approximately 16nm to the west of Melksham, which unit would you call if you wished to enter controlled airspace?

    a. Colerne Radio 120.075 MHz

    b. Bristol Radar 125.650 MHz

    c. Cotswold Information 105.0 MHz

    d. Lyneham Radar 123.4 Mhz

14. Overhead Melksham a fuel check shows 20 USG remaining. Assuming a fuel consumption of 9 USG per hour and the flight plan times to Wycombe and to Blackbushe. Allowing for a reserve of 6 USG, on arrival at the alternate what will be the remaining safe endurance?

    a. 55 minutes

    b. 1 hour 35 minutes

    c. 40 minutes

    d. 1 hour 10 minutes

15. 28 nm along the second leg from Melksham to Wycombe, you fix your position overhead Welford disused airfield, 2½ nm right of track. What correction needs to be made to route directly to Wycombe? Assume that a constant heading has been flown from Melksham.

    a. 058°M

    b. 051°M

    c. 075°M

    d. 069°M

The ATA overhead Melksham was 1340, and at 1351 you pinpoint your position overhead Membury 22 nm from Melksham, answer the following two questions.

16. What is the groundspeed being achieved?

    a. 112 knots

    b. 120 knots

    c. 107 knots

    d. 130 knots

17. What is your revised ETA at Wycombe?

    a. 1401

    b. 1411

    c. 1417

    d. 1406

18. On the diversion leg from Wycombe to Blackbushe, what is the lowest base of controlled airspace?

    a. 1,500 feet
    b. 2,500 feet
    c. 3,500 feet
    d. 4,500 feet

19. 20 nm west of Wycombe, at altitude 4,500 feet you wish to commence a descent to 2,000 feet to be level with five nm to run to Wycombe. What rate of descent is required assuming a groundspeed of 120 knots in the descent?

    a. 200 fpm
    b. 500 fpm
    c. 333 fpm
    d. 410 fpm

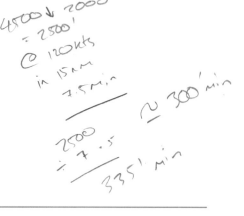

20. What is the airfield elevation at Blackbushe?

    a. 122 feet
    b. 325 feet
    c. 328 feet
    d. 227 feet

RADIO NAVIGATION

---

21. What range is displayed on the DME cockpit display?

    a. Slant range
    b. Horizontal Range
    c. Corrected slant range
    d. Arc range

22. Approximately what is the maximum number of aircraft that are able to use a DME station at any one time?

    a. 50
    b. 75
    c. 100
    d. 150

23. What is the name of the aircraft equipment needed for secondary surveillance radar?

    a. Transmitter
    b. Transposer
    c. Translator
    d. Transponder

24. A Non-Directional Beacon (NDB) is:

    a. An airborne system comprising of a loop antenna and a sense antenna
    b. A ground based station that radiates two signals out of phase
    c. An airborne system to measure the range and bearing from a ground station
    d. A ground based station that transmits omni-directionally

25. An aircraft is tracking away from an NDB maintaining a track of 040 with 9° of port drift. What bearing should the relative bearing indicator (RBI) be indicating?

    a.   189° relative

    b.   180° relative

    c.   031° relative

    d.   171° relative

END OF NAVIGATION PAPER 3

NAVIGATION PAPER 3: ANSWERS

	A	B	C	D
1.		X		
2.				X
3.	X			
4.		X		
5.	X			
6.			X	
7.	X			
8.				X
9.				X
10.			X	
11.				X
12.			X	
13.		X		
14.	X			
15		X		
16.		X		
17.				X
18.		X		
19.			X	
20.		X		
21.	X			
22.			X	
23.				X
24.				X
25.				X

$\frac{24}{25} = 96\%$

excellent, Smithers!

CORRECT ANSWERS: PERCENTAGES						
19	20	21	22	23	24	25
76%	80%	84%	88%	92%	96%	100%

INTENTIONALLY BLANK

TAKE OFF:

LAND:

FLIGHT TIME:

FROM	TO	ALT/FL	SAFE ALT	TAS	W/V	TRK T	DRIFT	HDG T	VAR	HDG M	GS	DIST	TIME	ETA
BODMIN	**MELKSHAM**													
50 30 06N	51 22 45N	As req.	2800	100	330/35	061	20 S	041	3W	044	95	109	69	
004 39 96W	002 08 30W													
MELKSHAM	**WYCOMBE**													
51 22 45N	51 36 70N	As req.	3300	100	320/25	074	13 S	061	2W	063	107	51.7	29	
002 08 30W	000 48 49 W													
										TOTAL		160.7	98	
ALTERNATE														
WYCOMBE	**BLACKBUSHE**													
51 36 70N	51 19 42N	As req.	1300	100	320/25	185	10 P	195	2W	197	116	17.3	9.1	
000 48 49W	000 50 90W													

Note: Safety Altitude is calculated from the higher of: i) the highest ground plus 1,299 feet; or ii) the highest structure plus 1,000 feet; Within 5 nm of track rounded up to the next 100 feet

1. **(Answer: B)** The magnetic heading from Bodmin to Melksham is 044°

   Method:

   1. Place the centre of the protractor over the track drawn on the map near the mid-point between the two ends of the track.
   2. Align the grid marks on the protractor with the graticule lines on the chart. Read off the True Track, in this case 061°
   3. Next, find the effect of the wind on the aircraft. Using the CRP computer set the wind direction (330) on the rotating inner scale under the Index on the fixed outer scale.
   4. Set the centre circle on a convenient speed arc – 100 is a handy round number. Mark down the wind speed, 35 knots for this question.
   5. The TAS is 100, so the centre circle is already in the correct place.
   6. Rotate the inner scale so that the measured true track, 061, is now below the index. Note the wind mark is now displaced 20° to the right
   7. Rotate the inner scale 20° to the right, 061 is now below 20° on the right hand side of the fixed drift scale. We are aiming for parity, so ensure that the wind dot is still displaced 20°.
   8. Read off the true heading under the Index = 041°
   9. Finally apply the variation, in this case 3°W. Remember "East is Least, West is Best", the variation is West, hence we add it giving a magnetic heading of 044°

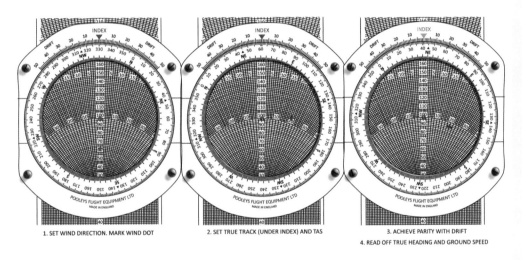

1. SET WIND DIRECTION. MARK WIND DOT   2. SET TRUE TRACK (UNDER INDEX) AND TAS   3. ACHIEVE PARITY WITH DRIFT

4. READ OFF TRUE HEADING AND GROUND SPEED

2. **(Answer: D)** Keeping the CRP as above read the groundspeed under the wind dot – 95 knots. The CRP can be very easy to misread, making a small sketch will give you a rough idea of the answer you expect to obtain to ensure that any amendments are applied correctly.

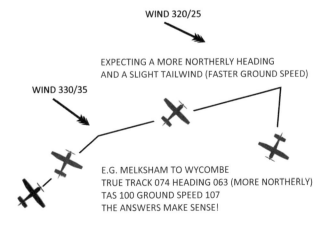

WIND 320/25

EXPECTING A MORE NORTHERLY HEADING
AND A SLIGHT TAILWIND (FASTER GROUND SPEED)

WIND 330/35

E.G. MELKSHAM TO WYCOMBE
TRUE TRACK 074 HEADING 063 (MORE NORTHERLY)
TAS 100 GROUND SPEED 107
THE ANSWERS MAKE SENSE!

3.   **(Answer: A)** The magnetic heading from Melksham to Wycombe 063°. Note the wind is different for this leg.

Method:

1. To find the effect of the wind on the aircraft. Using the CRP computer set the wind direction (320) on the rotating inner scale under the Index on the fixed outer scale.

2. Set the centre circle on a convenient speed arc – 100 is a handy round number.
    Mark down the wind speed, 25 knots for this leg.

3. The TAS is 100, so the centre circle is already in the correct place.

4. Rotate the inner scale so that the measured true track, 074, is now below the index. Note the wind mark is now displaced 12° to the right.

5. Rotate the inner scale 12° to the right, 074 is now below 12° on the right hand side of the fixed drift scale. However, now the pencil mark indicates 13° of starboard drift. What we are aiming for is parity, so move the rotating scale so that 074 is below 13° on the fixed drift scale and still right of the index. In so doing the drift remains at 13° and we have parity – the track is offset 13° and the wind mark still shows 13° of drift.

6. Read off the true heading under the Index = 061°.

7. Finally apply the variation, in this case 2°W. Remember "East is Least, West is Best", the variation is West, hence we add it giving a magnetic heading of 063°.

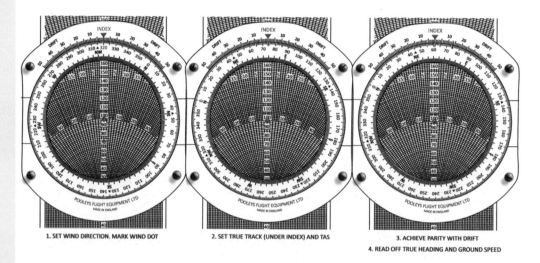

1. SET WIND DIRECTION. MARK WIND DOT   2. SET TRUE TRACK (UNDER INDEX) AND TAS   3. ACHIEVE PARITY WITH DRIFT
4. READ OFF TRUE HEADING AND GROUND SPEED

4.   **(Answer: B)** The magnetic heading from Wycombe to Blackbushe is 197°. The wind is the same as for the second leg, from the method above:

1. Rotate the inner scale so that the measured true track, 185, is now below the index. Note the wind mark is now displaced 7° to the left.

2. Rotate the inner scale 7° to the left, 185 is now below 7° on the left hand side of the fixed drift scale. However, now the pencil mark indicates 10° of port drift. What we are aiming for is parity, so move the rotating scale so that 185 is below 10° on the fixed drift scale and still left of the index. In so doing the drift remains at 10° and we have parity – the track is offset 10° and the wind mark still shows 10° of drift.

3. Read off the true heading under the Index = 195°.

4. Finally, apply the variation, in this case 2°W. Remember "East is Least, West is Best", the variation is West, hence we add it giving a magnetic heading of 197°.

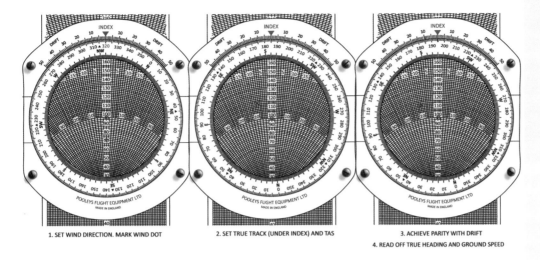

1. SET WIND DIRECTION. MARK WIND DOT
2. SET TRUE TRACK (UNDER INDEX) AND TAS
3. ACHIEVE PARITY WITH DRIFT
4. READ OFF TRUE HEADING AND GROUND SPEED

5. **(Answer: A)** The total flight plan time from Bodmin to Wycombe is 1 hour and 38 minutes. *(See completed PLOG on page 368)*

6. **(Answer: C)** FL 50. The quadrantal level is based on magnetic track. The magnetic track between Melksham and Wycombe is 077° (true track 074° plus 3° westerly variation). This track lies between 000° and 089°, so the flight level should be an odd one.

Enter the graph at the Minimum safe altitude (from the flight plan 3300 feet). Move horizontally across until you intercept the vertical line corresponding to the regional pressure of 1016 hPa. Trace vertically up to the next slanting line representing tracks between 000° and 089°, to the left of this number is another number showing the next flight level available for use.

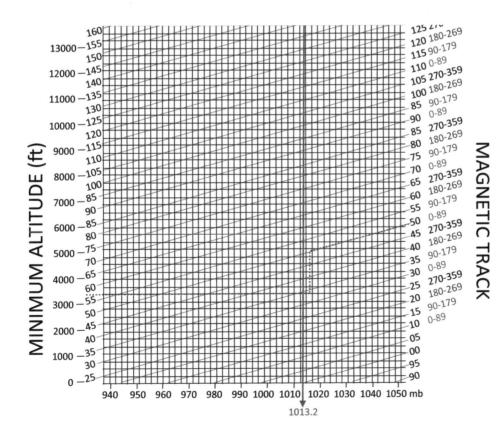

| MH 270 - 359 EVEN FLIGHT LEVEL + 500 | MH 000 - 089 ODD FLIGHT LEVEL |
| MH 180 - 269 EVEN FLIGHT LEVEL | MH 090 - 179 ODD FLIGHT LEVEL + 500 |

7. **(Answer: A)** 1,600 feet. The relevant Low Flying Rule is the one stating that except for helicopters or when aircraft are taking off or landing at a licensed or government aerodrome, you must not fly over the congested area of any city town or settlement below a height which would enable the aircraft to alight clear of the congested area in the event of a power unit failure or below 1000 ft above the highest fixed obstacle within 600 m of the aircraft. Whichever is the higher.

To the north of Glastonbury is a spot height of 520 feet. You must be 1000 feet above this, 1520 feet, rounded up to 1600 feet.

8. **(Answer: D)** 032°M. The first stage to solving this question is to find the Track Error. This can be done either using the formula:

Distance off track (nm) x 60 = **Track Error (degrees)**
Distance gone (nm)

$\frac{5.5}{62}$ x 60 = 5.3°

Or using the CRP flight computer:

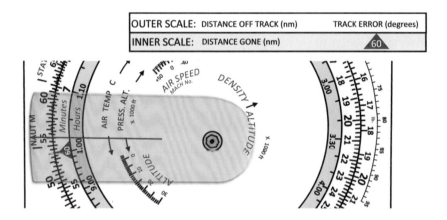

If a correction was made for Track Error alone we would merely parallel the required track, what we need to find now is the closing angle to route direct to the next turning point:

Distance off track (nm) x 60 = **Track Error (degrees)**
Distance to go (nm)

The total distance from Bodmin to Melksham is 109 nm, hence the distance to go is:

109 − 62 = 47.

$\frac{5.5}{47}$ x 60 = 7°

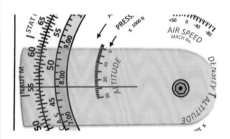

OUTER SCALE: DISTANCE OFF TRACK (nm)	TRACK ERROR (degrees)
INNER SCALE: DISTANCE TO GO (nm)	60

To find the heading correction to be made add the Track Error to the Closing Angle:

7 + 5.3 = 12.3°

As the aircraft is to the right of track, so the aircraft must be turned to the left. The original heading was 044°M, therefore the heading now required to reach Melksham is 044 – 12 = 032°M

9.   **(Answer: D)** The symbol represents multiple obstacles which are lit.

AIR NAVIGATION OBSTACLES

Exceptionally High Obstacle (Lighted) 100 ft or more AGL

Single Obstacle (Unlighted)

Multiple Obstacle (Lighted)

Cable joining Obstacles   **wwwww cables**

10.   **(Answer: C)** The feature at 51 01.11N 003 06.03W is a large town or city, in this case Taunton.

BUILT- UP AREAS

City or Large Town   over 2 Sq km

Town   1 to 2 Sq km

Small Town, Village or Hamlet   under 1 Sq km

Large Industrial Area

11.   **(Answer: D)** Microlight flying takes place at Halwell, 50 21.90N 003 42.52W, *See below.*

12.   **(Answer: C)** The symbol at Benson (51 36.85N 001 05.85W) denotes a Government Aerodrome available for Civil use.

Aerodrome - Civil

Aerodrome - Civil, limited or no facilities

Heliport - Civil

Aerodrome - Government, available for Civil use

Aerodrome - Government

Heliport - Government

Microlight Flying Sites

Disused or Abandoned Aerodrome

13.   **(Answer: B)** To obtain permission to transit the Bristol Control Zone you should contact Bristol Radar on 125.650 MHz.

14. **(Answer: A)** 55 minutes.

    The flight planned times for the subsequent legs are:
    Melksham to Wycombe: 29 minutes
    Wycombe to Blackbushe: 9.1 minutes
    Total: 38.1 minutes

Outer Scale:	Fuel Flow	Fuel Required
Inner Scale:	60	Time

Find out how much fuel the remaining flight time requires, using the CRP set the 60 index below 9 for the fuel flow.

Read off above the time (38.1 minutes) on the inner scale a fuel requirement of 5.7 USG. A rough check will determine where to place the decimal, the time is almost 40 minutes (⅔ of an hour), two thirds of 9 USG is 6, so we are expecting roughly 6 USG to be used in the remaining flight time.

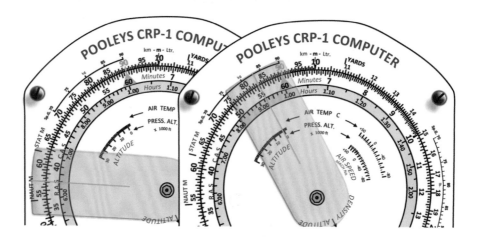

Overhead Swansea we had 20 USG of fuel and from this we need to subtract the 5.7 USG we are going to use and the 6 USG that we are told must be held in reserve:
20 − 5.7 − 6 = 8.3 USG
In determining the safe endurance we are expecting an answer of just under an hour. Keeping the CRP as above with the 60 index below the 9, this time read off below 8.3 on the outer scale a time of 55.4 minutes on the inner scale, which is the endurance remaining.

15. **(Answer: B)** 051°M. The first stage to solving this question is to find the Track Error. This can be done using the formula:

    Distance off track (nm) x 60 = Track Error (degrees)
    ** Distance gone (nm)**

    $$\frac{2.5}{28} \times 60 = 5.37°$$

    Or using the CRP flight computer:

OUTER SCALE:	DISTANCE OFF TRACK (nm)	TRACK ERROR (degrees)
INNER SCALE:	DISTANCE GONE (nm)	60

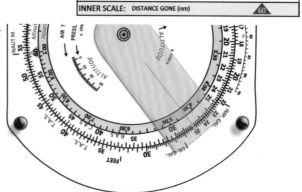

If a correction was made for Track Error we would merely parallel the required track, what we now need to find is the closing angle to route direct to the next turning point:

Distance off track (nm) x 60 = **Track Error (degrees)**
  Distance to go (nm)

The total distance from Bodmin to Melksham is 51.7 nm, hence the distance to go is
51.7 – 28 = 23.7 nm
$\frac{2.5}{23.7}$ x 60 = 6.33°

| OUTER SCALE: | DISTANCE OFF TRACK (nm) | TRACK ERROR (degrees) |
| INNER SCALE: | DISTANCE TO GO (nm) | 60 |

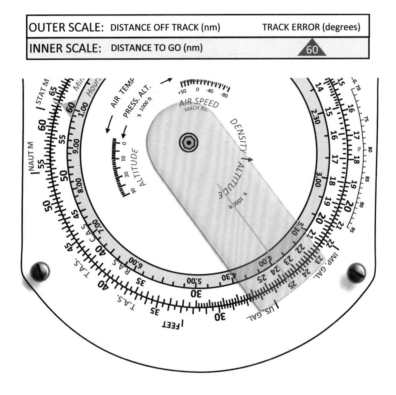

To find the heading correction to be made add the Track Error to the Closing Angle:
5.36 + 6.33 = 11.7°

As the aircraft is to the right of track, so the aircraft must be turned to the left. The original heading was 063°M, therefore the heading now required to reach Melksham is 063 – 12 = 051°M

16. **(Answer: B)** 120 knots. Your ATA overhead Swansea was 1340; at 1351 you fix your position on track and 22 nm from Melksham.

To find the new groundspeed: Speed = distance ÷ time
  $\frac{22\ nm}{11\ minutes}$ x 60 minutes = 120 knots

Alternatively using the CRP set 11 minutes on the rotating inner scale under the distance 22 nm on the outer scale; you may then read off the speed above the 60 index.

| **Outer Scale:** | Distance | Speed |
| **Inner Scale:** | Time | 60 |

17. **(Answer: D)** 1406

The distance remaining to Wycombe is 51.7 – 22 = 29.7 nm.

Time to Exeter = Distance remaining = 29.7 x 60 minutes = 14.85 minutes
                        Groundspeed   120

Or, using the CRP set the 60 index below the groundspeed (120), beneath distance 29.7 on the outer scale, read off the time on the inner scale, 14.85 minutes. (diag) The ETA at Exeter is therefore 1351 plus (for practical purposes) 15 minutes – 1406.

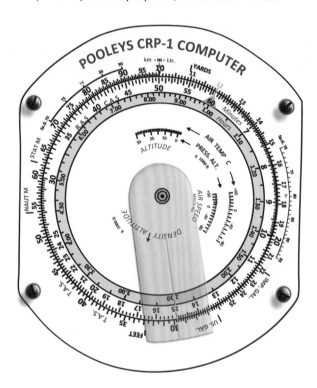

18. **(Answer:B)** **The** lowest base of controlled airspace between Wycombe and Blackbushe is 2,500 feet.

19. **(Answer: C)** 333 fpm

First we need to find the time it will take from the TOD to 2,000 feet:

Time   =   Distance   =   15 nm   x   60 minutes = 7.5 minutes
                Groundspeed   120 knots

Outer Scale:	Distance	Speed
Inner Scale:	Time	△60

Using the CRP, set the 60 index below the ground speed on the outer scale (12 representing 100 knots). Read off below 15 nm 7.5 (minutes) on the inner scale.

Rate of Descent = Altitude Reduction = (4,500 – 2,000) ft = 2,500 = 333 fpm
                        Time   7.5 minutes   7.5

20. **(Answer: B)** The airfield elevation at Blackbushe is 325 feet.

RADIO NAVIGATION

21. **(Answer: A)** Distance Measuring Equipment provides you with the distance of your aircraft from the ground station. It is important to remember that the information given is the slant range; when close to the ground station the information will be at its most inaccurate.

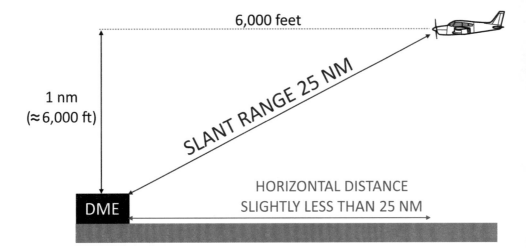

22. **(Answer: C)** DME operates by the aircraft equipment (the interrogator) transmitting a coded pulse signal on the selected frequency; the signal reaches the ground station where it is retransmitted. When the retransmitted signal reaches the aircraft the DME equipment recognises its own code and knows that the radio wave has travelled at a fixed speed. The interrogator can therefore work out how long it has taken for the pulse signal to travel to and return from the DME ground station and can calculate the distance.

There is a practical limit to how many aircraft can use or "lock on" to a DME station at any one time. Most can deal with no more than around 100 aircraft, when this limit is exceeded the ground station will begin to disregard the weaker signals, these will normally be the most distant from the station. Newer DME stations will be able to handle more aircraft.

DME operates in the UHF band. Each DME channel consists of two frequencies one for the interrogation signal from the aircraft and a separate, but automatically paired, response frequency from the ground station. There are 126 channels classified as either X or Y.

23. **(Answer: D)** A transponder is the airborne equipment required in the aircraft for the SSR system operate.

24. **(Answer: D)** A Non-Directional Beacon (NDB) is the most basic navigation aid. It is a ground station that transmits radio energy in all directions. NDBs operate in the low or medium frequency bands.

The accuracy of an NDB can be seriously reduced by:
Thunderstorm effect: The ADF needle can be deflected towards an electrical storm and away from the ground station
Night Effect: Strong sky waves can be present in the LF and MF frequency bands especially at dawn and dusk. At these times signals from the beacon can take different paths to the aircraft either by surface wave or sky wave, the two paths interfere with each other, the signal may fade and the needle wander.
Mountain Effect: Where signals from the beacon are reflected by terrain.
Coastal Effect: Caused by the radio wave bending (refracting) when it crosses a coast at an angle.

25. **(Answer: D)** 171° relative

Drift is measured from the heading (nose) to the track, and is classified in degrees port or starboard of heading.

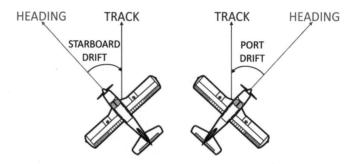

If there were to be no cross wind, when tracking away from the NDB flying the heading as a track would work. The needle would continue to show a steady relative bearing of 180° i.e. it will point to the tail of the aircraft. In cross wind conditions an allowance for drift is necessary.

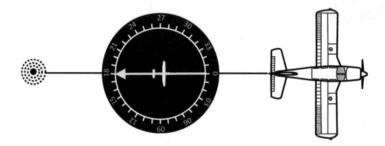

With a track of 040 and a drift 9° to port, the track lies to the left of the heading; therefore the heading is 049°. When using an RBI the "tail" of the ADF needle must be offset 9° I.e. by an equal amount in the opposite direction in order for the desired track to be maintained. To summarise, the aim is to achieve parity between the number of degrees by which the heading is offset in one direction and the number of degrees by which the tail of the ADF needle is displaced in the other direction.

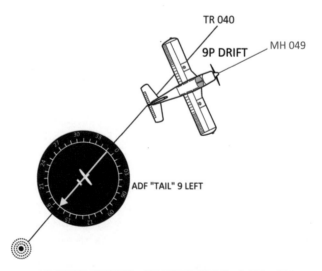

MAGNETIC HEADING + RELATIVE BEARING +/- 180 = QDR
049 + 171 = 220 - 180 = 040

INTENTIONALLY BLANK

TAKE OFF:

LAND:

FLIGHT TIME:

PLOG FOR NAVIGATION PAPER 4

FROM	TO	ALT/FL	SAFE ALT	TAS	W/V	TRK T	DRIFT	HDG T	VAR	HDG M	GS	DIST	TIME	ETA
ROCHESTER 51 21 17N 000 30 30E	ELMSETT 52 04 51N 000 58 65E	As req.	1900	95	040/20	022.5	4	26.5	2W	28.5	76	47	37	
ELMSETT 52 04 51N 000 58 65E	CONINGTON 52 27 90N 000 15 28W	As req.	1600	95	040/20	297.5	12	309.5	2W	311.5	97	50.5	31	
										TOTAL		97.5		
ALTERNATE CONINGTON 52 27 90N 000 15 28W	BOURN 52 12 88N 000 02 47W	As req.	1300	95	050/15			146	2W	148				

Note: Safety Altitude is calculated from the higher of: i) the highest ground plus 1,299 feet; or ii) the highest structure plus 1,000 feet; Within 5 nm of track rounded up to the next 100 feet

You are planning the following VFR flight:

From: **Rochester (51 21 07N 000 30 30E)**
To: **Peterborough/Conington (52 27 90N000 15 28W)**
Via: **Elmsett (52 04 51N 000 58 65E)**
Alternate: **Bourn (52 12 88N 000 02 47W)**

Complete the Flight Plan before answering questions 6 to 20

1. What is the magnetic heading from Rochester to Elmsett?

    a.   026°M
    b.   023°M
    c.   028°M
    d.   035°M

2. What is the ground speed from Rochester to Elmsett?

    a.   75 knots
    b.   80 knots
    c.   70 knots
    d.   85 knots

3. What is the magnetic track from Elmsett to Conington?

    a.   310°M
    b.   298°M
    c.   308°M
    d.   312°M

4. What is the total flight plan time from Rochester to Conington?

    a.   1 hour 37 minutes
    b.   1 hour 9 minutes
    c.   1 hour 21 minutes
    d.   58 minutes

5. What is the magnetic heading from Conington to Bourn?

    a.   145°M
    b.   155°M
    c.   143°M
    d.   147°M

6. What is the total distance from Rochester to Conington?

    a.   48 nm
    b.   68.9 nm
    c.   97.7 nm
    d.   114.6 nm

7. In the vicinity of Rochester what agencies are able to provide LARS services?

    a.   Thames Radar 132.7 MHz to the west, Southend Radar 130.775 MHz to the north
    b.   Thames Radar 132.7 MHz to the west, Essex Radar 120.625 MHz to the north
    c.   Southend Radar 130.775 MHz to the north, Farnborough East Radar 123.225 Mhz to the west
    d.   Essex Radar 120.625 MHz to the north, Farnborough East Radar 123.225 MHz to the west

8. The turning point at Elmsett lies within a light blue shaded area surrounded by darker blue dots. What does this area denote and which agency should you contact and why?

    a.   It denotes a Control Zone, pilots should contact Elmsett 130.9 MHz for permission to transit

    b.   It denotes a MATZ, pilots should contact Wattisham 125.8 MHz for penetration

    c.   It denotes a Control Area, pilots should contact Wattisham 109.3 MHz for information

    d.   It denotes a MATZ, pilots should contact Wattisham 109.3 MHz for penetration

9. Given the following, what is the minimum amount of fuel required?

Start Up, Taxi, Run up and Take Off	2 USG
Fuel Consumption	7 USG per Hour
Flight Planned Time	1 Hour 25 Minutes
Diversion	10 Minutes
Approach and Landing (or missed approach)	2 USG
Reserve at Diversion Airfield	6 USG

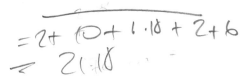

    a.   21.6 USG

    b.   19.6 USG

    c.   28.6 USG

    d.   23.6 USG

10. Assume that conditions allow the aircraft to be operated at MTWA. Given the following what is the maximum payload that can be carried? Given:

MTWA	2,100 lbs
Aircraft Basic Empty Weight	1,460 lbs
Pilot's Weight	210 lbs
Fuel Required 37 USG (Sp.G 0.72)	?

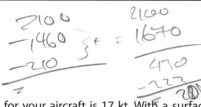

    a.   164 lbs

    b.   189 lbs

    c.   208 lbs

    d.   222 lbs

11. The maximum demonstrated cross wind for your aircraft is 17 kt. With a surface wind speed of 35 kt, by how many degrees can the surface wind differ from the runway direction before the crosswind component equals 17 kt?

    a.   20°

    b.   30°

    c.   40°

    d.   50°

12. 18 nm along the first leg, you fix your position over head South Woodham Ferrers VRP, 2½ nm left of track. What correction needs to be made to route directly to Elmsett? Assume that a constant heading has been flown from Rochester.

    a.   015°M

    b.   041°M

    c.   033°M

    d.   010°M

The ATA overhead Elmsett was 1515, and at 1525 you pinpoint your position overhead Newmarket 22 nm from Elmsett, answer the following two questions.

13. What ground speed is being achieved?

    a.   97 knots

    b.   88 knots

    c.   125 knots

    d.   132 knots

[handwritten: 22nm in 10m = 133nm/h]

14. What is the revised ETA at Conington?

    a.   1538

    b.   1528

    c.   1548

    d.   1544

[handwritten: 50.8nm]

15. What feature can be found at 52 00.86N 000 48.33W? What does the associated notation mean?

    a.   It is a Danger Area, and must be avoided by all aircraft

    b.   It is a Prohibited Area, and must be avoided by fixed wing aircraft

    c.   It is a Restricted Area, and must be avoided by all aircraft

    d.   It is a Restricted Area, and must be avoided by helicopters

[handwritten: READ ... PARKING NOTES]

16. What is the lowest base of the controlled areas around the Stansted Control Zone?

    a.   2,500 feet

    b.   2,000 feet

    c.   3,500 feet

    d.   1,500 feet

17. What feature is found at 52 31N 000 06W?

    a.   A windfarm

    b.   An aerodrome (Benwick)

    c.   A microlight and parachute site

    d.   A gliding site

18. What is the meaning of the following symbol?

    a.   A Prohibited Area

    b.   A Restricted Area

    c.   A High Intensity Radio Transmission Area

    d.   An Area of Intense Aerial Activity

19. Overhead Elmsett a fuel check shows 18 USG remaining. Assuming a fuel consumption of 7 USG per hour and the flight plan times to Conington and to Bourn. Allowing for a reserve of 6 USG, on arrival at the alternate what will be the remaining safe endurance?

    a.   1 hour 57 minutes

    b.   1 hour and 20 minutes

    c.   96 minutes

    d.   65 minutes

[handwritten: 12 USG ... 50.5min = 5.9 USG ... = 6.1 USG]

20. Along the second leg from Elmsett, you call Lakenheath to request permission to transit the MATZ. No reply is received, what is the best course of action to take?

    a.   Climb above 2,032 feet aal to avoid the MATZ

    b.   Make a second call, if there is still no answer proceed on track with caution.

    c.   Climb to 2,500 aal to fly above the MATZ

    d.   Call Mildenhall to obtain permission

RADIO NAVIGATION

---

21. You are flying towards a VOR on the 255 radial. In order to obtain CDI indications in the correct sense the OBS should be set to:

   a. 075° with a TO indication
   b. 255° with a FROM indication
   c. 255° with a TO indication
   d. 075° with a FROM indication

22. An aircraft is tracking away from an NDB maintaining a track of 300 with 5° of starboard drift. What bearing should the relative bearing indicator (RBI) indicate?

   a. 185° relative
   b. 180° relative
   c. 175° relative
   d. 300° relative

23. An aircraft is tracking towards an NDB maintaining a track of 270 with 8° of port drift. What bearing should the relative bearing indicator (RBI) indicate?

   a. 008° relative
   b. 360° relative
   c. 270° relative
   d. 352° relative

24. A QDM is:

   a. Magnetic bearing of the aircraft from the VDF station
   b. Magnetic heading (in nil wind) to steer to reach the VDF station
   c. True bearing of the aircraft from the VDF station
   d. True heading (in nil wind) to steer to reach the VDF station

25. An aircraft is tracking away from an NDB maintaining a track of 090 with 8° of port drift. What bearing should the relative bearing indicator (RBI) indicate?

   a. 180° relative
   b. 188° relative
   c. 172° relative
   d. 099° relative

END OF NAVIGATION PAPER 4

INTENTIONALLY BLANK

	A	B	C	D
1.			X	
2.	X			
3.				X
4.		X		
5.				X
6.			X	
7.			X	
8.		X		
9.	X			
10.			X	
11.		X		
12.		X		
13.				X
14.	X			
15				X
16.				X
17.	X			
18.			X	
19.				X
20.		X		
21.	X			
22.	X			
23.				X
24.		X		
25.			X	

CORRECT ANSWERS: PERCENTAGES						
19	20	21	22	23	24	25
76%	80%	84%	88%	92%	96%	100%

INTENTIONALLY BLANK

TAKE OFF:

LAND:

FLIGHT TIME:

FROM	TO	ALT/FL	SAFE ALT	TAS	W/V	TRK T	DRIFT	HDG T	VAR	HDG M	GS	DIST	TIME	ETA
ROCHESTER	ELMSETT													
51 21 07N	52 04 51N	As req.	1900	95	040/20	023	4 P	026	2W	028	75	46.8	37.4	
000 30 10E	000 58 65E													
ELMSETT	CONINGTON													
52 04 51N	52 27 90N	As req.	1600	95	040/20	298	12 P	310	2W	312	97	50.9	31.5	
000 58 65E	000 15 28W													
										TOTAL		97.7	68.9	
ALTERNATE														
CONINGTON	BOURN													
52 27 90N	52 12 88N	As req.	1300	95	050/15	154	9 S	145	2W	147	98	16.9	10.4	
000 15 28W	000 02 47W													

Note: Safety Altitude is calculated from the higher of: i) the highest ground plus 1,299 feet; or ii) the highest structure plus 1,000 feet; Within 5 nm of track rounded up to the next 100 feet

1. **(Answer: C)** The magnetic heading from Rochester to Elmsett is 028°M

    Method:
    1. Place the centre of the protractor over the track drawn on the map near the mid-point between the two ends of the track.
    2. Align the grid marks on the protractor with the graticule lines on the chart. Read off the TrueTrack, in this case 023°.
    3. Next, find the effect of the wind on the aircraft. Using the CRP computer set the wind direction(040) on the rotating inner scale under the Index on the fixed outer scale.
    4. Set the centre circle on a convenient speed arc – 100 is a handy round number. Mark down the wind speed, 20 knots for this question.
    5. Move the sliding scale so that the centre circle is over the TAS 95.
    6. Rotate the inner scale so that the measured true track, 023, is now below the index. Note the wind mark that was drawn is now displaced 5° to the left.
    7. Now rotate the inner scale 5° to the left, 023 is now below 5° on the left hand side of the fixeddrift scale. However, the wind dot is now only displaced by 4°; adjust the inner scale so that 023 isnow under 4° on the fixed drift scale. Check to ensure that the wind dot is still displaced 4° to theleft. We are aiming for parity, so if 023 is below 4° on the fixed drift scale and the wind dot is alsodisplaced by 4° then the computer is set correctly.
    8. Read off the true heading under the Index = 026°.
    9. Finally apply the variation, in this case 2°W. Remember "East is Least, West is Best", thevariation is West, hence we add it giving a magnetic heading of 028°.

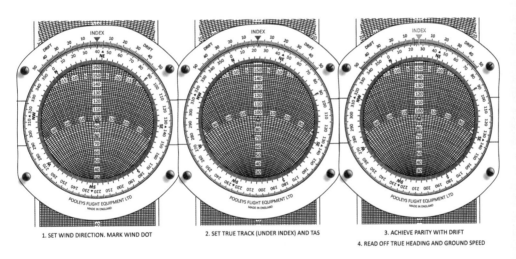

1. SET WIND DIRECTION. MARK WIND DOT   2. SET TRUE TRACK (UNDER INDEX) AND TAS   3. ACHIEVE PARITY WITH DRIFT
4. READ OFF TRUE HEADING AND GROUND SPEED

2. **(Answer: A)** The ground speed from Rochester to Elmsett is 75 knots. Keeping the CRP as above read the groundspeed under the wind dot – 75 knots. The CRP can be very easy to misread, drawing a small sketch will give you a rough idea of the answer you expect to obtain to ensure that any amendments are applied correctly. In this instance we would expect the wind to be almost all head wind and therefore have a big effect on the speed, reducing it, but the cross wind component will be fairly small with only a small correction to the east being necessary.

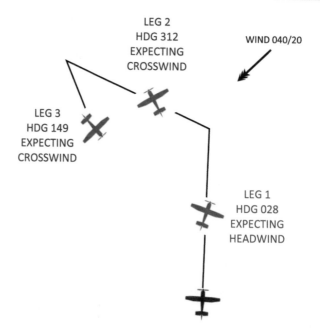

LEG 2
HDG 312
EXPECTING
CROSSWIND

WIND 040/20

LEG 3
HDG 149
EXPECTING
CROSSWIND

LEG 1
HDG 028
EXPECTING
HEADWIND

3.   **(Answer: D)** The magnetic track from Elmsett to Conington is 312°M

Method:

1. To find the effect of the wind on the aircraft. Using the CRP computer set the wind direction (040) on the rotating inner scale under the Index on the fixed outer scale.

2. Set the centre circle on a convenient speed arc – 100 is a handy round number. Mark down the wind speed, 20 knots for this question.

3. Move the sliding scale so that the centre circle is over the TAS 95.

4. Rotate the inner scale so that the measured true track, 298, is now below the index.
    Note the wind mark that was drawn is now displaced 12° to the left

5. Rotate the inner scale 12° to the left, 298 is now below 12° on the left hand side of the fixed drift scale.
    The wind dot is still indicating 12° of port drift, so we have parity between the wind dot and the displacement of the true track.

6. Read off the true heading under the Index = 310°

7. Finally apply the variation, in this case 2°W. Remember "East is Least, West is Best", the variation is West, hence we add it giving a magnetic heading of 312°

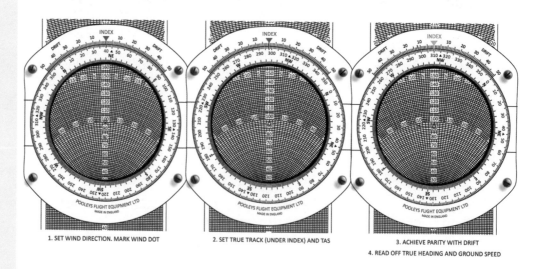

1. SET WIND DIRECTION. MARK WIND DOT   2. SET TRUE TRACK (UNDER INDEX) AND TAS   3. ACHIEVE PARITY WITH DRIFT
                                                                                        4. READ OFF TRUE HEADING AND GROUND SPEED

4.   **(Answer: B)** The total flight plan time from Rochester to Conington is 1 hour and 9 minutes.
      (see completed flight PLOG on page 388)

5. **(Answer: D)** The magnetic heading from Conington to Bourn is 147°

Method:
1. To find the effect of the wind on the aircraft. Using the CRP computer set the wind direction (050) on the rotating inner scale under the Index on the fixed outer scale.
2. Set the centre circle on a convenient speed arc – 100 is a handy round number. Mark down the wind speed, 15 knots for this question.
3. Move the sliding scale so that the centre circle is over the TAS 95.
4. Rotate the inner scale so that the measured true track, 154, is below the index.
   Note the wind mark that was drawn is now displaced 9° to the right.
5. Rotate the inner scale 9° to the right, 154 is now below 9° on the right hand side of the fixed drift scale. The wind dot is still indicating 9° of starboard drift, so we have parity between the wind dot and the displacement of the true track.
6. Read off the true heading under the Index = 145°.
7. Finally apply the variation, in this case 2°W. Remember "East is Least, West is Best", the variation is West, hence we add it giving a magnetic heading of 147°.

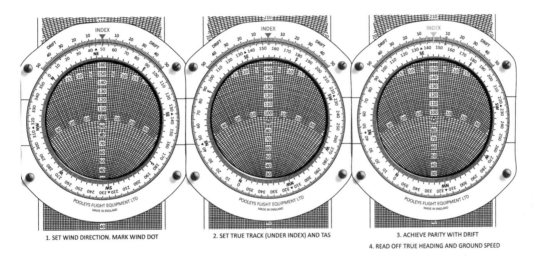

1. SET WIND DIRECTION. MARK WIND DOT   2. SET TRUE TRACK (UNDER INDEX) AND TAS   3. ACHIEVE PARITY WITH DRIFT
                                                                                                4. READ OFF TRUE HEADING AND GROUND SPEED

6. **(Answer: C)** 97.7 nm. The distance is found by measuring the track drawn on the chart. As we are using a 1:500,000 chart ensure that you are measuring with the correct scale.

7. **(Answer: C)** The designated LARS units in the vicinity of Rochester are Southend 130.775 MHz and Farnborough East Radar 123.225 MHz.

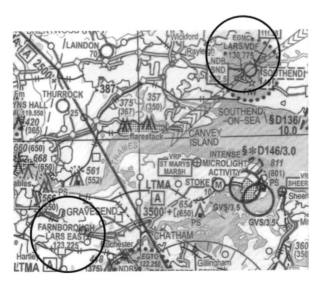

8.   **(Answer: B)** The area is a MATZ (Military Aerodrome Traffic Zone); pilots should contact Wattisham 125.8 MHz when 15 nm or 5 minutes flying time from the MATZ boundary (whichever is sooner) to request permission to penetrate the MATZ.

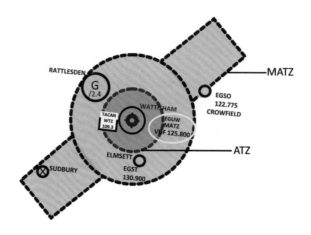

9.   **(Answer: A)** The minimum fuel required is 21.6 USG

Start Up, Taxi, Run up and Take Off	2 USG	2 USG
Fuel Consumption	7 USG per Hour	
Flight Planned Time	1 Hour 25 Minutes	9.9 USG
Diversion	10 Minutes	1.6 USG
Approach and Landing (or missed approach)	2 USG	2 USG
Reserve at Diversion Airfield	6 USG	6 USG
Total		**21.5 USG**

FUEL FOR ROUTE   FUEL FOR DIVERSION

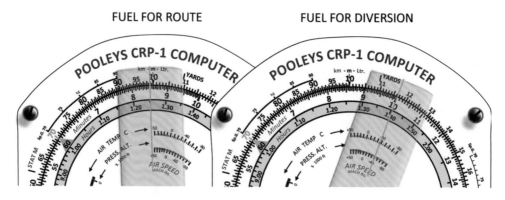

Outer Scale:	Fuel Flow	Fuel Required
Inner Scale:	60	Time

A rough estimate of the fuel required will help in deciding where to put the decimal place. With a fuel flow of 7 USG per hour and a total flight time of 1 hour 35, we are expecting an answer slightly more than 10.5 USG (real answer 9.9 + 1.6 = 11.5 USG).

10. **(Answer: C)** To find the payload, which is the weight of passengers, cargo and baggage, we first find the weight of the fuel that is needed for the flight. This can be done either using the CRP, or by using 6 lb per USG. This is a handy figure to commit to memory, one USG with a Specific Gravity of 0.72 weighs 6 lb.

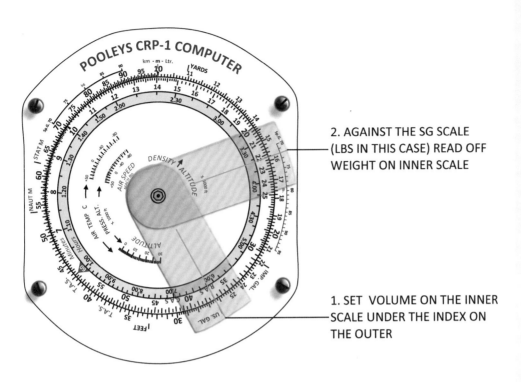

2. AGAINST THE SG SCALE (LBS IN THIS CASE) READ OFF WEIGHT ON INNER SCALE

1. SET VOLUME ON THE INNER SCALE UNDER THE INDEX ON THE OUTER

MTWA	2,100 lbs
Aircraft Basic Empty Weight	1,460 lbs
Pilot's Weight	210 lbs
Fuel Required 37 USG (Sp.G 0.72)	**222 lbs**

Next find the sum of the weight used so far: 1,460 + 210 + 222 = 1,892 lbs
Finally subtract this figure from the MTWA:
Payload available = 2,100 – 1,892 = 208 lbs.

11. **(Answer: B)** 30°. To find the crosswind component use the wind triangle side of the CRP and the square grid at the bottom of the low speed side of the sliding plate.

Set the rotating inner scale to North, and place the centre dot at the zero speed point at the top of the square grid. Make a mark to represent the wind speed – 35 knots for this question.

Rotate the inner scale until your pencil mark reaches the maximum cross wind limit of 17 knots. Now read off on the inner scale the number directly below the index, this represents the degrees from runway heading at which the crosswind will be 17 knots.

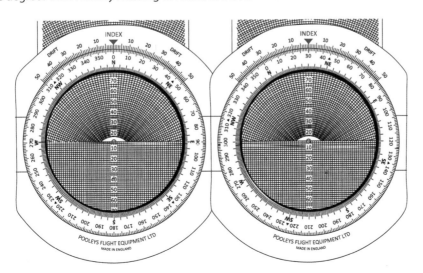

12. **(Answer: B)** 041°M

The first stage to solving this question is to find the Track Error.

This can be done using the formula:

Distance off track (nm) x **60 = Track Error (degrees)**
  Distance gone (nm)

$\frac{2.5}{18}$ x 60 = 8.3°

Or using the CRP flight computer:

Outer Scale:	Distance Off Track (nm)	Track Error (degrees)
Inner Scale:	Distance Gone (nm)	60

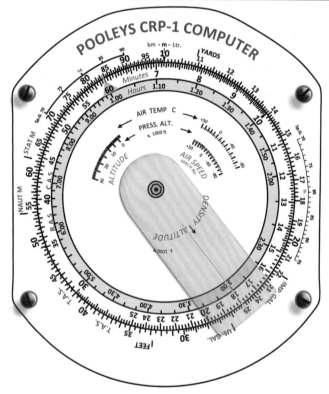

If a correction was made for Track Error alone we would merely parallel the required track, what we now need to find is the closing angle to route direct to the next turning point:

Distance off track (nm) x **60** = **Track Error (degrees)**
  Distance to go (nm)

The total distance from Rochester to Elmsett is 46.8 nm; hence the distance to go is:
46.8 – 18 = 28.8 nm

$\frac{2.5}{28.8}$ x 60 = 5.2°

OUTER SCALE:	DISTANCE OFF TRACK (nm)	CLOSING ANGLE (degrees)
INNER SCALE:	DISTANCE TO GO (nm)	60

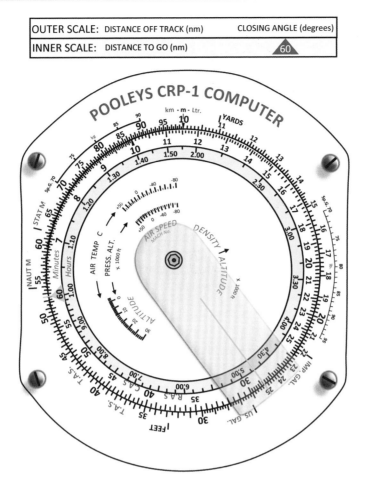

To find the heading correction to be made, add the Track Error to the Closing Angle:
8.3 + 5.2 = 13.5°

As the aircraft is to the left of track, the aircraft must be turned to the right. The original heading was 028°M, therefore the heading now required to reach Elmsett is 028 + 13.5 = 041°M

13. **(Answer: D)** 132 knots. The ATA overhead Elmsett was 1515; at 1525 you fix your position on track and 22 nm from Elmsett.

To find the new groundspeed: Speed = distance ÷ time

$$\frac{22 \text{ nm}}{10 \text{ minutes}} \times 60 \text{ minutes} = 132 \text{ knots}$$

Alternatively using the CRP set 10 minutes on the rotating inner scale under the distance 22 nm on the outer scale; you may then read off the speed above the 60 index.

Outer Scale:	Distance	Speed
Inner Scale:	Time	60

14. **(Answer: A)** The distance remaining to Conington is 50.9 – 22 = 28.9 nm.

Time to Conington = $\frac{\text{Distance remaining}}{\text{Groundspeed}} = \frac{28.9}{132} \times 60 \text{ minutes} = 13.1 \text{ minutes}$

Or, using the CRP set the 60 index below the groundspeed (132), beneath distance 28.9 on the outer scale, read off the time on the inner scale, 13.1 minutes.

The ETA at Conington is therefore 1525 plus (for practical purposes) 13 minutes – 1538.

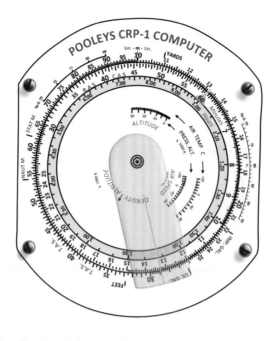

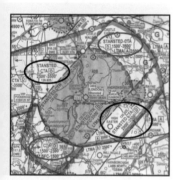

15. ANSWER D

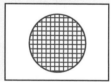

16. ANSWER D

17. ANSWER A

18. ANSWER C

15. **(Answer: D)** It is a Restricted Area number R214 with a maximum altitude of 2,400 feet. The annotation "see note 2" means that the restriction only applies to helicopters. Usually these areas are established around prisons.

16. **(Answer: D)** The lowest base of controlled areas around the Stansted CTR is 1,500 feet.

17. **(Answer: A)** The feature at 52 31N 000 06W is a windfarm

18. **(Answer: C)** The symbol represents a HIRTA, a High Intensity Radio Transmission Area. This is an area of defined dimensions within which there is intense radio energy which may cause interference or damage to an aircraft's radio equipment. These areas should be avoided.

19. **(Answer: D)** 65 minutes

The flight planned times for the subsequent legs are:
Elmsett to Conington: 31.5 minutes
Conington to Bourn: 10.4 minutes
Total: 41.9 minutes

Find out how much fuel the remaining flight time requires, using the CRP set the 60 index below 7 for the fuel flow.

FUEL REQUIRED   SAFE ENDURANCE

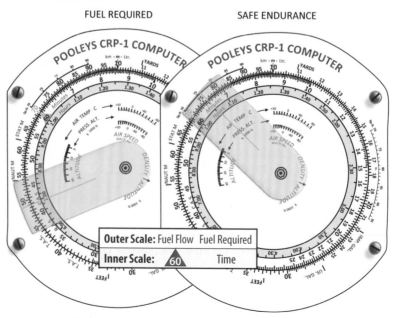

| Outer Scale: | Fuel Flow | Fuel Required |
| Inner Scale: | 60 | Time |

Read off above the time (41.9 minutes) on the inner scale a fuel requirement of 4.4 USG. A rough check will determine where to place the decimal, the time is just over 40 minutes (⅔ of an hour), two thirds of 7 USG is 4.6, so we are expecting roughly 4.6 USG to be used in the remaining flight time.

Overhead Elmsett we had 18 USG of fuel and from this we need to subtract the 4.4 USG we are going to use and the 6 USG that we are told must be held in reserve:
18 – 4.4 – 6 = 7.6 USG.

In determining the safe endurance we are expecting an answer of just over an hour. Keeping the CRP as above with the 60 index below the 7, this time read off below 7.6 on the outer scale a time of 65 minutes on the inner scale, which is the endurance remaining.

20. **(Answer: B)** The advice in the UKAIP states that when requesting penetration of a MATZ if no reply is received to two consecutive calls proceed with caution. Avoiding the area by turning left, or climbing above 3,032 feet aal to fly above the MATZ are also good options!

RADIO NAVIGATION

---

21. **(Answer: A)** In this question we are told that the aircraft is on the 255 radial, i.e. it is to the west of the beacon. In order to fly to the beacon with correct sense indications the OBS should be set to 075 with a TO indication.

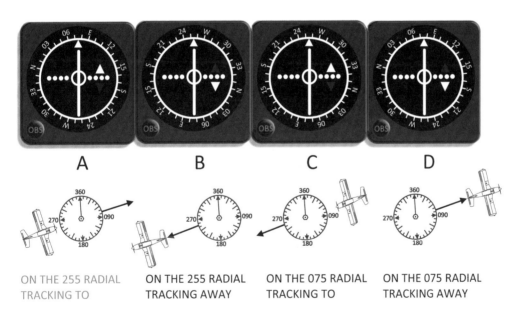

A	B	C	D
ON THE 255 RADIAL TRACKING TO	ON THE 255 RADIAL TRACKING AWAY	ON THE 075 RADIAL TRACKING TO	ON THE 075 RADIAL TRACKING AWAY

22. **(Answer: A)** 185° relative. Drift is measured from the heading (nose) to the track, and is classified in degrees port or starboard of heading.

If there were to be no cross wind, when tracking away from the NDB flying the heading as a track would work. The needle would continue to show a steady relative bearing of 180° i.e. it will point to the tail of the aircraft.

In cross wind conditions an allowance for drift is necessary.

With a track of 300 and a drift 5° to starboard, the track lies to the right of the heading; therefore the heading is 305°. When using an RBI the "tail" of the ADF needle must be offset 5° right: an equal amount but to the opposite side of the nose in order for the track to be maintained.

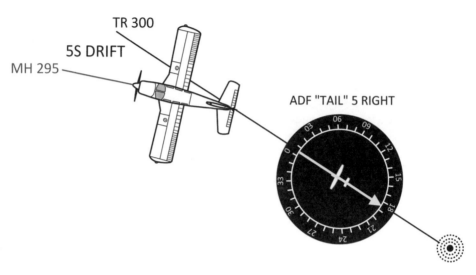

MAGNETIC HEADING + RELATIVE BEARING +/- 180 = QDR
295 + 185 = 480 - 180 = 300

To summarise, when tracking away from an NDB the aim is to achieve parity between the number of degrees by which the heading is offset in one direction and the number of degrees by which the tail of the ADF needle is displaced in the other direction.

23. **(Answer: D)** 352° relative. When tracking towards an NDB in nil wind, the RBI would indicate 000° relative, the needle would point directly to the nose. With 8° of port drift the heading is right of track, the RBI should therefore point 8° left of the nose.

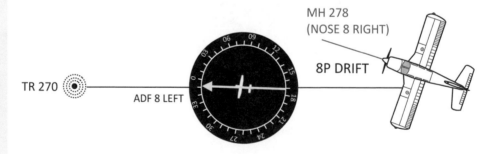

TRACKING TOWARDS THE NDB:
MAGNETIC HEADING + RELATIVE BEARING = QDR
278 + 352 = 630 - 360 = 270

24. **(Answer: B)**

QDM   Aircraft's magnetic heading to steer in zero wind to reach the station
QDR   Aircraft's magnetic bearing from the station
QTE   Aircraft's true bearing from the station
QUJ   Aircraft's true track to the station

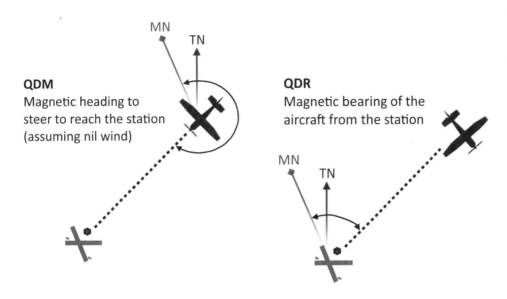

QDM
Magnetic heading to
steer to reach the station
(assuming nil wind)

QDR
Magnetic bearing of the
aircraft from the station

25. **(Answer: C)** 172° relative

With a track of 090 and a drift 8° to port, the track lies to the left of the heading; therefore the heading is 098°. When using an RBI the "tail" of the ADF needle must be offset 8° left - an equal amount but to the opposite side of the nose in order for the QDR to be maintained.

To summarise, when tracking away from an NDB the aim is to achieve parity between the number of degrees by which the heading is offset in one direction and the number of degrees by which the tail of the ADF needle is displaced in the other direction.

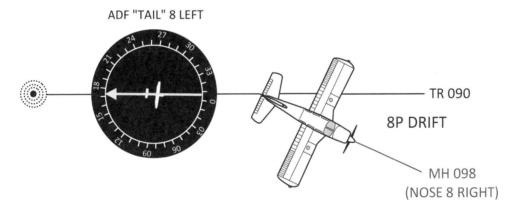

TRACKING AWAY FROM THE NDB
MAGNETIC HEADING + RELATIVE BEARING +/- 180 = QDR
098 + 172 = 270 - 180 = 090

INTENTIONALLY BLANK

JAA PPL REVISION PAPERS

INTENTIONALLY BLANK

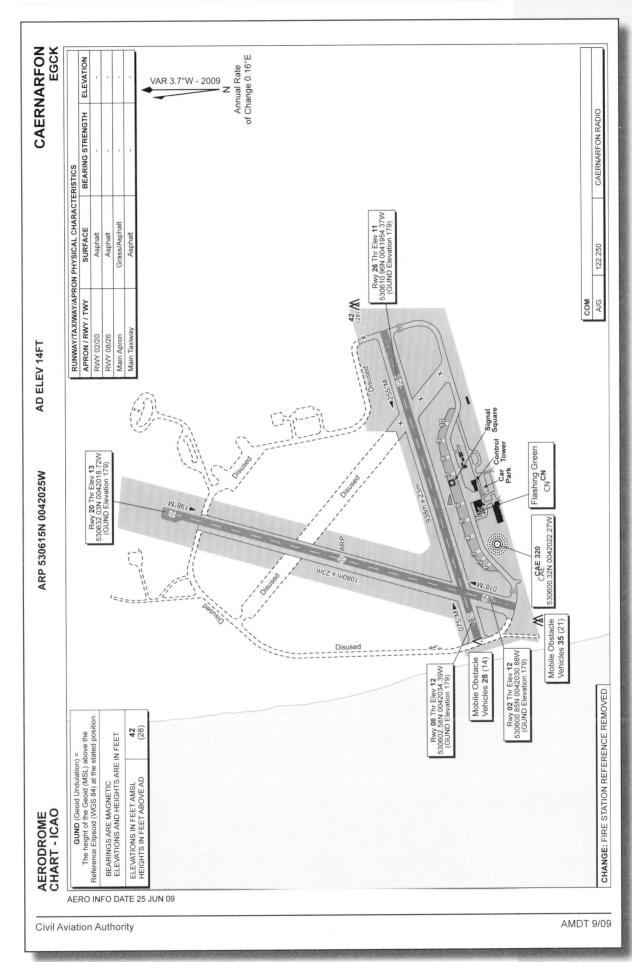

AERODROME CHART - ICAO

CAERNARFON EGCK

ARP 530615N 0042025W   AD ELEV 14FT

VAR 3.7°W - 2009
Annual Rate of Change 0.16°E

RUNWAY/TAXIWAY/APRON PHYSICAL CHARACTERISTICS

APRON / RWY / TWY	SURFACE	BEARING STRENGTH	ELEVATION
RWY 02/20	Asphalt	-	-
RWY 08/26	Asphalt	-	-
Main Apron	Grass/Asphalt	-	-
Main Taxiway	Asphalt	-	-

GUND (Geoid Undulation) = The height of the Geoid (MSL) above the Reference Ellipsoid (WGS 84) at the stated position.

BEARINGS ARE MAGNETIC
ELEVATIONS AND HEIGHTS ARE IN FEET

ELEVATIONS IN FEET AMSL   42
HEIGHTS IN FEET ABOVE AD   (28)

AERO INFO DATE 25 JUN 09

Rwy 20 Thr Elev 13
530632.03N 0042018.72W
(GUND Elevation 179)

Rwy 26 Thr Elev 11
530610.96N 0041954.37W
(GUND Elevation 179)

Rwy 08 Thr Elev 12
530602.58N 0042034.39W
(GUND Elevation 179)

Rwy 02 Thr Elev 12
530600.85N 0042030.88W
(GUND Elevation 179)

CAE 320
530600.32N 0042022.27W

Mobile Obstacle Vehicles 28 (14)
Mobile Obstacle Vehicles 35 (21)

Signal Square
Control Tower
Car Park
Flashing Green

1080m x 23m
938m x 23m
255°M
198°M
018°M
075°M

COM

A/G	122.250	CAERNARFON RADIO

CHANGE: FIRE STATION REFERENCE REMOVED.

INTENTIONALLY BLANK

CAERNARFON

EGCK AD 2.1 - CAERNARFON

EGCK AD 2.2 — AERODROME GEOGRAPHICAL AND ADMINISTRATIVE DATA

1	ARP co-ordinates and site at Aerodrome:	**Lat:** 530615N **Long:** 0042025W Mid Point of Runway 02/20
2	Direction and distance from the city:	4 nm SW of Caernarfon.
3	Elevation/Reference temperature:	14 ft – °C
4	Geoid undulation at AD ELEV PSN:	179 ft.
5	MAG VAR/Annual change:	W3.7° (2009) – 0.16° decreasing
6	AD Administration:	Air Caernarfon Ltd.
	Address:	Caernarfon Aerodrome, Dinas Dinlle, Gwynned, LL54 5TP.
	Telephone:	01286-830800.
	Fax:	01286-830280.
7	Types of traffic permitted (IFR/VFR):	VFR
8	Remarks:	

EGCK AD 2.3 — OPERATIONAL HOURS

1	AD Administration:	**Winter:** 0900-1630.
		Summer: 0800-1700.
2	Customs and Immigration:	By arrangement.
3	Health and Sanitation:	
4	AIS Briefing Office:	
5	ATS Reporting Office (ARO):	
6	MET Briefing Office:	
7	ATS:	As AD hours. See also AD 2.18.
8	Fuelling:	**Winter:** 0900-1630.
		Summer: 0800-1700.
9	Handling:	
10	Security:	
11	De-icing:	
12	Remarks:	This aerodrome is **PPR**. The aerodrome and fuel may be available by arrangement outside the above hours, **but** the aerodrome may be unlicensed.

EGCK AD 2.4 — HANDLING SERVICES AND FACILITIES

1	Cargo handling facilities:	
2	Fuel/oil types:	AVGAS 100LL, AVTUR JET A-1. Oil: W80, W100.
3	Fuelling facilities/capacity:	
4	De-icing facilities:	
5	Hangar space available for visiting aircraft:	
6	Repair facilities for visiting aircraft:	
7	Remarks:	Pilots requiring fuel on arrival should make this request when inbound on A/G frequency

EGCK AD 2.17 — ATS AIRSPACE

Designation and lateral limits		Vertical limits	Airspace Classification
1		2	3
Caernarfon Aerodrome Traffic Zone (ATZ) Circle radius 2 nm centred on longest notified runway (02/20) 530615N 0042025W.		2000 ft aal/ SFC	G †

4	ATS unit call sign: Language(s):	Caernarfon Radio English
5	Transition altitude:	ft
6	Remarks:	Hours: See AD 2.18 † Refer to section ENR 1.4 for notifications. Special procedures are in operation for aircraft arriving at and departing from Caernarfon: See AD 2.22.

EGCK AD 2.18 — ATS COMMUNICATION FACILITIES

Service Designation	Callsign	Channel MHz	Hours of Operation		Remarks
			Winter	Summer	
1	2	3	4		5
A/G	Caernarfon Radio	122.250	0900-1630	0800-1700	ATZ hours co-incident with A/G hours, but not by arrangement.

EGCK AD 2.19— RADIO NAVIGATION AND LANDING AIDS

Type of Aid MAG VAR Type of supported OP (VOR/ILS/MLS declination)	IDENT	Frequency	Hours of Operation		Position of transmitting antenna co-ordinates	Elevation of DME transmitting antenna	Remarks
			Winter	Summer			
			# and by arrangement				
1	2	3	4		5	6	7
NDB	CAE	320 kHz	HO	HO	530600.32N 0042022.27W		On AD. Range 15 nm. Normally radiates H24.

EGCK AD 2.20 — LOCAL TRAFFIC REGULATIONS

1. **Airport Regulations**

   a. The wearing of high visibility vests by pilots and visiting aircrew is mandatory whilst operating airside during normal hours of operation.

2. **Ground Movement**

   Not applicable

3. **CAT II/III Operations**

   Not applicable

4. **Warnings**

   a. Turbulance might on occassion be experienced when there is an easterly wind.

   b. In the event of heavy rain, Runway 20 may have standing water approaximately 70 m from the threshold.

5. **Helicopter Operations**

   Not applicable

6. **Use of Runways**

   a. **Back-tracking Procedure RWY 02/20.** Pilots unfamiliar with these procedures should telephone for details prior to departure.

7. **Training**

   Not applicable

UK AIP   AD 2-EGCK-1 - 5
CAERNARFON   27 Aug 09

EGCK AD 2.21 — NOISE ABATEMENT PROCEDURES

Helicopters must not overfly any caravan site within the ATZ below 1000 ft on the QFE.

EGCK AD 2.22 — FLIGHT PROCEDURES

a.   The aerodrome is in the vicinity of the Valley MATZ. Civil aircraft are to fly at 1500 ft or below (Holyhead QNH) in the Menai Straits area.

b.   **Arriving aircraft.** From the south and southeast should call Llanbedr ATC on 122.500 MHz at least 5 minutes before abeam Llanbedr aerodrome. Unless otherwise instructed, these aircraft should subsequently call Valley ATC on 125.225 MHz at least 15 minutes before ETA Caernarfon ATZ boundary.
All other aircraft should call Valley ATC on 125.225 MHz at least 15 minutes before ETA Caernarfon ATZ boundary.

c.   **Departing aircraft.** Unless otherwise instructed, departing aircraft should call Valley ATC on 125.225 MHz immediately after take-off.

d.   Circuit height: 800 ft aal. Aircraft are requested to join overhead not above 1300 ft aal. Circuit direction: Runways 02 and 26 - RH.

EGCK AD 2.23 — ADDITIONAL INFORMATION

Not applicable

EGCK AD 2.24 — CHARTS RELATED TO THE AERODROME

Chart Name	Page
Aerodrome Chart - ICAO	AD 2-EGCK-2-1

EGCK AD 2.5 — PASSENGER FACILITIES

Not applicable

EGCK AD 2.6 — RESCUE AND FIRE FIGHTING SERVICES

1	AD category for fire fighting:	RFF Category 1.
2	Rescue equipment	
3	Capability for removal of disabled aircraft:	
4	Remarks:	

EGCK AD 2.7 — SEASONAL AVAILABILITY - CLEARING

Not applicable

EGCK AD 2.8 — APRONS, TAXIWAYS AND CHECK LOCATIONS/POSITIONS DATA

Not applicable

EGCK AD 2.9 — SURFACE MOVEMENT GUIDANCE AND CONTROL SYSTEM AND MARKINGS

Not applicable

EGCK AD 2.10 — AERODROME OBSTACLES

In Approach/Take-off Areas			In circling area and at aerodrome		
1			2		
Runway/Area affected	Obstacle type Elevation Markings/Lighting	Co-ordinates	Obstacle type Elevation Markings/Lighting		Co-ordinates
a	b	c	a		b
		ft amsl		ft amsl	
02/Approach 20/Take-off	Vehicles on road	26	530556.97N 0042031.00W	TV Mast (Lgtd)	2050	*530109.30N 0041624.40W
	Vehicles on road	35	530553.90N 0042033.85W			
08/Approach 26/Take-off	Vehicles on road	28	530601.65N 0042037.47W			
	Tree	42	530614.00N 0041945.77W			
	Tree	40	530612.46N 0041945.66W			
	Telegraph Pole	35	530613.24N 0041944.44W			
3	Remarks:	High ground beyond 6 nm southeast of the aerodrome rising to 3559 ft aal/amsl. Runway 08 take-off; Beyond 11000 m there is a mountainous terrain, rising to 3485 ft.			

EGCK AD 2.11— METEOROLOGICAL INFORMATION PROVIDED

Not applicable

EGCK AD 2.12 — RUNWAY PHYSICAL CHARACTERISTICS

Designations RWY Number	True bearing	Dimensions of RWY (m)	Strength (PCN) and surface of RWY and Stopway	Threshold co-ordinates RWY end co-ordinates THR Geoid undulation	THR elevation and highest elevation of TDZ of precision APP RWY
1	2	3	4	5	6
02	013.21°	1080 x 23	Asphalt	530600.85N 0042030.88W — GUND 179 ft	THR 12 ft
20	193.21°	1080 x 23	Asphalt	530632.03N 0042018.72W — GUND 179 ft	THR 13 ft
08	070.81°	938 x 23	Asphalt	530602.58N 0042034.39W — GUND 179 ft	THR 12 ft
26	250.82°	938 x 23	Asphalt	530610.96N 0041954.37W — GUND 179 ft	THR 11 ft

Slope of RWY-SWY	Stopway dimensions (m)	Clearway dimensions (m)	Strip dimensions (m)	OFZ
7	8	9	10	11

12	Remarks:	Runway 02 landing threshold displaced by 77 m from start of pavement to allow 1:25 slope over vehicles using the road outside the aerodrome boundry.
		Runway 08 landing threshold displaced by 56 m to allow 1:20 over 1 m high fence plus 30 m strip end.
		Runway 26 landing threshold displaced by 89 m to allow 1:20 approach surface over trees and HT cable.

EGCK AD 2.13 — DECLARED DISTANCES

RWY Designator	TORA (m)	TODA (m)	ASDA (m)	LDA (m)	Remarks:
1	2	3	4	5	6
02	1080	1080	1080	1003	
20	1044	1044	1044	1044	
08	799	799	799	880	
26	799	799	799	759	

EGCK AD 2.14 — APPROACH AND RUNWAY LIGHTING

Not applicable

EGCK AD 2.15 — OTHER LIGHTING, SECONDARY POWER SUPPLY

Not applicable

EGCK AD 2.16 — HELICOPTER LANDING AREA

Not applicable

This page is intentionally left blank

THRUXTON

EGHO AD 2.1 - THRUXTON

EGHO AD 2.2 — AERODROME GEOGRAPHICAL AND ADMINISTRATIVE DATA

1	ARP co-ordinates and site at Aerodrome:	**Lat:** 511238N **Long:** 0013600W
2	Direction and distance from the city:	4.5 nm W of Andover.
3	Elevation/Reference temperature:	319 ft – °C.
4	Geoid undulation at AD ELEV PSN:	155 ft.
5	MAG VAR/Annual change:	W2.3° (2009) – 0.14° decreasing.
6	AD Administrator:	Western Air (Thruxton) Ltd.
	Address:	Thruxton Aerodrome, Nr. Andover, Hampshire, SP11 8PW.
	Telephone:	01264-772352 (A/G). 01264-772171 (Administration).
	Fax:	01264-882259 (A/G). 01264-733193 (Administration).
7	Types of traffic permitted (IFR/VFR):	
8	Remarks:	

EGHO AD 2.3 — OPERATIONAL HOURS

1	AD Administration:	**Winter:** 0900-1700; and by arrangement.
		Summer: 0800-1600; and by arrangement.
2	Customs and immigration:	By arrangement.
3	Health and sanitation:	
4	AIS Briefing Office:	
5	ATS Reporting Office (ARO):	
6	MET Briefing Office:	
7	ATS:	As AD hours. See also AD 2.18.
8	Fuelling:	As AD hours.
9	Handling:	
10	Security:	
11	De-icing:	
12	Remarks:	This aerodrome is **PPR**.

EGHO AD 2.4 — HANDLING SERVICES AND FACILITIES

1	Cargo handling facilities:	
2	Fuel/oil types:	AVTUR JET A-1 (AL48 additive not included), AVGAS 100LL.
3	Fuelling facilities/capacity:	
4	De-icing facilities:	
5	Hangar space available for visiting aircraft:	
6	Repair facilities for visiting aircraft:	
7	Remarks:	

EGHO AD 2.5 — PASSENGER FACILITIES

Not applicable

EGHO AD 2.6 — RESCUE AND FIRE FIGHTING SERVICES

1	AD category for fire fighting:	RFF Category 1/H1. Category 2 on request.
2	Rescue equipment	
3	Capability for removal of disabled aircraft:	
4	Remarks:	

CIVIL AVIATION AUTHORITY

AMDT 005/10

AD 2-EGHO-1 - 2
6 May 10

UK AIP
THRUXTON

EGHO AD 2.7 — SEASONAL AVAILABILITY - CLEARING

Not applicable

EGHO AD 2.8 — APRONS, TAXIWAYS AND CHECK LOCATIONS/POSITIONS DATA

1	Apron surface and strength:	Aircraft Parking Area: **Surface:** Concrete **Strength:** Northern Parking Area **Surface:** Asphalt **Strength:**
2	Taxiway width, surface and strength:	**Width: Surface: Strength:**
3	Altimeter checkpoint location and elevation:	
4	VOR checkpoints:	
5	INS checkpoints:	
6	Remarks:	

EGHO AD 2.9 — SURFACE MOVEMENT GUIDANCE AND CONTROL SYSTEM AND MARKINGS

Not applicable

EGHO AD 2.10 — AERODROME OBSTACLES

In Approach/Take-off Areas			In circling area and at aerodrome		
1			2		
Runway/Area affected	Obstacle type Elevation Markings/Lighting	Co-ordinates	Obstacle type Elevation Markings/Lighting		Co-ordinates
a	b	c	a		b
		ft amsl		ft amsl	
			Hangar (Lgtd)	340	511234.50N 0013618.05W
			Tree	530	511302.85N 0013724.69W
			Tree	537	511303.58N 0013722.75W
			Tree	539	511304.01N 0013722.53W
			Mast	357	511222.26N 0013556.29W
3	Remarks:				

EGHO AD 2.11— METEOROLOGICAL INFORMATION PROVIDED

Not applicable

EGHO AD 2.12 — RUNWAY PHYSICAL CHARACTERISTICS

Designations RWY Number	True bearing	Dimensions of RWY (m)	Strength (PCN) and surface of RWY and Stopway	Threshold co-ordinates RWY end co-ordinates THR Geoid undulation	THR elevation and highest elevation of TDZ of precision APP RWY
1	2	3	4	5	6
07	067°	770 x 23	— Asphalt	511235.60N 0013606.89W — GUND 155 ft	THR 303 ft
25	247°	770 x 23	— Asphalt	511245.23N 0013530.89W — GUND 155 ft	THR 305 ft
13	123°	750 x 31	— Grass	511243.21N 0013613.49W — GUND 155 ft	THR 319 ft
31	303°	750 x 31	— Grass	511229.89N 0013540.64W — GUND 155 ft	THR 279 ft

Slope of RWY-SWY	Stopway dimensions (m)	Clearway dimensions (m)	Strip dimensions (m)	OFZ
7	8	9	10	11

12	Remarks: Runway 07 threshold displaced by 181 m.	Runway 25 threshold displaced by 30 m.

EGHO AD 2.13 — DECLARED DISTANCES

RWY Designator	TORA (m)	TODA (m)	ASDA (m)	LDA (m)	Remarks:
1	2	3	4	5	6
07	770	770	770	760	
25	770	770	770	770	
13	750	750	750	750	
31	750	750	750	750	

EGHO AD 2.14 — APPROACH AND RUNWAY LIGHTING

Runway	Approach lighting Type Length Intensity	Threshold lighting colour Wingbars	PAPI VASIS Angle Dist from THR (MEHT)	TDZ lighting Length	Runway Centre-line Lighting Length Spacing Colour Intensity	Runway edge lighting Length Spacing Colour Intensity	Runway End Lighting Colour Wingbars	Stopway Lighting Length (M) Colour
1	2	3	4	5	6	7	8	9
07		LI Green wingbars	APAPI 4° LHS (20 ft)			LI	Red	
25		LI Green wingbars	APAPI 4° LHS (20 ft)			LI	Red	
10	Remarks							

EGHO AD 2.15 — OTHER LIGHTING, SECONDARY POWER SUPPLY

Not applicable

EGHO AD 2.16 — HELICOPTER LANDING AREA

Not applicable

EGHO AD 2.17 — ATS AIRSPACE

Designation and lateral limits	Vertical limits	Airspace Classification
1	2	3
Thruxton Aerodrome Traffic Zone (ATZ) Circle radius 2 nm centred on longest notified runway (07/25) 511240N 0013549W.	2000 ft aal/ SFC	G †

4	ATS unit call sign: Language(s):	Thruxton radio. English
5	Transition altitude:	
6	Remarks:	Hours: See AD 2.18 † Refer to Section ENR 1.4 for Notifications.

EGHO AD 2.18 — ATS COMMUNICATION FACILITIES

Service Designation	Callsign	Channel MHz	Hours of Operation		Remarks
			Winter	Summer	
1	2	3	4		5
A/G	Thruxton radio	130.450	0900-1700	0800-1600	ATZ hours coincident with A/G hours.

EGHO AD 2.19— RADIO NAVIGATION AND LANDING AIDS

Not applicable

EGHO AD 2.20 — LOCAL TRAFFIC REGULATIONS

1. **Airport Regulations**

   a. While airside each aircraft commander is responsible for the safety of his passengers and other crew members. Passengers are at all times to be escorted by the aircraft commander or a crew member who is known to be competent to ensure both his/her and the passengers safety. The wearing of high visibility clothing is mandatory.

   b. Aircraft commanders or crew members, as applicable, are responsible for ensuring that a total ban on smoking whilst airside is observed.

   c. Use of the aerodrome not permitted by aircraft with a maximum weight authorised in excess of 5700 kg if operating for the public transport of passengers.

   d. Permission to use the aerodrome will not normally be granted to microlight aircraft.

   e. Use of the Main Apron is restricted to aircraft with a wingspan not exceeding 12 m and fuselage length not exceeding 9.5 m. Subject to specific approval from A/G, use by other aircraft may be permitted. This approval is to be requested when permission to use the aerodrome is requested.

2. **Ground Movement**

   Not applicable

3. **CAT II/III Operations**

   Not applicable

4. **Warnings**

   a. Danger Areas EG D126, EG D127 Boscombe Down and Middle Wallop ATZ are located adjacent to the Thruxton ATZ. All are active H24.

   b. Thruxton ATZ is situated on the approach/departure path for the main runway at Boscombe Down. During Boscombe Down Combined Military Air Traffic Zone (CMATZ) hours of operation, aircraft being provided Air Traffic Service by ATC Boscombe Down will transit the Thruxton ATZ above 1450 ft above Thruxton aerodrome level.

   c. Extensive military helicopter, transport and tactical jet aircraft operations can be anticipated at any time in the vicinity of Thruxton ATZ, associated with the Boscombe Down CMATZ.

   d. Aircraft movements may take place outside notified aerodrome/ATZ operating hours involving aircraft that do not require the use of a licensed aerodrome.

   e. Two large birds of prey are released daily at 1430 (local) from London Hill, approximately 800 m southeast of Runway 31 threshold. Pilots are requested to avoid the area during this activity. A/G will notify when the activity is completed.

5. **Helicopter Operations**

   a. Helicopters may operate to/from two aiming points. One is designated Heli North, and is located 130 m south of the intersection of Runways 07/25 and 13/31 marked by two white concentric circles. Approaches and departures to/from Heli North will be parallel to the fixed wing runways in use. A second aiming point is located in the south-west corner of the aerodrome and is marked with a white triangle. Circuits flown by helicopters will be as follows, in relation to the specified runway in use, and at the specified height:

   - Runway 07 - RH, 1000 ft aal
   - Runway 25 - LH, 1000 ft aal
   - Runway 13 - RH, 800 † ft aal
   - Runway 31 - LH, 800 † ft aal

      † 1000 ft if Boscombe CMATZ is not active.

   b. Unless other arrangements have been made with the A/G station, helicopters must arrive and depart the ATZ via the Heli North, in accordance with the procedures set out at paragraph (a).

6. **Use of Runways**

   a. Aircraft vacating Runway 07/25 must vacate to the south. When Runway 13/31 is in use, vacate to the west.

7. **Training**

   Not applicable

EGHO AD 2.21 — NOISE ABATEMENT PROCEDURES

a. Aircraft are to be operated in a manner to cause the least disturbance in areas surrounding the aerodrome. All aircraft should avoid overflying the following residential areas:

- Kimpton Village (adjacent to northern aerodrome boundary);
- Fyfield Village (1 nm northeast of the aerodrome);
- Quarley Village (1.25 nm southwest of the aerodrome);
- Thruxton Village (adjacent to eastern aerodrome boundary);
- The Hawk Conservancy (bird sanctuary 1.5 nm southeast of the aerodrome).

EGHO AD 2.22 — FLIGHT PROCEDURES

1. **Boscombe Down/Middle Wallop CMATZ**

    a. During Boscombe Down/Middle Wallop CMATZ hours of operation, it is a condition of use of Thruxton aerodrome that the flight procedures set out below are complied with. Information on the CMATZ activity status may be obtained from the A/G station.

    i. **Arriving aircraft**

    1. Contact Boscombe Down on frequency 126.700 MHz for a MATZ penetration service (in accordance with ENR 2.2). To reduce the possibility of inadvertent CMATZ or ATZ penetration, arriving traffic may be routed via a point 1 nm north of Andover. Once an aircraft has reported at this point it will be advised to free-call Thruxton A/G. Remain outside the Thruxton ATZ and contact 'Thuruxton Radio' (130.450 MHz) for ATZ entry information. ATZ entry should be at 1200 ft aal, or a maximum height to remain in VMC, not above 1200 ft aal; or

    2. Avoid the Boscombe Down CMATZ, contact Thruxton Radio for ATZ entry information. ATZ entry should be not above 1200 ft aal. If contact with the A/G Station is not possible, ATZ entry must be not above 1200 ft aal.

    ii. **Departing to west/southwest/northwest**

    1. Prior to departure, notify flight details to, and request approval from Boscombe Down ATC via telephone (01980-663246) After departure, aircraft are to maintain VMC and contact Boscombe Down on notified frequency as soon as possible. Any SSR code allocation should be selected immediately prior to departure.

    iii. **Departing to north/northeast/southeast**

    1. Leave the ATZ not above 1200 ft, or 900 ft aal (Thruxton QNH). Before climbing above 1200 ft ALT (Thruxton QNH), either free-call Boscombe Zone after leaving the Thruxton ATZ or delay further climb until clear of the CMATZ lateral limits

2. **Communications**

    a. Transponder equipped aircraft operating within the Thruxton ATZ not above 1000 ft aal are requested to squawk Mode 3/A code 2660, without Mode C.

    b. Aircraft that are given approval to use the aerodrome, but are unable to communicate with the A/G station via radio, must obtain the current Thruxton QFE prior to arrival by telephoning the A/G station (01264-772352). Aircraft departing Thruxton are to obtain the current Thruxton QNH from the A/G station prior to departure.

3. **Arrivals/Departures**

    a. Aircraft arriving/departing from/to the southeast should exercise caution due the possibility of aircraft operating IMC while making an instrument approach Runway 26 at Middle Wallop.

4. **Circuits**

    a. Unless otherwise notified by the A/G Station, circuit height is 800 ft aal (Thruxton QFE) for all runways.

    b. During times that the Boscombe Down CMATZ is not in operation, circuit joining height is 1500 ft aal, or the maximum possible below this level to maintain VMC and circuit height 1000 ft aal.

    c. There is no dead-side for Runway 07/25. Helicopters operate south of Runway 07/25 up to 1000 ft aal.

    d. The following circuit directions apply for fixed wing aircraft when the specified runways are in use:

    - Runway 07 - LH
    - Runway 25 - RH
    - Runway 13 - RH
    - Runway 31 - LH

EGHO AD 2.23 — ADDITIONAL INFORMATION

Not applicable

EGHO AD 2.24 — CHARTS RELATED TO THE AERODROME

Chart Name	Page Number
Aerodrome Chart - ICAO	AD 2-EGHO-2-1

This page is intentionally left blank

ANSWER SHEETS

PAPER NO.				
	A	B	C	D
1				
2				
3				
4				
5				
6				
7				
8				
9				
10				
11				
12				
13				
14				
15				
16				
17				
18				
19				
20				
21				
22				
23				
24				
25				
26				
27				
28				
29				
30				
31				
32				
33				
34				
35				
36				
37				
38				
39				
40				

PAPER NO.				
	A	B	C	D
1				
2				
3				
4				
5				
6				
7				
8				
9				
10				
11				
12				
13				
14				
15				
16				
17				
18				
19				
20				
21				
22				
23				
24				
25				
26				
27				
28				
29				
30				
31				
32				
33				
34				
35				
36				
37				
38				
39				
40				

PAPER NO.				
	A	B	C	D
1				
2				
3				
4				
5				
6				
7				
8				
9				
10				
11				
12				
13				
14				
15				
16				
17				
18				
19				
20				
21				
22				
23				
24				
25				
26				
27				
28				
29				
30				
31				
32				
33				
34				
35				
36				
37				
38				
39				
40				

PAPER NO.				
	A	B	C	D
1				
2				
3				
4				
5				
6				
7				
8				
9				
10				
11				
12				
13				
14				
15				
16				
17				
18				
19				
20				
21				
22				
23				
24				
25				
26				
27				
28				
29				
30				
31				
32				
33				
34				
35				
36				
37				
38				
39				
40				

PAPER NO.				
	A	B	C	D
1				
2				
3				
4				
5				
6				
7				
8				
9				
10				
11				
12				
13				
14				
15				
16				
17				
18				
19				
20				
21				
22				
23				
24				
25				
26				
27				
28				
29				
30				
31				
32				
33				
34				
35				
36				
37				
38				
39				
40				

PAPER NO.				
	A	B	C	D
1				
2				
3				
4				
5				
6				
7				
8				
9				
10				
11				
12				
13				
14				
15				
16				
17				
18				
19				
20				
21				
22				
23				
24				
25				
26				
27				
28				
29				
30				
31				
32				
33				
34				
35				
36				
37				
38				
39				
40				

PAPER NO.				
	A	B	C	D
1				
2				
3				
4				
5				
6				
7				
8				
9				
10				
11				
12				
13				
14				
15				
16				
17				
18				
19				
20				
21				
22				
23				
24				
25				
26				
27				
28				
29				
30				
31				
32				
33				
34				
35				
36				
37				
38				
39				
40				

PAPER NO.				
	A	B	C	D
1				
2				
3				
4				
5				
6				
7				
8				
9				
10				
11				
12				
13				
14				
15				
16				
17				
18				
19				
20				
21				
22				
23				
24				
25				
26				
27				
28				
29				
30				
31				
32				
33				
34				
35				
36				
37				
38				
39				
40				

PAPER NO.				
	A	B	C	D
1				
2				
3				
4				
5				
6				
7				
8				
9				
10				
11				
12				
13				
14				
15				
16				
17				
18				
19				
20				
21				
22				
23				
24				
25				
26				
27				
28				
29				
30				
31				
32				
33				
34				
35				
36				
37				
38				
39				
40				

PAPER NO.	A	B	C	D
1				
2				
3				
4				
5				
6				
7				
8				
9				
10				
11				
12				
13				
14				
15				
16				
17				
18				
19				
20				
21				
22				
23				
24				
25				
26				
27				
28				
29				
30				
31				
32				
33				
34				
35				
36				
37				
38				
39				
40				

PAPER NO.	A	B	C	D
1				
2				
3				
4				
5				
6				
7				
8				
9				
10				
11				
12				
13				
14				
15				
16				
17				
18				
19				
20				
21				
22				
23				
24				
25				
26				
27				
28				
29				
30				
31				
32				
33				
34				
35				
36				
37				
38				
39				
40				

PAPER NO.	A	B	C	D
1				
2				
3				
4				
5				
6				
7				
8				
9				
10				
11				
12				
13				
14				
15				
16				
17				
18				
19				
20				
21				
22				
23				
24				
25				
26				
27				
28				
29				
30				
31				
32				
33				
34				
35				
36				
37				
38				
39				
40				